CW00663249

A
NATURAL HISTORY
OF THE
LAKES, TARNS AND STREAMS
OF THE
ENGLISH LAKE DISTRICT

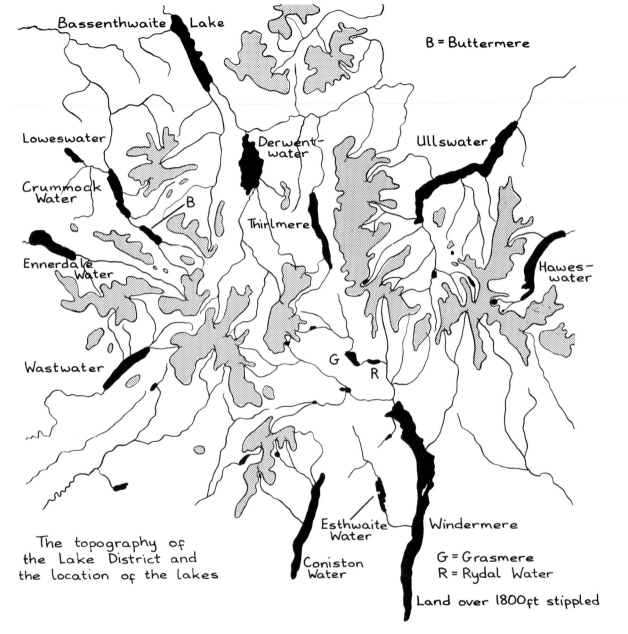

Frontispiece

B = Buttermere

Bassenthwaite Lake

Loweswater

Derwent-water

Ullswater

Crummock Water

B

Thirlmere

Hawes-water

Ennerdale Water

Wastwater

G
R

Esthwaite Water

Windermere

The topography of the Lake District and the location of the lakes

Coniston Water

G = Grasmere
R = Rydal Water

Land over 1800ft stippled

A
NATURAL HISTORY
OF THE
LAKES, TARNS AND STREAMS
OF THE
ENGLISH LAKE DISTRICT

GEOFFREY FRYER

CALLIGRAPHY BY
SHARON MURPHY

Published by The Freshwater Biological Association,
The Ferry House, Far Sawrey, Ambleside, Cumbria LA22 0LP, England.

© FRESHWATER BIOLOGICAL ASSOCIATION 1991

ISBN 0 900386 50 9

Hand-written text, photographed and printed by Titus Wilson & Son, Kendal.

Cover illustration: Ullswater

IN MEMORY OF MY MOTHER AND FATHER

The earth is the Lord's and the fulness thereof;
the world and they that dwell therein.

Ps. 24

CONTENTS

Preface

There are several books of a technical nature that deal with lakes and rivers. Others serve as guides to the plants and animals that live in them. However, there is nothing written in simple language that tells how the lakes and tarns of the English Lake District were formed, what happened to them during the course of their histories, how and why they differ among themselves, what goes on within them (how they 'work'), and at the same time gives an account of the plants and animals that are to be found there. Yet there are many to whom such things are of potential interest — those who live in the area and the many who visit it who like to know what is going on around them and what happened in the past, teachers keen to stimulate young minds, university students in their elementary years, amateur naturalists, and all who delight in the wild things of this earth. This book tries to meet the needs of such people and, while attempting to maintain scientific accuracy, to explain in non-technical language what goes on in the English lakes, tarns and streams, and to reveal what fascinating organisms are to be found living there.

While no text book, this work tries to introduce the reader to most of the major aspects of the study of lakes and their inhabitants, but in a way that requires little or no previous knowledge. It is deliberately produced in sections, often of only a few pages. Each, complete in itself, can be read or consulted, usually without reference to other sections. One can dip, but the whole can, if desired, be read right through.

The sections dealing with animals aim not only to indicate what the creatures look like, but to give some idea of their structure, habits and ways of life. Not all the facts related are to be found in general textbooks. While not an identification manual, the book contains more illustrations of freshwater animals than do some such guides, and while concerned specifically with organisms living in the English Lake District, it provides a broad introduction to the freshwater fauna and flora of the British Isles. It is in fact an introduction to freshwater biology.

Simple words are used whenever possible and terse factual statements are employed in preference to long descriptions. Where a technical term has to be used it is defined — more than once if this seems helpful. Specialists may quibble about the balance. Some groups of animals receive more coverage than their number of species or ecological importance perhaps warrant, but this is deliberate. Fishes receive more space than the far more numerous one-celled animals (the Protozoa) because they are more likely to be encountered by the non-specialist, and because more readers will wish to know about fishes than about protozoans. The whole of the plant and animal kingdoms are, however, covered, if only briefly, so far as their freshwater representatives in the Lake District are concerned.

Throughout the text due respect is accorded to scientific facts. However science has little to say about beauty, aesthetic appreciation, wonderment, reverence and the other emotions evinced by consideration of the natural world, though it is almost impossible to consider the things dealt with here without being affected by such matters. Contrary to what some would have us believe, this applies even to most practitioners of science, who are not devoid of human emotions. To many these intangibles are indeed more meaningful than factual knowledge about the world around us. However, I believe that some familiarity with how that world is structured and has evolved, with the nature of its components, and with the ways in which it operates, heightens such emotions and enhances one's appreciation of its beauty and its complexity. If this small work brings added enjoyment to those who already appreciate the wonders of creation or induces others to look a little more carefully, and with a little more understanding, at the remarkable world in which we live, it will have achieved one of its objectives.

Contemplation of the things considered here can bring immense pleasure and lasting satisfaction, and is an unrestricted priviledge, available to all, no matter how little they may be endowed with the material possessions by which some set such store. If enjoyment leads to the desire to protect and conserve the things that are to be seen, or that live in, this small and therefore vulnerable region this will be an added bonus.

The work had its genesis in some hand-out sheets prepared for a course given to students of the University of Lancaster. John Horne suggested that these could be expanded into a guidebook. At first I rejected the idea but when Robin Clarke said the same thing I wrote out a few rough pages just to see what such a guide might look like. From then on there was no retreat though there were times when I wished there was!

The approach is at times idiosyncratic and the layout adopted is unusual but, I hope, less forbidding than that of a type-set book. My original draft, complete with pictures, at that stage sometimes rough, was prepared as a mock-up of what the book would look like. From this Sharon Murphy wrote out the final version, and has, I believe, done so in a clear and attractive way. Much of the appeal of the final product is due to the care and skill that she has devoted to the task.

A note on names and numbers

Many scientific names are used in the text. A lot of organisms have no other. These should not deter. They are no more complicated than the two (or more) names borne by every reader. Their use, and the elements of biological classification, are simply explained on page 114.

Both metric and traditional units are employed. Often both are given for convenience, but small dimensions are given chiefly in millimetres (mm) or parts thereof, though the equivalent in inches is given as well where this seems helpful. Sometimes the size of very small organisms is given in microns (μm). 1 micron = $\frac{1}{1000}$ mm. Temperatures are given in degrees centigrade. No excuse is made for usually giving altitudes only in feet.   To most readers this is still more meaningful than metres, but for those who prefer the latter, 1 foot = 0.3048 m and 1 m = 3.282 ft.

Acknowledgements

My debt to Sharon Murphy for her calligraphy is self-evident.   Her attractive and intelligent translation of my rough version to its final form is a monument to her skill and patience and I count myself fortunate to have found such a skilled and co-operative collaborator.

I have at times sought, and obtained, information or help from various colleagues and friends and I thank Toby Carrick, Gina Devlin, Malcolm Elliott, Terry Gledhill, David Glen George, John Gwynfryn Jones, Elizabeth Haworth, Ivan Heaney, John Hilton, David Morley, Harold Mundie and Jack Talling, as well as my son, David, for telling me what I wanted to know or for dispelling my ignorance.   Coral Hogben and Olive Jolly helped in various ways and Barry Tullet provided a photograph from which one of the illustrations was made.

The book relies heavily on illustrations — there are about 800 of them.   Many of these I prepared myself, but others are borrowed from various sources, care having been taken to select good examples. Many of these were copied photographically by Trevor Furnass for whose invaluable help and advice I am most grateful.   Permission to use illustrations has been granted by :— Cambridge University Press (pollen grains, page 32, being part of a figure in H. Godwin's 'History of the British Flora'); Pat Wolseley and the Field Studies Council (flowering plants on pages 133—136 and 143); Sarah Corbet and the same body (Difflugia tests, page 158), Eric Hollowday and the Quekett Microscopical Club (figures of Euspongilla, page 169); the same artist-naturalist (rotifers, page 179, Notholca, page 180, Callotheca, page 181 and Pleurotrocha and Philodina, page 183, all from 'The Microscope'; T. B. Reynoldson and the Linnean Society of London (Dugesia polychroa, page 186 and the other triclad flatworms, pages 187—189; Alastair Graham (leech locomotion, page 207); N. Møller Andersen (Microvelia, page 264, the feeding Hydrometra, page 265, and some of the bugs used in the figure on page 267); Sir Richard Southwood (nymph of Nepa, page 269 and Micronecta, page 271); N. E. Hickin (caddises, pages 274—276, Philopotamus, page 278, Hydropsyche, page 279, Plectrocnemia, page 280, and the figures on pages 281—284); Petur Jonasson (Chironomus, page 306); the British Museum (Natural History) (mosquito figures, pages 300 and 301, Pericoma, page 314 and the larva of Eristalis, page 315); the Zoological Society of London (chironomid larvae pages 307 and 308) and the Quekett Microscopical Club (Rheotanytarsus, page 308), all by Barbara Walshe who I have been unable to locate; the British Ecological Society (Ancylus, page 219, slightly modified, and the head of the male minnow, page 334); the British Mammal Society (mammals on pages 350 and 351); and the Royal Society and the Yorkshire Naturalists' Union for permission to use some of my own illustrations previously published in their journals.

Clive Pinder, Bland Findlay and John Gwynfryn Jones provided certain figures of chironomid larvae, protozoans and bacteria respectively while Eric Hollowday specially drew what he regarded as an improved version of his already elegant illustration of the rotifer Polyarthra. These I gratefully acknowledge.

I have also been fortunate to be allowed to make use of illustrations by various workers that have appeared in the Scientific Publications series of the Freshwater Biological Association and its now associated Culture Collection of Algae and Protozoa of the Natural Environment Research Council, for which I am also grateful. While it may seem invidious to mention particular individuals in this connection, Alan Brook's attractive illustrations of desmids and Noel Hynes' stonefly nymphs demand such. Some illustrations are modified from those of others and yet others are from old works, copyright to which has lapsed and which would in any case usually have been untraceable, but I express gratitude to artists and naturalists long gone whose work is, I hope usefully, perpetuated here. Modified figures include those of certain algae (G. Prescott) internal seiches (C.H. Mortimer), vegetation maps and shorelines (W.H. Pearsall) and certain prosobranch molluscs (V. Fretter and A. Graham).

The arrangement of the illustrations and the task of fixing them in position proved to be more complicated and time-consuming than anticipated. For help in this I am grateful to my wife, Vivien, who also 'proof read' all the sheets and checked the index, and who tolerated heaps of paper — the original sheets are larger than the printed version — debris on the floor, and such inconveniences as the loss of the dining room table, or part of it, for long periods.

A special word of thanks is due to David Sutcliffe who not only dealt with the mechanics of seeing the work through the press but read the entire script and drew attention to certain recent changes in nomenclature, a matter that prompted the following postscript.

For various, often good, reasons, the scientific names of plants and animals sometimes change. Some of those used here may do so in the future. Indeed, I recently learned that the snail long known as Potamopyrgus jenkinsi, and so called herein, which is an invader of Britain whose origin was mysterious, is evidently a New Zealand species that had been given the name P. antipodarum as long ago as 1843. Henceforth, unless recent work can be disproved, the snail in question should therefore go by the latter name. While granted this mention on the threshold, the new (or old!) name is not, however, used in the text.

The rocks beneath : the geological setting

Apart from the superficial, but dramatic, sculpturing of the area by the last glaciation and the gradual and ever-present changes wrought by weathering and deposition (page 10) the main structural features of the Lake District were established millions of years ago. The present rock formations are the result of a long series of events, sometimes gradual, sometimes cataclysmic, which included volcanic activity, submergence beneath the sea, re-emergence, earth movements, deposition and erosion.

In essence the Lake District consists today of a central dome of Palaeozoic rocks laid down in the Ordovician and Silurian periods between 400 and 500 million years ago, encircled by younger, but in some cases ancient, rocks of various ages. The oldest rocks, of Ordovician age, lie in the north of the district; the Silurian rocks, which follow next in geological time, in the south. The Ordovician rocks are of two types. To the north, and the oldest, are the Skiddaw Slates. These take their name from Skiddaw, a mountain carved from them. They are sedimentary rocks — built up from material eroded from even older rocks. Mostly of a clayey nature, they include also beds of grit and even conglomerate. In spite of their name they do not generally make good slates. Leaden blue, sometimes darker, even black in colour, they usually break into small pieces

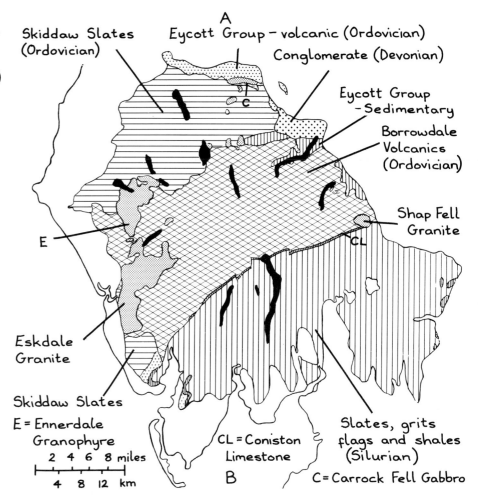

Skiddaw Slates (Ordovician)

A
Eycott Group - volcanic (Ordovician)

Conglomerate (Devonian)

Eycott Group - Sedimentary

Borrowdale Volcanics (Ordovician)

Shap Fell Granite

E

Eskdale Granite

Skiddaw Slates
E = Ennerdale Granophyre

2 4 6 8 miles
4   8   12 km

CL = Coniston Limestone

B

Slates, grits flags and shales (Silurian)

C = Carrock Fell Gabbro

The geological setting of the English Lakes
(Some regard the sedimentary Eycott rocks as Skiddaw Slates)

1

		Time before present in millions of years.	
	Present		
The Ice Ages ———→	Pleistocene		
	Pliocene	2	
When the final doming of the region may have occurred	Miocene		Tertiary
	Oligocene		
———→	Eocene		
		65	
	Cretaceous		
	Jurassic		Mesozoic
	Triassic		
	Permian		
The Lake District rocks were laid down in these periods.	Carboniferous		
	Devonian	350	
	Silurian	400	Palaeozoic
	Ordovician	440	
	Cambrian	500	
	Pre-Cambrian		

The chronology of major events in the geological history of the Lake District.

when weathered. Because of this even the mountains composed of them, of which Blencathra (= Saddleback) is the most splendid example, have rounded rather than angular contours. A small inlier of Skiddaw Slate occurs in the south west of the area, around Black Combe.

Because the Skiddaw 'slates' are not all of the same composition and some of them have been metamorphosed by heat or pressure (see page 5) they provide a variety of settings for lakes and tarns. Thus Bassenthwaite Lake lies in almost pastoral surroundings and has a shore-line that is much less rocky than those of Buttermere and Crummock Water whose setting is in rocks that have been metamorphosed by heat.

More Ordovician rocks make up the central part of the district. These are of volcanic origin — the Borrowdale Volcanic group. Of them such mountains as the Scafell, Helvellyn, Coniston and High Street ranges are composed. These are hard rocks, derived from the ejecta- menta either poured or shot out by volcanoes — sometimes beneath the sea — and are very varied in nature. Most common are slates and porphyries, often green in colour — the green slates of certain quarries are famous — but include also ashes, agglomerates and a variety of others. The lavas are very resistant to weathering. Ashes might be thought to be otherwise but these are often also very hard, having been altered by heat and pressure to give rise to flinty rock. The volcanic rocks break into large pieces. Beds of weaker slates add to the irregularity, and rugged, craggy scenery results. Many present-day crags of Borrowdale Volcanic rocks are the result of tearing and plucking by glaciers in what, geologically speaking, were very recent times. Lakes and tarns on these rocks are often bounded by such crags, as is readily apparent to the traveller along Thirlmere, or to those who ascend to Stickle Tarn. It is Wastwater, however, that is the classic example of a lake lying on the Borrowdale Volcanic rocks.

Formerly confused with the Borrowdale Volcanics, but now known to be older, are rocks of the <u>Eycott Group</u>. These are mostly volcanic, but those around the north end of Ullswater, still regarded as Skiddaw Slates by some, are sedimentary (largely mudstones).

A final zone of Ordovician rocks, the youngest, is a thin band of limestone which traverses the district at the southern boundary of this series. This is the Coniston Limestone - actually more of a calcareous mudstone - which was laid down under water. Although it crosses the Windermere basin its extent is too small to exert a significant influence upon the nature of the lake.

In the south most of the <u>Silurian rocks</u> are slates, shales, grits and flags. The so-called Bannisdale Slates, which cover most of this area, are clayey mud-stones, leaden grey, bluish or sometimes almost black in colour. Being much jointed and roughly cleaved they do not make good slates. Grits, often greenish, sometimes alternate rapidly with mud-stones to give characteristically striped rocks. The Bannisdale Slates, often with a covering of soil of moderate quality, give rise to relatively gentle scenery with occasional outcrops of rock, familiar to users of the roads between Kendal and Windermere. Of the major lakes Windermere, Coniston Water and Esthwaite Water lie largely or entirely on these rocks which, while hard, are less so than the Borrowdale Volcanics.

<u>Devonian rocks</u> are confined to a mass of conglomerate of which Great Mell Fell and adjacent areas are composed. These rocks impinge on the lower end of Ullswater but make up only a small part of its shore-line and drainage area.

As well as the major rock formations there are in the Lake District numerous <u>igneous intrusions</u>, large and small. These represent areas where the deep-lying molten magma has forced its way into the country rock and cooled slowly to form crystalline rocks such as granite that have been exposed by subsequent weathering over enormous periods of time. Intrusions occurred in Ordovician and Late Silurian - Early Devonian times, often many thousands of feet below the surface. These granitic outcrops are very diverse.

← North   South →

Skiddaw Slates	Borrowdale Volcanics	Silurian slates and grits
Sedimentary.	Volcanic.	Sedimentary.
Hard but less so than the volcanics.	Very hard.	Hard but less so than the volcanics.
Clayey 'slates', grits, some conglomerates.	Slates, porphyries, ashes, agglomerates etc.	Clayey and sandy mudstones, sandstones, grits.
Often bluish.	Often greenish.	Leaden grey, bluish or very dark.
Break into small pieces.	Shatter into large angular lumps.	Much jointed; often weather smoothly.
Give rise to scenery with smooth rounded contours.	Give rise to rugged, craggy scenery.	Produce relatively gentle scenery with occasional outcrops.

A synopsis of Lake District geology as it would appear in a section A–B on the map on page 1.

Most famous is the Shap Fell Granite in the east; perhaps most familiar is the Eskdale Granite which gives the red colour to the rocks and walls of the area, and which extends to the foot of Wastwater. Other igneous intrusions include the Ennerdale Granophyre, a very hard fine-grained rock of a pleasing pink colour which cradles the upper half of Ennerdale Water, and whose northernmost outpost is the appropriately named Red Pike whose feet are washed by Buttermere. A small intrusion of dolerite at Castle Head, Keswick, abuts Derwentwater, and there are diorites near Embleton and important microgranites at Threlkeld. Carrock Fell is famous for its complex intrusions of gabbro, granophyre and diabase and their associated minerals.

The great heat of these intrusions often altered the nature of the rocks into which they forced their way, frequently rendering them harder and more resistant to erosion than was originally the case. The region of metamorphosed rocks around the intrusion is called a <u>metamorphic aureole</u>. Thus the Ennerdale Granophyre has produced a metamorphic aureole up to 2 miles (more than 3 km) wide, and there is an unexposed igneous mass beneath Grasmoor with an equally wide aureole. These have hardened the rocks around Buttermere and Crummock Water and are responsible for the greater extent of crags and scree in the Grasmoor area than is typical of the Skiddaw Slates. Likewise an intrusion of granite that surfaces in three places north of Blencathra has metamorphosed the Skiddaw Slates into which it was injected, and hardened them sufficiently to permit the formation of two corrie tarns (Ice Ages and Lake formation – page 15), Bowscale and Scales Tarns. Such features are more usually associated with the Borrowdale Volcanic rocks. Chemical changes were also sometimes induced by the intrusion of molten rocks, and minerals are sometimes associated with sedimentary rocks so metamorphosed.

The history of an igneous intrusion and its effects

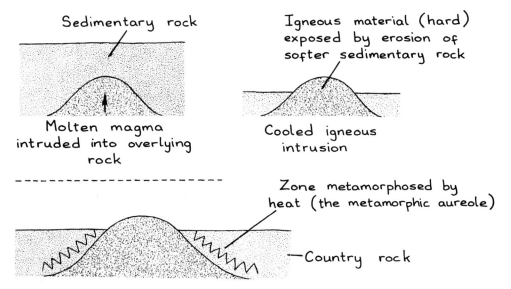

Sedimentary rock

Molten magma intruded into overlying rock

Igneous material (hard) exposed by erosion of softer sedimentary rock

Cooled igneous intrusion

Zone metamorphosed by heat (the metamorphic aureole)

—Country rock

The final uplift of the dome that forms the present Lake District occurred some time after the Triassic — probably in the Tertiary.   The shape of the dome was such that rivers ran down its slopes in a more or less radial pattern.   However, some of them evidently followed lines of weakness established before the uplift.   Over a long period of time denudation reputedly removed the younger rocks that many believe then covered the area and through which these rivers at first flowed.   Eventually they cut down to the older rocks beneath — those seen today — but retained their direction of flow.   If such a sequence of events occurred — and the idea certainly contains much truth — it provides a good example of what is called superimposed drainage.   However, if some rivers follow pre-existing lines of weakness in the underlying rock, these at least do not exhibit this phenomenon.

The uplift, like earlier movements, gave rise to faults — fractures on either side of which the rocks are displaced relative to each other.   The Lake District is criss-crossed by faults, many minor, some major.   The ancient (Palaeozoic) Coniston and Brathay faults displaced rocks by almost 2 km (well over a mile), as the obviously broken line of the Coniston Limestone on maps reveals.   Faults give rise to lines of weakness and facilitate erosion.   The largest dislocation in the Lake District is the Coniston Fault that runs north from Coniston Water, through Grasmere, up the Rothay Valley to the top of Dunmail Raise, through Thirlmere and away to the north through the Vale of St. John, separating the mountains into eastern and western blocks.

The lines of radial drainage, and the Coniston Fault, were later followed by ice streams and it was along these routes that the major lakes were formed.   This is why the present-day lakes are arranged rather like the spokes of a wheel radiating from the centre of the district.   An exception to this radial pattern is provided by Loweswater, a small lake that drains inland to the extreme northern end of Crummock Water, and not directly to the perimeter of the district.

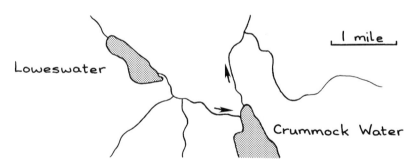

The inland drainage of Loweswater

6

Geology and the nature of lake basins

The kind of rock on which a lake lies, and which make up its drainage area, greatly influences its character. Different geological settings are often readily apparent. Wastwater and Esthwaite Water differ in many ways, not least in geology. Save for a small portion on the equally hard Eskdale Granite, Wastwater lies entirely on the Borrowdale Volcanic rocks, splendidly exposed in its famous screes. Bare rock is much in evidence and the wild mountainous scenery and paucity of human settlement bear testimony to the inhospitable nature of the terrain. The hard rocks produce poor soil and the land is ill-suited to agriculture. A few small fields at Wasdale Head and others below the lake, and therefore outside its drainage area, represent the only enclosed agricultural enterprises.

Being hard and resistant to weathering the rocks on which Wastwater lies, and from which it receives its drainage, yield salts grudgingly. Their soils are thin or peaty and of low fertility, being poor, or even lacking, in nitrates. The waters of the lake are therefore poor in those substances which, in water as on the land, serve as plant nutrients. Just as land plants produce meagre crops in poorly fertilized fields, so do the microscopic plants (algae- page 117) that live in suspension in ill-nourished waters such as Wastwater. Sparse crops in a lake mean a lack of green turbidity, and its waters, free also from silt of which hard rocks yield little, are beautifully clear and the lake looks blue in the sunshine. Only clear lakes are so blue. Different wavelengths of light penetrate water to different depths (page 83). Blue light (short wavelength) penetrates Wastwater deeply and is reflected back from the depths. If the lake supported dense crops of green plants it would look green. A clear-water lake such as Wastwater, whose waters contain little lime and are therefore also 'soft', produces water of high quality, much sought after by water engineers for domestic and industrial purposes.

The shores of Wastwater are predominantly rocky. Reed beds and stands of luxuriant vegetation are conspicuous by their absence. Only a limited number of animals like such shores and, reflecting the unproductive nature of the lake, such animals generally occur only in small numbers.

Wastwater — a fjord-like, rock-girt lake on hard volcanic rocks in mountainous terrain.

Area	2·91 km² (1·124 sq. miles)
Maximum depth	76m (249 ft)
Mean depth	39·7m (130 ft)
Percentage of shore-line rocky	73%
Percentage of drainage area cultivated	5·2%
Transparency	9–12m (29–39 ft)

No reed beds

8

Esthwaite Water — a lake on softer (but still hard) rocks in a drift-covered landscape. The mountains behind are composed of Borrowdale Volcanic rocks.

Area	1·00 km² (0·39 sq. miles)
Maximum depth	15·5m (50·8 ft)
Mean depth	6·4m (21·1 ft)
Percentage of shore-line rocky	12%
Percentage of drainage area cultivated	c.45·5%
Transparency	c.3m (10 ft)

Reed beds present

By contrast, Esthwaite Water lies entirely on the Bannisdale Slates that, while hard, are much softer than the Borrowdale Volcanic rocks. The area is well plastered with glacial debris (drift), (page 13) and the lake is located in gentle terrain. Rounded contours and modest heights prevail. Here the rocks and soils more readily yield up their salts. On land this gives rise to fertile fields which produce good crops of grass for hay and grazing, for the area has proved attractive to human settlement and exploitation. Likewise the lake produces good crops of microscopic algae - in sufficient numbers for them to render the water green at times. Blue light penetrates less deeply than in the clear waters of Wastwater, and Esthwaite is not noted for its blueness. Such water is of less interest to the water engineer than is that of a lake like Wastwater: it requires more treatment before it can be used.

The shore line of Esthwaite is 'gentler' than that of Wastwater, and more varied in nature. There are some stony areas, but reed beds abound, floating-leaved plants are in evidence in places and there is much submerged vegetation. A variety of animals frequents such a diversity of places.

Wastwater and Esthwaite operate as very different dynamic systems (page 72). Many of their differences stem from the nature of the rocks on which they lie.

Visual contrasts such as that between Wastwater and Esthwaite Water can be made from a single vantage point. The walker standing at the summit of Coniston Old Man can survey the wild scenery of the Borrowdale Volcanic rocks in the uplands and see Blind Tarn, Low Water and Levers Water, and, if he walks a little, Goats Water, all set in these hard, rugged rocks. There is no sign of cultivation here, and no trees. The tarns have predominantly rocky shores and no reed-beds. At the same time he can look down on the full length of Coniston Water which lies entirely on the softer sedimentary Silurian rocks. The contrast is striking. Here the land is of low relief, there are no crags, contours are smooth, green fields line a considerable proportion of the lakeshore, and woodlands do likewise. Only part of the shore is rocky and one can see reed beds even from this distant viewpoint.

The last Ice Age and the making of the English Lakes and tarns.

The English Lakes were born at the end of the last Ice Age, whose retreat was the last act in the drama referred to technically as the Pleistocene glaciations. The Pleistocene period lasted for almost 2 million years. During this period there were several glaciations – 'Ice Ages' – with a total duration of close on a million years. These were separated by intervals during which the ice retreated. The intervals are called interglacials. We may be living in one now. The last glaciation was the Devensian glaciation. This is the British equivalent of the Würm glaciation of Central Europe and the Weichsel glaciation of Northern Europe.

The great ice sheets.

In cold climates ice accumulates in valleys to form glaciers. At times of maximum glaciation, however, not only were Lake District valleys filled with ice, but the glaciers in adjacent valleys became so large as to over-ride the intervening ridges and coalesced to form a huge ice-cap which engulfed the whole area and was so thick that only the highest peaks protruded. Because, as now, there was much precipitation in the area – then as snow – the Lake District at times became a centre of glaciation from which ice flowed outwards.

It was however, only one of several centres of glaciation. Ice sheets covered the greater part of northern Britain, and the Irish Sea and North Sea basins were more or less filled with ice. Scottish ice from Galloway flowed southwards and met that flowing northwards down the northern slopes of the Lake District, much of which was deflected westwards – where it met the southward – moving Irish Sea ice, and was swung to the south. Ice from the Lake District also flowed eastward through the Tyne and Stainmore gaps as well as to the south.

At times congestion in the northern part of the Lake District caused ice from the Thirlmere Valley to flow backward over the col at Dunmail Raise, and some ice from the Brotherswater Valley likewise slid over the Kirkstone Pass.

As it flowed, the ice plucked boulders from the rock over which it passed and carried them elsewhere. Boulders of Lake District origin are abundant on the Lancashire and Cheshire Plain and occur in north and west Yorkshire and as far away as Nottinghamshire. Such ice-carried boulders are called <u>erratics</u>.

The power and work of the ice

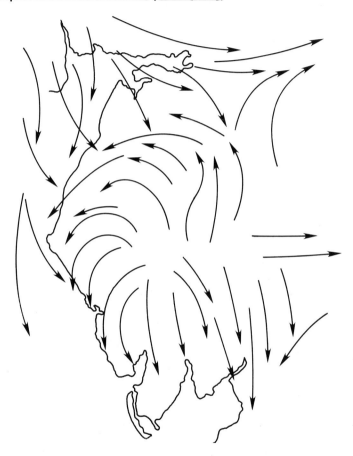

Ice movements in the Lake District during the 'Ice Ages'. In the Solway region the direction of flow differed as circumstances changed.

Ice is mobile, and as many millions of tons of it were on the move for long periods of time it scraped and tore the surface of the land and was responsible for many of the major landscape features of the present-day Lake District, including its lakes and tarns.

The ice naturally moved down the valleys. These were originally cut by streams and were V-shaped in section. The hallmark of a glaciated (ice-gouged) valley is its U-shaped section. A splendid example can be seen from the vicinity of Grasmere as one looks up Dunmail Raise. Because the major lakes lie in glaciated valleys they tend to be U-shaped in section.

The former direction of flow is often indicated by ice-scratched rock. Projecting rocks were left smooth and polished on the upstream side: often rough and irregular on the downstream side, and are often deeply scratched (striated) in the direction of flow. Such smoothed and striated projecting rocks are called roches moutonées. Travellers with a few minutes to spare as they wait for the Windermere ferry at the Bowness side can see an example of an ice-scratched rock. Now partly covered with soil and tree roots, this beautifully smoothed rock has deep parallel striations.

The power of ice is often demonstrated in valleys. Streams meander but ice tries to flow in a straight line. Thus when spurs of hills projected into a valley the ice often tore them away.

11

Such torn-off spurs are said to be truncated. A majestic example is provided by the truncated spurs of Blencathra on the north side of the Glenderamakin Valley. Such truncation, and deepening of a valley, by a glacier often leaves tributary valleys hanging above the main valley. Such hanging valleys, which often debouch into the main valley by a waterfall, are common in the Lake District. They provide habitats for a restricted, but specialised, assemblage of animals that like fast-flowing water.

The excavation and over-deepening of lake basins by ice

The power of the ice is also dramatically revealed by the way it excavated valley lakes. A notable feature of some of these lakes is that their lowest points lie below sea level. No such excavation could have been carried out by a river. Ice was the agent. When it gouged out such basins, of which Windermere and Wastwater are examples, the ice must have moved up the slope at the foot of the lake. This clearly reveals the mobility of ice, which in bulk flows under its own weight and behaves as a rheid.

Glaciers may move at a speed of several feet per day in summer. Rocks dislodged (plucked) and carried in the sole of the glacier serve as teeth and increase its abrasive power.

The basin of Windermere has been so over-deepened by ice-gouging that although its surface lies only 39 m (c. 128 ft) above sea level its maximum depth is 64 m (c. 210 ft). Furthermore, many metres of sediment have accumulated since the lake was

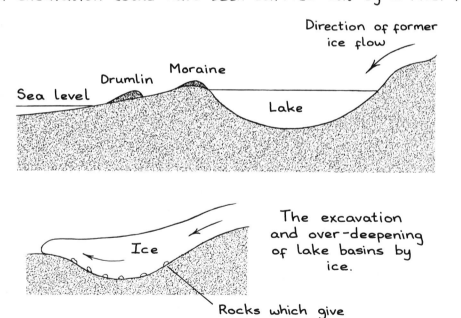

Direction of former ice flow

Moraine

Drumlin

Sea level

Lake

The excavation and over-deepening of lake basins by ice.

Ice

Rocks which give the glacier teeth

formed so its rock bed lies even further below sea level than these figures suggest. For Wastwater the comparable figures are 61m (c. 200ft.) and 76m (c. 249ft.). Some Scottish lochs have been much more over-deepened than this. The deepest parts of Lochs Lomond, Ness and Morar lie respectively 193m (633ft), 219m (718ft) and 301m (987ft) below sea level.

Glacial rubbish : its production and its disposal

Much material was ripped and scraped from the land by the ice and often ground into small pieces or into clay. This rubbish had to go somewhere and was dumped in various ways, often outside the Lake District. Because each successive glaciation swept away the debris of its predecessor, what remains today is the refuse of the last (Devensian) glaciation. Sometimes glacial debris, or drift, covers extensive areas : sometimes the material is concentrated into ridges or hummocks.

As glaciers melted they dropped loads of debris from their snouts at places at which they halted for a time. These are called terminal moraines. They are not particularly well developed in the Lake District where, apparently, the ice retreated quickly at the end of the last glaciation. Lateral moraines were left at the sides of the glaciers. Terminal moraines sometimes form natural dams across valleys that hold up lakes or tarns. Windermere appears to provide an example. Although it lies in rock basins, this lake is also apparently damned near Newby Bridge by glacial drift, including what is perhaps a terminal moraine. However, a seismic study has revealed that this material is scanty and lies over a lip of rock that would retain the lake at its present level even if it were removed, so Windermere cannot be regarded as a moraine-dammed lake.

Drumlins are also composed of glacial debris. These are low, smoothly rounded, whale-backed mounds that are found where the ice impinged on lower ground. They were formed beneath the ice. Their steep ends face the direction whence came the ice and their long axes lie parallel to its flow. Many drumlins derived from material originating in the Lake District diversify the landscape between Kendal and Lancaster and a splendid series extends around the northern perimeter of the Lake District. Their distribution shows most beautifully the anti-clockwise flow of the ice in the latter area. Excellent examples are to be seen rising from the margin of Esthwaite Water (page 22) and the islands of Derwentwater are the summits of drowned drumlins. Adelaide Hill, Windermere is another.

Corries and corrie tarns.

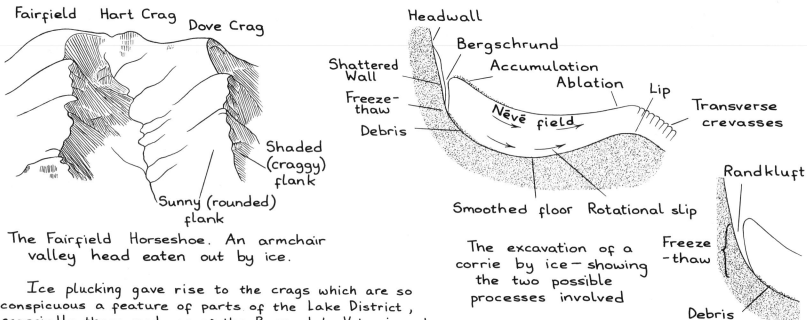

Fairfield Hart Crag Dove Crag

Shaded (craggy) flank

Sunny (rounded) flank

The Fairfield Horseshoe. An armchair valley head eaten out by ice.

Headwall

Bergschrund

Shattered Wall

Accumulation

Freeze-thaw

Ablation

Névé field

Lip

Transverse crevasses

Debris

Smoothed floor Rotational slip

The excavation of a corrie by ice – showing the two possible processes involved

Randkluft

Freeze-thaw

Debris

Ice plucking gave rise to the crags which are so conspicuous a feature of parts of the Lake District, especially those made up of the Borrowdale Volcanic rocks. Crags are often better developed on the eastern (shady) than on the western (sunny) side of the valley, showing that glaciers tended to melt on the sunny side of the valley. Ice plucking gradually ate back into the valley head. The Fairfield Horseshoe is a good example of a valley head eaten out by ice, which also shows craggy and rounded flanks and a basically U-shaped section.

A corrie or cirque, locally called a coum (or combe), has not infrequently been eroded at a valley head and is sometimes occupied by a tarn. A snow-filled hollow in such a situation causes freezing and thawing on the marginal rocks which disintegrate or 'rot'. The process is called nivation. Melt water removes debris to give a nivation hollow. Once a certain critical depth is reached, pressure turns the snow into ice, which continues the erosion. As the ice-filled hollow grows it nourishes a small névé field, or even a corrie glacier, which plucks rocks from its bed. Melt water, either trickles down the back wall of the corrie and down the so called Bergschrund –

14

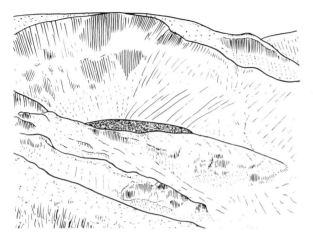

Bleawater - Lakeland's deepest corrie tarn

Corrie tarns Levers Water (centre) and Low Water excavated in Borrowdale Volcanic rocks in the Coniston Fells.

a crevasse near the back wall - or, as recent observations on ice-filled corries suggest, trickles between the back wall and the ice - the so-called Randkluft. This helps, by freezing and thawing, to eat away the wall. The latter process enables freeze-thaw action to take place over much of the headwall and leads to its rapid destruction. This basal sapping maintains steepness of the wall and provides abrasive debris. Rotational slipping of the ice, or plastic flow, lead to overdeepening of the basin.

 <u>Moraines</u>, sometimes crescentic in shape, often help to build up the margins of the corries.

 When such corries are occupied by tarns these are sometimes remarkably deep for their size. Blea Water, above Haweswater, with an area of only 0.173 sq. km, is 63.1m (207ft) deep and the somewhat smaller Levers Water is 38.1m (125ft) deep. Even the tiny Angle Tarn (Bowfell), only 0.034 sq. km in area, is more than 16m (53ft) deep.

 These tarns do <u>not</u>, as is popularly supposed, and as is stated in certain guidebooks, occupy volcanic craters. Far from being associated with hot processes they were excavated by ice. Although many of them lie on the Borrowdale Volcanic rocks this is not always so. Bowscale Tarn and Scales Tarn are fine examples on the sedimentary Skiddaw Slates. The rocks on which Bowscale Tarn lies are indeed of sedimentary origin, but beneath them is a granite intrusion (with small outcrops in the region of the Upper Caldew Valley) whose intense heat produced around itself a metamorphic aureole (page 5). The rocks so affected became metamorphosed into chiastolite slate. Scales Tarn

15

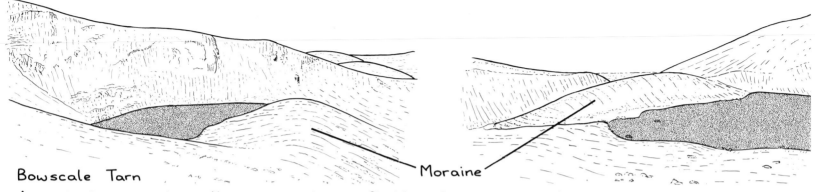

Bowscale Tarn

A corrie tarn on thermally metamorphosed Skiddaw Slates, dammed by a magnificent moraine

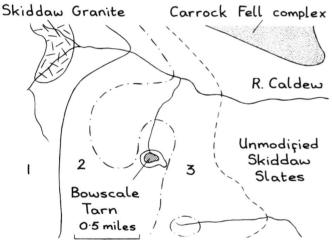

The location of Bowscale Tarn in relation to an intrusion of Skiddaw Granite and its metamorphic aureole. The granite is exposed in certain places. The nearer to the intrusion, the more strongly are the slates metamorphosed. Three zones are recognisable. Because the rocks on which Bowscale Tarn lies form a deep hollow, and therefore come close to the intrusion, they are highly metamorphosed.

lies just beyond the recognised limits of the aureole, but the rocks on which it lies were probably hardened by the intrusion.

The moraines that dam, and make deeper, some of these corrie tarns are sometimes impressive from below, even when the tarn itself cannot be seen. Such is the case at Bowscale

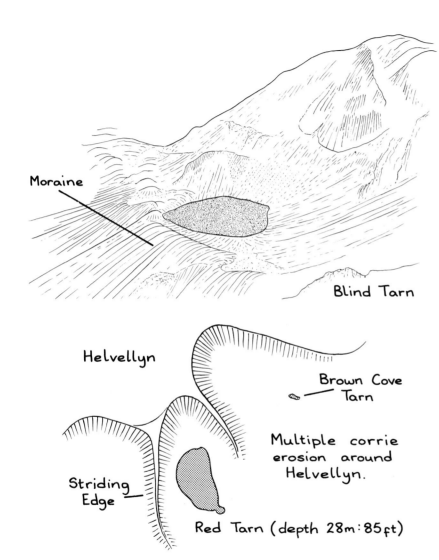

Moraine

Blind Tarn

Helvellyn

Brown Cove
Tarn

Multiple corrie
erosion around
Helvellyn.

Striding
Edge

Red Tarn (depth 28m : 85ft)

Tarn and Blind Tarn, Coniston. On a clear day the moraine of the latter can be well seen with binoculars from Orrest Head above Windermere!

Not all corrie tarns have a moraine, crescentic or otherwise. Low Water on Coniston Old Man, under the towering 275m (900ft) Buckbarrow Crag, lacks such. A morainic mound at its lip, containing many huge boulders, rent from the crag by ice, does nothing to contain its waters, which escape to one side of it. To the south, well up the hillside, is morainic debris that, had it continued around the tarn, would have rendered it much deeper than it is. This corrie too can be contemplated from Orrest Head and compared with that holding Blind Tarn.

Sometimes corrie erosion has eaten back into adjoining corries to such an extent that the ridge which separates them is reduced to a narrow knife-edge — an arête — of which Striding Edge on Helvellyn is the finest Lake District example. Helvellyn has been subjected to corrie erosion from several sides and Striding Edge is only the most striking of the ridges which separate adjoining corries. One of the corries holds a substantial tarn — Red Tarn — and there is a small tarn in the adjacent Brown Cove.

Upland ice-scooped lakes and tarns

The major Lake District lakes lie in valleys. This is where the maximum weight and abrasive power of the ice was concentrated. However, the ice sheet also covered the uplands, in some of the flatter tracts of which it scraped out shallow basins which, sometimes dammed by drift, became lakes or tarns when the ice retreated. As the highest parts of the district are mountainous, such ice-scraped regions and their tarns lie at no great altitude. Devoke Water, 234m (766ft) and Burnmoor Tarn, 254m (833ft) are examples, as are the small tarns on Haystacks. Ice-scooping may also have played a part in the formation of Blea Tarn (Armboth).

There are, however, a few upland valley tarns rather like the lowland lakes in some respects. A southward moving tongue of ice gouged out the basin in which Seathwaite Tarn, 370m (1210ft) now lies. A lobe of this ice also slid down the adjacent valley that now holds Goatswater, 502m (1646ft). This lobe evidently ate back to some extent in a combe-like manner towards the present col at Goats House, but Goatswater is not a true corrie tarn. It is dammed by a congested mass of rocks that have fallen from Dow Crag, through which its waters seep out. It is only 13m (43ft) deep at its deepest point. Hayeswater, 417m (1373ft), with a depth of 17m (56ft) is another upland ice-scooped valley tarn.

Tarns amid morainic debris

Jumbled morainic debris can provide hollows in which ponds and tarns can form. When the parallel valleys of Kentmere and Longsleddale were each occupied by a glacier there was a period when they were separated by the ridge of high land between them. Here, as a product of both glaciers, morainic debris accumulated. Among this debris Skeggles Water occupies a hollow as, at a somewhat lower altitude, does Gurnal Dubs.

Blea Tarn (Armboth) – there are three Blea Tarns in the Lake District – may have had a similar origin amid debris produced by glaciers moving down Borrowdale and the Thirlmere Valley and local debris from Ullscarf, but snow-field erosion (nivation) has been suggested as a means of its formation, and ice-scooping may have been involved. Not every detail of lake and tarn formation is yet understood.

Kettles and kettle-holes

Small lakes or tarns known as kettles or kettle-holes owe their origin to a yet different consequence of glacial action. Because of the way they form, these are more common in flat than in hilly country and are rare in the Lake District. Sometimes glacial outwash, itself derived from glacial drift, carried lumps of ice, icebergs in effect; or such lumps were left stranded by the retreating glacier or ice sheet and became embedded in detritus. When these melted, lakes or tarns were formed. Such tarns tend to be steep sided.

Mockerkin Tarn on the western fringe of the Lake District is an example of a kettle hole. Although reputed to be 'bottomless' it is only 3m (10ft) deep.

Such tarns were sometimes small and some have become extinct since they were formed. Two small kettle holes formerly existed alongside Blelham Tarn but were gradually converted into mires. These are now protected as the Blelham Bog National Nature Reserve.

The name kettle does not indicate any similarity to the utensil used for boiling water. It comes from the Kettle Range in N. America where such lakes are numerous.

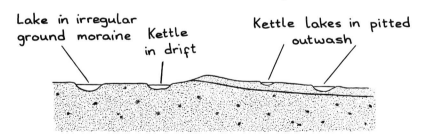

How kettle holes are formed

Ice action and subsequent events in the Buttermere Valley

The Buttermere Valley displays many features that illustrate glacial and post-glacial moulding of the landscape and the making of lakes and tarns. Two glaciers which carved Fleetwith Pike, one grinding down the valley of Gatesgarth Beck, the other down that of Warnscale Beck, united to form a single ice stream that scooped out the U-shaped valley now occupied by Buttermere and Crummock Water, which were originally one lake. In so doing it tore away spurs of the hills on the western side of the valley, leaving hanging valleys. From these, streams now tumble precipitously, the most spectacular being Sourmilk Gill — best seen after rain. Corries were also excavated on that, the shaded, side of the valley. That from which Sourmilk Gill issues contains a tarn — Bleaberry Tarn — almost 6m (19ft) deep.

Subsequent events — deposition of debris — produced an alluvial flat at the head of the lake, and another that eventually divided it into the present day Buttermere and Crummock Water. The formation of a dividing flat was made easier by the shallowness of the lake at this point. Only a few feet beneath the deposited material is a rock bar. The resistance of this bar to the ice may be due to metamorphic hardening by the adjacent intrusion of Ennerdale granophyre.

It seems likely that these large expanses of debris were for the most part deposited shortly after the retreat of the ice, at which time lots of large stones and unconsolidated detritus would be lying around. Two deltas are seen in Buttermere. These are not particularly common features on such exposed shores where deposited material tends to be carried away by wave action and redistributed.

Geological and physiographic features of the Buttermere area

Crummock Water — Alluvial flat dividing former lake — Buttermere — Flat — Delta — Sourmilk Gill — Dolerite intrusion

BVS = Borrowdale Volcanic Series

Unstippled areas are of Skiddaw Slate.

Ennerdale granophyre

Ling Comb   Red Pike   Bleaberry Tarn   High Stile   BVS

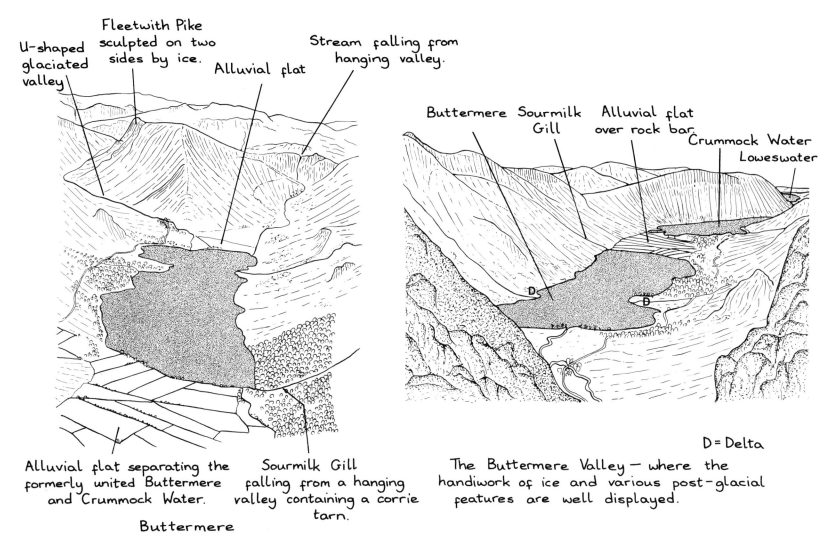

U-shaped glaciated valley

Fleetwith Pike sculpted on two sides by ice.

Alluvial flat

Stream falling from hanging valley.

Buttermere Sourmilk Gill

Alluvial flat over rock bar

Crummock Water Loweswater

D = Delta

Alluvial flat separating the formerly united Buttermere and Crummock Water.

Sourmilk Gill falling from a hanging valley containing a corrie tarn.

Buttermere

The Buttermere Valley — where the handiwork of ice and various post-glacial features are well displayed.

The Windermere Valley ice-stream and its offspring:
the making of Esthwaite Water and Blelham Tarn.

Except for the complication that it is made up of twin basins, Windermere is a good example of an ice-gouged valley lake. During its excavation, some ice from the mainstream glacier was, at least for a time, diverted over the low ground on which Blelham Tarn and Esthwaite Water now lie and was responsible for their excavation. This ice stream continued down the Cunsey Valley to rejoin the main flow. The extra abrasive power conferred by its contribution to the main ice stream may help to explain why a second, southern, basin was excavated in Windermere. As it passed over what is now Esthwaite Water the ice deposited several drumlins, the largest of which today constitutes what is almost an island on the west shore, Strickland Ees.

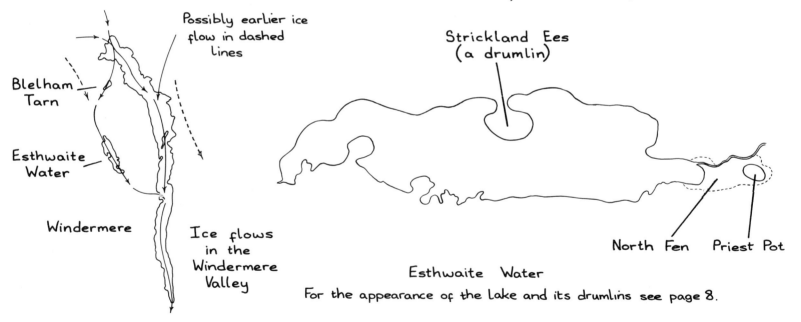

Possibly earlier ice flow in dashed lines

Blelham Tarn

Esthwaite Water

Windermere

Ice flows in the Windermere Valley

Strickland Ees (a drumlin)

North Fen   Priest Pot

Esthwaite Water
For the appearance of the lake and its drumlins see page 8.

Derwentwater and Bassenthwaite Lake.

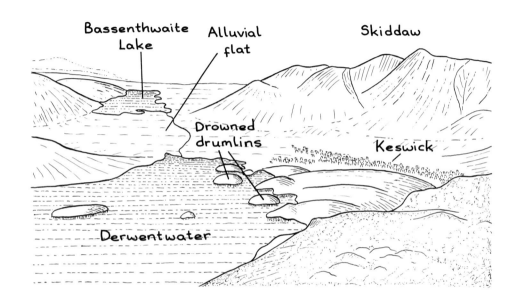

Bassenthwaite Lake

Alluvial flat

Skiddaw

Drowned drumlins

Keswick

Derwentwater

The lower part of Borrowdale reveals the work of ice in a broad valley and is also instructive in showing the great changes that can be wrought in a short time as soon as the ice has departed. Like Buttermere and Crummock Water, Derwentwater and Bassenthwaite Lake were formerly parts of a single lake. This was the widest lake in the Lake District and, although narrower than its predecessor, the shallow Derwentwater retains this distinction today. When the ice of Upper Borrowdale had squeezed through the restricting gorge known as the Jaws of Borrowdale, whose hard volcanic rocks even the glacier could not dislodge, it spread out in the wider valley below carving the softer Skiddaw Slates into a broad U-shape. As the ice spread on this lower ground it deposited several drumlins which later, partially drowned, became islands. While wide, the upper reaches of Derwentwater are, however, still constrained, especially by a steep wall of Borrowdale Volcanic rock on its eastern side.

The originally large, but shallow, lake was divided in its middle region by material deposited by the River Greta and Newlands Beck. Today this is a large alluvial flat. It lies a little above the level of Bassenthwaite whose exit to the north has been somewhat lowered by erosion. Derwentwater is also being encroached upon at its head by extensive post-glacial infilling.

The tarns of the Langdale Valleys.

A side-stream of ice was involved in the making of Blea Tarn, Langdale. During the period of intense glaciation, some of the ice flowing down Great Langdale slid over the col below Side Pike and flowed into Little Langdale. When the glacier began to retreat there came a time when it no longer over-rode the col, and a huge lump of ice, deprived of its nourishment, lay stranded where Blea Tarn now lies, probably in an already ice-scooped hollow which its movements may have deepened. This lump, which probably grew each winter, and must have persisted for many years, eventually melted to give rise to the 7m (23ft.) deep Blea Tarn.

The adjacent, higher-lying, Stickle Tarn, excavated in a hanging corrie and partly held up by morainic debris, has been artificially enlarged to supply a former gunpowder factory in Elterwater. The lower-lying, formerly much larger, Little Langdale Tarn is situated on the valley floor and is moraine-dammed. Each of this trio of tarns thus owes its origin to a distinctive and different kind of glacial activity.

The tarns of Easdale.

When a glacier flowed down Easdale towards Grasmere it encountered a hard and resistant outcrop of rock at Belles Knott where there is today a steep, narrow gorge. As it melted, masses of clayey debris and boulders were held back here. These dammed an area on a shelf of more or less level ground to the north of the valley. Here Codale Tarn, with a maximum depth of only about 7m (23ft) formed.

Lower down the valley, below Eagle Crag, a smaller tarn was impounded by glacial debris but is now overgrown and no more than a marshy hollow.

Still further down, with crags behind it, lies the larger Easdale Tarn, with some features of a corrie tarn but also gouged longitudinally, and with a depth of 21m (69ft). Around its margin at its lower end, adjacent to the narrow gorge through which Sour Milk Gill escapes from it to the valley below, are many large mounds of glacial debris. (More than one steep, turbulent stream in the Lake District is called Sour Milk Gill). Here stagnant ice evidently melted, dropping its load to form this complex of hummocks that now hold back the tarn. These are some of the most striking and most easily accessible such hummocks to be seen in the Lake District. They represent the work of the last ice to be active in the area (page 31).

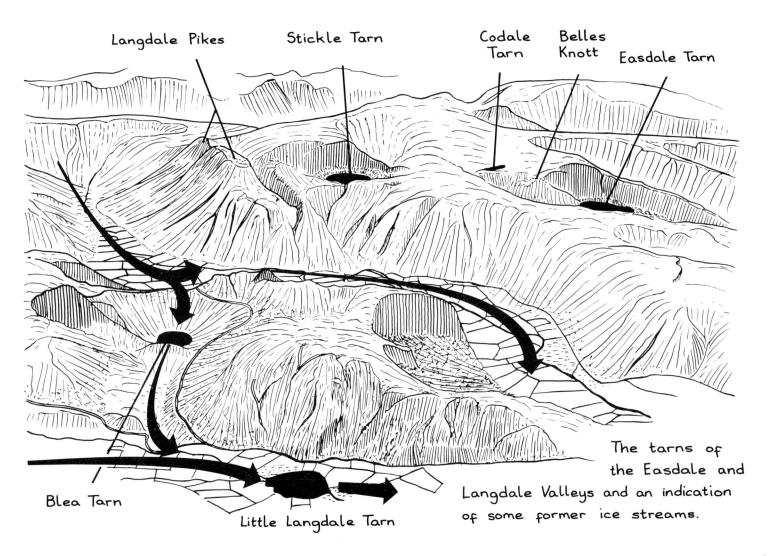

Langdale Pikes

Stickle Tarn

Codale Tarn

Belles Knott

Easdale Tarn

Blea Tarn

Little Langdale Tarn

The tarns of the Easdale and Langdale Valleys and an indication of some former ice streams.

The mystery of Ennerdale Water

Like other Lake District lakes Ennerdale is an ice-gouged basin. In its upper reaches the excavating ice was constricted, and gouged deeply. Here the lake is up to 42 m deep. Lower down the valley it was able to spill out laterally, losing much of its erosive power. Here the lake is shallow, nowhere more than 7 or 8 m deep, and often less.

In late glacial times Irish Sea ice blocked the valley. Behind this ice dam a _pro-glacial_ lake formed, as was the case in other western valleys. Its level once lay at about 244 m (800 ft) but gradually fell as the ice melted. Deltas formed where streams entered it and remain today stranded on the side of Herdus to the north of the present lake. Sediments from this vanished glacier lake occur in lower Ennerdale.

Today Ennerdale contains three crustaceans found in no other English lake. Elsewhere they are associated with glaciated regions. In the British Isles <u>Mysis relicta</u> (page 228) occurs in Ireland, <u>Limnocalanus macrurus</u> (page 232) nowhere else. <u>Salmincola edwardsii</u> (page 235), a parasite of the Char, occurs in a few Scottish lochs. How did these animals get into Ennerdale? <u>Mysis</u> and <u>Limnocalanus</u> may have migrated from the east along the margin of the retreating ice cap, and followed it north. About 12,000 years ago a surge of the still present sea ice may have trapped them below Ennerdale and given rise to a temporary lake — not to be confused with the earlier pro-glacial lake. Char carrying <u>Salmincola</u> could have become land-locked at the same time. Char colonising other lakes would be able to migrate (page 330) and may have lost their parasites later in the warming waters of the Irish Sea, then cut off from northern, colder, waters. The temporary lake, fed by meltwater and the overflow of Ennerdale, would fill rapidly and grant easy access to the latter lake.

A possible scenario about 12,000 years ago, and Ennerdale's present-day distinctive assemblage of crustaceans.

26

Lakes have a history. They are born, in the case of the Lake District lakes as a result of ice action; they age; and eventually they die. Already some Lake District lakes have died, having become silted up or drained (page 42). The lakes and tarns of the English Lake District came into existence only as the ice of the last Ice Age (the Devensian glaciation of the Pleistocene glaciations) retreated and melted away. In concise technical language they are said to be post-glacial in origin. Geologically speaking they are very young.

By various means the history of a lake can be unravelled. The most informative way is by reading the 'documents' preserved in its bed. Each year material is deposited on the bottom of a lake. For various reasons the nature of this material changes with time. The oldest deposits lie at the bottom of the pile, more recent deposits higher up. If one can obtain a series of samples of these deposits, from bottom to top, it is possible to deduce from what they contain, something about the conditions that prevailed at the time they were laid down.

The study of the deposits of Lake District lakes has not only helped us to understand the histories of the lakes but also to piece together the history of the district as a whole and to reconstruct the changes in climate, vegetation and human activity that have taken place during the past 15,000 years or so.

The sediments; their thickness and where they came from.

The thickness of the layer of sediment differs from lake to lake and in different parts of the same lake. There are several reasons for this, but in general they relate to different rates of deposition. A seismic survey enables the thickness of the deposits to be measured easily. This employs 'echo sounding'. A sound impulse is sent vertically downwards. It hits the deposits and is reflected back. Its speed is known so the time taken to make the double journey measures the depth at which the mud surface lies. Some of the sound waves also continue, at a different speed, through the deposits. These hit the rock floor and are reflected back from there. Again the double journey, this time from the surface to the rock bed and back, is measured. Simple subtraction gives the thickness of the sediment. In the North Basin of Windermere the sediments are more than 30m (100ft) thick in places.

Material sinking to the bottom of a lake can come from two sources. It can come from outside the basin, in the form of silt brought in by rivers and streams, as dust blown by

27

the wind, as dead leaves and other plant remains, and as faecal matter dropped by animals. In the unpleasant, but useful, language of the specialist, this material is said to be 'allochthonous'. It can also come from within. Such material consists of the remains of plants and animals that have lived and died in the lake; that were produced there, and is said to be 'autochthonous'.

Sampling the sediments.

The best way to obtain a continuous record of the sediments is by means of a core. If a tube, like a drain-pipe, is driven into the bottom muds and forced through the sediments to the bed rock it will penetrate 15,000 years of history. If it can be withdrawn with its contents intact, these — the core — will contain a neat sample of this history. Different sections of the core can then be studied.

A corer is rather more elaborate than a drain-pipe but the principle is exactly the same as if such a pipe were used. In practice the pipe is driven into the mud by some means — compressed air has proved convenient — and is extracted by blowing compressed air into a barrel-like extension of the tube, which drags it out of the mud and lifts it to the lake surface (and beyond!) where it can be recovered.

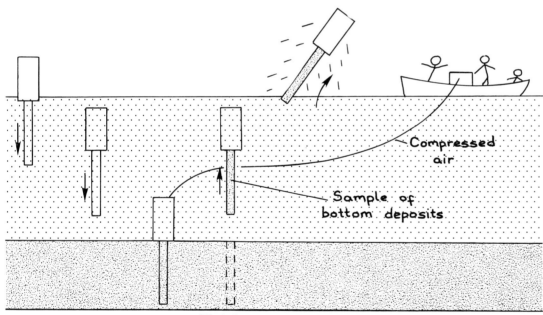

Compressed air

Sample of bottom deposits

Taking a core

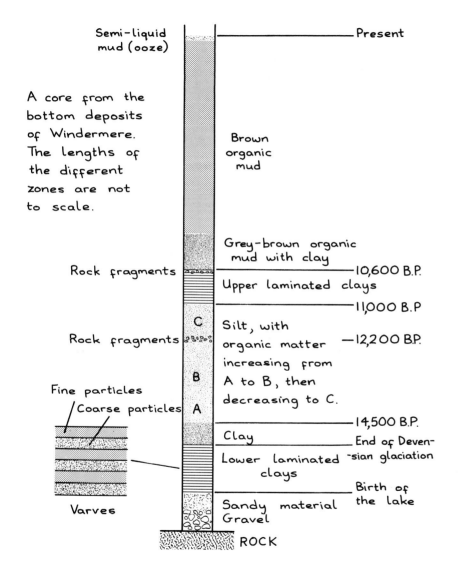

Semi-liquid mud (ooze)

A core from the bottom deposits of Windermere. The lengths of the different zones are not to scale.

Rock fragments

Rock fragments

Fine particles
Coarse particles

Varves

Present

Brown organic mud

Grey-brown organic mud with clay
——10,600 B.P.
Upper laminated clays
——11,000 B.P
Silt, with organic matter increasing from A to B, then decreasing to C.
——12,200 B.P.

——14,500 B.P.
Clay
End of Deven-
Lower laminated -sian glaciation
clays
Birth of the lake
Sandy material
Gravel
ROCK

C
B
A

By a happy circumstance some of the deepest (earliest) deposits are of sticky clay which effectively bung up the tube and retain the more friable upper layers.

A core and what it looks like.

In practice it is very difficult to take a complete core, but some clays deposited about 11,000 years ago make a convenient bung, and cores from deeper deposits can be 'joined' to these. Because of shore erosion and inwash of material, cores taken near the shore also differ somewhat from those taken in deep water. A deep water core is described here.

In Windermere the oldest deposits are cobbly gravels, fine gravels and clay which give way to sandy material. These were dumped by the ice as it melted.

Above them is a zone of regularly alternating bands of clay. At first as much as 2 cm (c. ¾ in.) thick, the bands get thinner towards the top where they are about 3 mm (⅛ in.) thick. The point where these laminated clays begin marks the time when the ice left the basin — when the lake was born.

The presence of laminated clays indicates that valley glaciers still persisted. Because everything froze, probably for

29

several months, in winter, material was brought in by melt-water only during the warmer months when the lake was open and stirred by winds. Coarse particles settled quickly. During winter, when all was calm beneath the ice and the glaciers were well frozen, the fine particles settled out. Thus each year a layer of coarse and a layer of fine particles were deposited, which gives these deposits their laminated appearance. These annual layers are called <u>varves</u>. They are analogous to tree rings. In some parts of Windermere there are about 15m (50ft.) of such laminated clays. Their upper boundary marks the end of the Devensian glaciation.

These clays give way to a zone of non-laminated clay, then to silts.

Following the retreat of the ice, the land around the lakes was bare—there were no trees and no grass, apparently only mosses and a few alpine plants (page 35) — and the lakes themselves, which were cold, were only just beginning to be colonised by plants and animals. The earliest deposits were therefore largely of inorganic origin—clay and silt. Because the silts contain at least some, but not much, organic matter (carbon), derived from plants and animals which gradually colonised both lakes and the surrounding land, it is possible to date them by the technique of radio-carbon dating. We can thus obtain a series of dates at different depths—an absolute chronology. The silts began to be deposited about 14,500 years ago — at about 14,500 BP (Before Present). At this time both the lakes and the surrounding land were becoming increasingly colonised by plants and animals. The bare 'soil', mostly clay and easily eroded, became clothed by a protective, but still sparse, layer of vegetation, fragments of which were washed and blown into the lakes. Remains of organisms living in the lakes also sank to the bottom. Some of these disintegrated and were reduced to minute unrecognisable fragments: others were preserved, in effect as fossils. The nature of the inhabitants of both the lakes and the surrounding land changed with time, and climate, so the fossils did likewise. They throw much light on lake history and on the history of the Lake District as a whole.

For a time the carbon content of the silts gradually increased—indicating favourable conditions for life. At about 12,200 BP rock fragments appear for a time, indicating increased erosion on the land, which, with the fossil evidence (page 31) indicates a sudden cooling of the climate. The carbon content then began to fall. Animals and plants were less abundant.

At about 11,000 BP laminated clay again made its appearance and about 400 varves were laid down to form a layer of clay about 50cm (20in.) thick. This indicates a return of the ice to corries and valley heads in the drainage area, which made the lake turbid with clay from the ice melt. The varves show that these conditions persisted for 400 years or rather more. The hummocks so familiar in valley heads e.g. in Great Langdale and around Easdale Tarn (page 24) are the terrestrial remnants of material dumped by this ice. This was the last fling of the ice. It disappeared about 10,600 years ago, since when it has never formed even small glaciers.

Above the upper laminated clays is a long column of organic muds. At first grey-brown, with an admixture of clay, they are mostly brown in colour and represent the last 10,000 years or so of the lake's history. They are topped by a thin layer of semi-liquid black ooze derived from the most recent material to fall to the bottom.

What we find in a core and what the findings tell us.

The gross examination of a core tells us quite a lot. Examination of its organic remains tells us a lot more. Although the mud at first seems uninteresting it contains a diverse assemblage of plant and animal remains. Although many of these are fragmented, they can often be identified with considerable precision. This is largely because parts of certain organisms preserve extremely well. It is convenient first to consider the kinds of remains that are found, without paying too much attention to their precise location, then to see whereabouts in the sediments they occur and what this tells us.

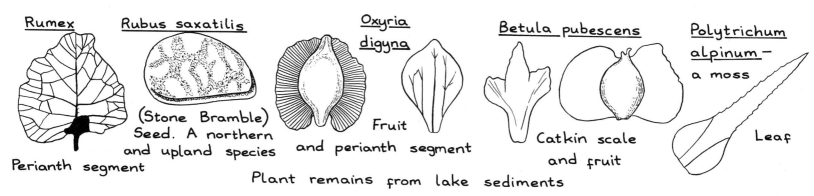

Rumex — Perianth segment

Rubus saxatilis (Stone Bramble) Seed. A northern and upland species

Oxyria digyna — Fruit and perianth segment

Betula pubescens — Catkin scale and fruit

Polytrichum alpinum — a moss — Leaf

Plant remains from lake sediments

31

Many of the most informative remains are microscopic but a few large chunks of terrestrial plants occur in some of the silts between the two zones of laminated clays. In Windermere these have been found in deposits in shallow water, which is where such material is most likely to settle. They include the leaves of various mosses, fruits and catkin scales of the Downy Birch, <u>Betula pubescens</u>, leaf fragments of broad-leaved flowering plants, twigs, bark and seeds, some of which can be accurately identified. Fruits of sedges, <u>Carex</u> and <u>Scirpus</u>, are common.

In shallow-water deposits the same zone contains the abundant remains of an aquatic plant, one of the Milfoils, almost certainly <u>Myriophyllum alterniflorum</u>, whose pollen grains are also present.

<u>Pollen grains</u> preserve extremely well thanks to their tough coat. Fortunately they are also very diverse in shape and ornamentation and many of them can be readily and accurately identified. Naturally it is pollen from wind-pollinated plants, which is widely dispersed by winds and often falls into lakes, that is best represented in the deposits. By a happy circumstance various tree pollens come into this category.

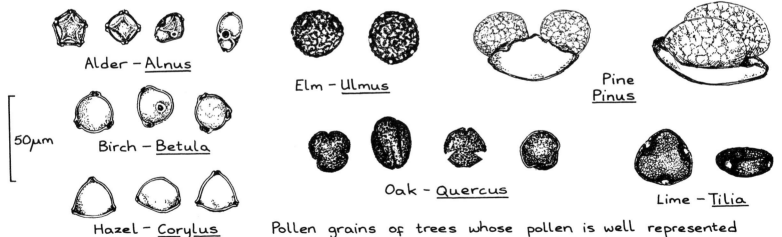

Alder – <u>Alnus</u>

50μm

Birch – <u>Betula</u>

Hazel – <u>Corylus</u>

Elm – <u>Ulmus</u>

Oak – <u>Quercus</u>

Pine
<u>Pinus</u>

Lime – <u>Tilia</u>

Pollen grains of trees whose pollen is well represented in the bottom deposits of Lake District lakes.

Trees are often the dominant plants in the landscape. If one knows which trees occurred at a particular time one can deduce a lot about the vegetation and about the climate that then prevailed. Furthermore tree pollen is often sufficiently abundant in the deposits to give a reasonable idea of the relative abundance of the different kinds of trees that were present at any given time and to trace changes in the fortunes of different kinds (species) of trees with the passage of time.

Fossil evidence is also provided by a group of minute aquatic plants — <u>diatoms</u>. Diatoms are algae (page 117) which have a skeleton of silica (silicon dioxide) — familiar as quartz — which naturally preserves very well. Diatoms can be so abundant in lake sediments as to form deposits that consist largely of their skeletons. Such deposits of <u>diatomite</u> or <u>diatomaceous earth</u>, are frequently exploited commercially. Diatomite is used in fine industrial filters, insulators and building materials, and as a very gentle abrasive in polishes and toothpaste. A Lake District source, exploited for many years, was an extinct lake in Kentmere (page 43).

Many different species of diatoms are found in the deposits of Windermere. Some are tolerant and were present throughout much of the lake's history without significant changes in abundance; others were plentiful when the lake was young and are now absent or rare; others made a late appearance or increased greatly in abundance in recent times, and one, formerly common, is now extinct in Britain.

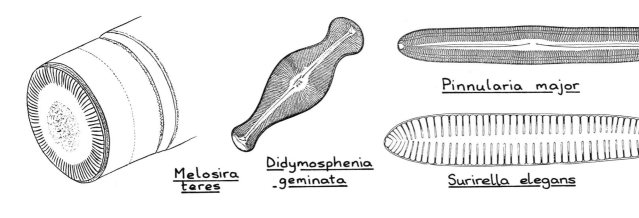

<u>Melosira teres</u>

<u>Didymosphenia -geminata</u>

<u>Pinnularia major</u>

<u>Surirella elegans</u>

Fossil diatoms from the sediments of Windermere

Even when no tangible remains are preserved, some organisms may leave traces that can be detected by suitable techniques. Thus pigments derived from algae are sometimes preserved in the sediments. In some cases the kinds of algae from which these came can be ascertained. For example, myxoxanthophyll, a pigment found in most Blue-Green Algae (page 128), is specific to these organisms. Likewise oscillaxanthin is specific to Blue-Green Algae of the family Oscillatoriaceae, and indeed is found only in Oscillatoria and one other genus. These pigments are to be found in certain sediments. Futhermore, the amounts present at different levels in the cores can be measured. By reference to the conditions under which their producers flourish, or fare badly, changes in the amounts of pigment with time can be related to changing environmental conditions.

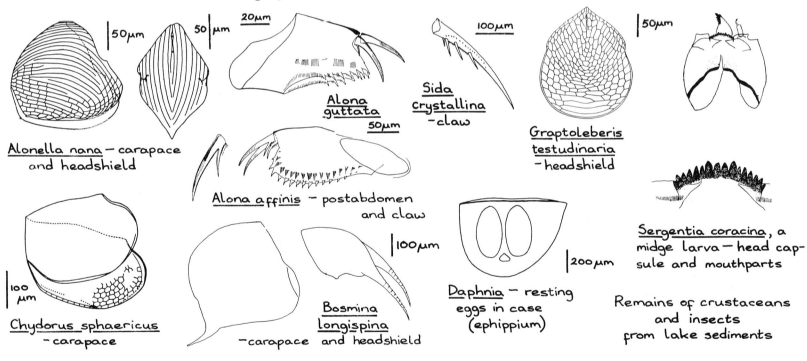

50μm

50μm

20μm

Alona guttata

100μm

50μm

Sida crystallina -claw

Graptoleberis testudinaria -headshield

Alonella nana – carapace and headshield

50μm

Alona affinis – postabdomen and claw

100μm

Sergentia coracina, a midge larva – head capsule and mouthparts

100μm

Chydorus sphaericus - carapace

Bosmina longispina -carapace and headshield

200μm

Daphnia – resting eggs in case (ephippium)

Remains of crustaceans and insects from lake sediments

<u>The animal remains</u> are also derived from both terrestrial and aquatic sources. Beetles have a hard exoskeleton, and even their detached wing cases (elytra) can often be accurately identified. Beetles also prove to be very sensitive indicators of climate. During cold periods, warmth-loving species are replaced by arctic-alpine forms : when the climate warms up the reverse process occurs. Some informative terrestrial beetle remains have been recovered from certain levels of the Windermere sediments but the record is less good than that of, for example, terrestrial deposits near the Cumbrian coast.

Remains of aquatic animals are diverse.* They include the tests of rhizopods (case or shell-bearing amoebae — page 157), the egg capsules of flatworms (page 189), resting stages (statoblasts) of the polyzoan <u>Cristatella</u> (page 177), the skeletal fragments of a variety of insects and crustaceans, fish scales, and occasional fish bones. The most significant remains of aquatic insects are those of the larvae of various midges. Midge larvae (page 305) have hard head capsules and it is these that survive. Most numerous of all are skeletal fragments of small crustaceans (water fleas — page 239) which are major components of some deposits.

Plotting the position in cores of these various remains and estimating their relative abundance whenever possible, enables a picture of change to be built up which can be dated by the radio-carbon technique. If we know which plants and animals like warm, or cold, climates, and under what conditions they flourish best, or find life hard, the changing assemblages in a core, added to the information provided by the silts and clays, tell us a lot about past climates, terrestrial vegetation and the changing conditions of the lakes themselves. Partly for convenience and partly because the muds of Esthwaite Water tell us something specific to that lake, the revelations of the Windermere plants and the Esthwaite animals are reported separately, but the general story applies to the whole district and to its lakes. The essence of this story is contained in the diagrams.

<u>What the plant remains of the Windermere sediments tell us.</u>

Until the glaciers left the valleys about 15,000 years ago it was very cold. Mosses and club mosses grew on the land, as did sedges and the Least Willow, <u>Salix herbacea</u>, a plant of mountain tops in Britain today. Gradually Birches, <u>Betula</u>, colonised the land,

*For living representatives of the animals mentioned here see page 157 et seq.

thinly spread at first, then forming woodland for a time with Juniper, <u>Juniperus communis</u>, as the climate gradually warmed up. Grasses and various herbaceous plants also began to colonise the district which had an apparently temperate climate by about 13,000 BP.

In the lakes various diatoms established themselves at the end of the Devensian glaciation, as did the Alternate-flowered Milfoil, <u>Myriophyllum alterniflorum</u>, which flourished in shallow water near the shore of Windermere. One of the diatoms common in the earliest deposits above the Lower laminated clays is called <u>Melosira teres</u>. This persisted for several thousand years then died out and is now extinct in Britain. It apparently occurs today only in areas of Russia and Alaska that experience severe winters. All the early colonisers among the diatoms were bottom-dwellers (benthic forms). Only considerably later did open-water (planktonic) species manage to establish themselves.

Midges, caddis flies, water 'fleas' (Cladocera) and the polyzoan <u>Cristatella</u> were among the first animals to arrive.

More or less temperate conditions prevailed for something like 900 years from 13,000 BP, then came a sudden cooling which reduced the amount of woodland in the Lake District. A beetle whose name, <u>Helophorus glacialis</u>, indicates its preferences, is recorded from this cool period which persisted for a thousand years or more before, about 11,000 years ago, arctic conditions temporarily re-asserted themselves. It is in the deposits laid down as they began to do so that remains of the Mountain Sorrel, <u>Oxyria digyna</u>, have been found. This is an Arctic-Alpine plant that today has one of its southern outposts in the uplands of the Lake District. The remains were accompanied by those of the moss <u>Polytrichum alpinum</u>, a species of mountains and moorlands. Glaciers were re-established in corries and valley heads, laminated clays were again laid down in the lakes, and many animals and plants were either exterminated or greatly reduced in numbers.

The final departure of the ice about 400 years later, to whose former presence the 'morainic' hummocks near so many valley heads bear witness, saw the beginning of a period of relative stability during which there were climatic fluctuations but of a less drastic nature than those experienced in the first 5000 years or so of the history of the lakes. As the climate gradually warmed up, being sometimes wet, sometimes dry, before eventually cooling again, woodland and forest covered much of the district. Scots Pine, <u>Pinus sylvestris</u>, quickly established itself and, in the early cool period about 10,000 years ago, it dominated the forests, but was early accompanied by Birch, Oak, <u>Quercus</u>, and Hazel, <u>Corylus avellana</u>.

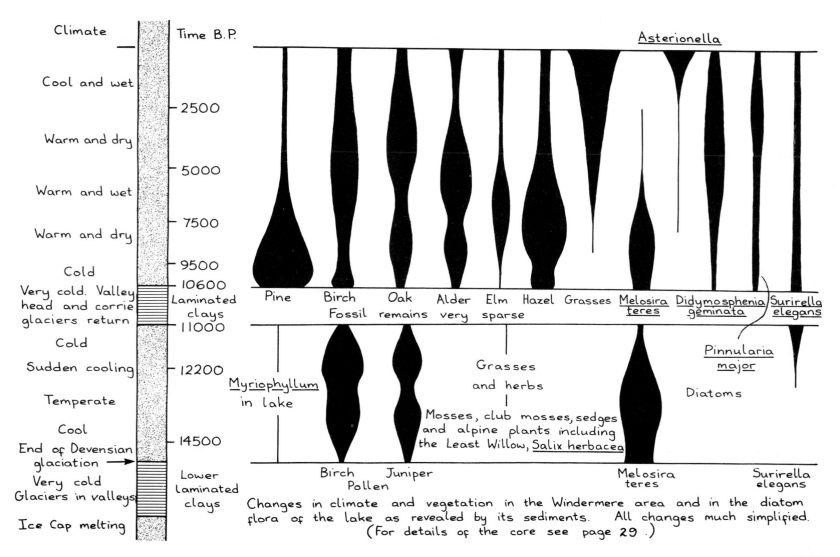

Climate

Time B.P.

Cool and wet

— 2500

Warm and dry

— 5000

Warm and wet

— 7500

Warm and dry

— 9500

Cold

— 10600

Very cold. Valley head and corrie glaciers return

Laminated clays

— 11000

Cold

Sudden cooling

— 12200

Temperate

Cool

— 14500

End of Devensian glaciation

Very cold Glaciers in valleys

Lower laminated clays

Ice Cap melting

Asterionella

Pine   Birch   Oak   Alder   Elm   Hazel   Grasses   Melosira teres   Didymosphenia geminata   Surirella elegans

Fossil remains very sparse

Pinnularia major

Diatoms

Myriophyllum in lake

Grasses and herbs

Mosses, club mosses, sedges and alpine plants including the Least Willow, _Salix herbacea_

Birch Pollen   Juniper

Melosira teres

Surirella elegans

Changes in climate and vegetation in the Windermere area and in the diatom flora of the lake as revealed by its sediments. All changes much simplified. (For details of the core see page 29.)

37

These latter gradually became more abundant than Pine.   Alder, <u>Alnus glutinosa</u>, established itself, presumably in the wetter places, and became important, and Elm, <u>Ulmus</u>, also arrived and became well represented.   Grasses, sparse at first, gradually increased, as did herbaceous plants.

In the lakes, diatoms, which had received a set-back during the minor triumph of the ice, quickly re-asserted themselves. Many species soon colonised Windermere and, with varying fortunes, persisted until today. <u>Melosira teres</u> was one of those which flourished at first but eventually it disappeared. In contrast, another diatom, <u>Asterionella</u>, although long present in Windermere, was unimportant until very recently and is now a dominant member of the plankton (page 126).

<u>Midges and Water fleas and what they tell us about the history of Esthwaite Water.</u>

The larvae of certain midges frequent the bottom muds in the deep water of lakes. Different midge larvae have different requirements and preferences.   In Esthwaite, larvae of <u>Sergentia</u> and <u>Tanytarsus</u> dominated the bottom muds until about 1000 years ago.   This indicates that the lake was well oxygenated in the deep water (page 73).   Another midge, <u>Chironomus</u>, then appeared.   Its remains are abundant in recent sediments, and living larvae abound in the lake.   Its arrival and subsequent increase in abundance was paralleled by a decrease in the abundance of <u>Sergentia</u> and <u>Tanytarsus</u>.   <u>Chironomus</u> belongs to a group of midges whose larvae can tolerate low levels of oxygen.   Its arrival and establishment indicate that Esthwaite was getting 'richer' (page 73) and perhaps suffering oxygen deficits in deep water in summer.   A similar story is told by the midges of Blelham Tarn, where <u>Sergentia</u> in particular was originally abundant but declined drastically as <u>Chironomus</u> gradually became dominant.

A tiny water flea, the cladoceran <u>Bosmina longispina</u>, was abundant in the open waters until about 1000 years ago.   This indicates that Esthwaite was until then a somewhat impoverished lake.   It was then joined by its close relative <u>Bosmina longirostris</u>, which likes 'richer' conditions, and which quickly became dominant, though <u>B. longispina</u> persisted in greatly reduced numbers.   The change-over occurred at the same time as that of the midges.   At the same time water fleas of the genus <u>Ceriodaphnia</u> appeared in the lake for the first time.   Remains of three species have been found.   These also indicate that the lake was becoming richer and supporting larger crops of algae which these open-water species used as food. A very different kind of water flea, <u>Bythotrephes longimanus</u>, present in the lake for 10,000 years, became scarce in the most recent deposits and is no longer to be found. This is probably another reflection of increasing enrichment, for <u>Bythotrephes</u> prefers the 'poorer' types of lakes. As was the case among the midges, similar changes took place in the water flea fauna of Blelham Tarn.

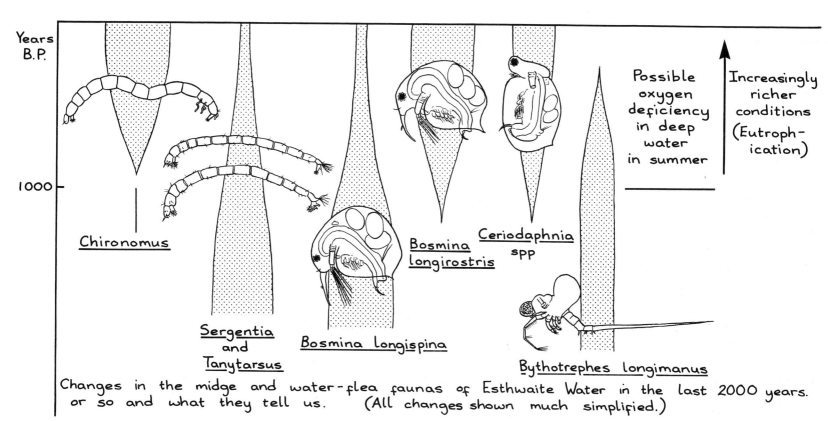

Years
B.P.

1000

<u>Chironomus</u>

<u>Sergentia</u>
and
<u>Tanytarsus</u>

<u>Bosmina Longispina</u>

<u>Bosmina</u>
<u>longirostris</u>

<u>Ceriodaphnia</u>
spp

<u>Bythotrephes longimanus</u>

Possible
oxygen
deficiency
in deep
water
in summer

Increasingly
richer
conditions
(Eutroph-
ication)

Changes in the midge and water-flea faunas of Esthwaite Water in the last 2000 years. or so and what they tell us. (All changes shown much simplified.)

Fossil magnetism

Preserved in lake sediments are what might be called invisible fossils: fossil magnetism. The horizontal component of the earth's magnetic field differs from place to place as mariners have long known. This variation is called magnetic declination. Further, at any given point on earth, deviations of the magnetic needle — a compass needle — from the true (astronomical) North Pole change with time. These changes with time are recorded in the sediments of the Lake District lakes. As they were laid down the sediments acquired a degree of magnetisation. Although slight, this is measurable with sensitive instruments. This magnetic remanence as it is called was aligned with the ambient field at that time — particles as it were lined up north – south in the then direction of magnetic north. Further, the magnetic remanence is sufficiently stable to have retained its direction during subsequent changes in the ambient field. The sediments of Windermere show that the horizontal component of magnetisation oscillates about the mean deviation with an amplitude of about plus or minus 20° with a frequency of about 2,700 years. This provides an accurate record of these directional variations since sedimentation began. The variations can be correlated with C^{14} dates and themselves provide a useful time scale.

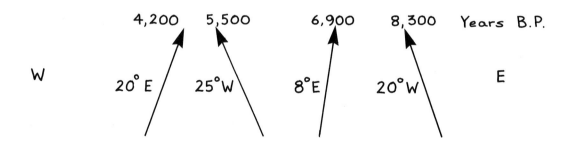

Change in the direction of fossil magnetism detected in the bottom deposits of Windermere.

Youthful exuberance, senility and death of some English Lakes.

When the lake basins became filled with water as the ice retreated, they were at first cold, barren places, inhabited by relatively few kinds of plants and animals. Paradoxically they were also, for a time, more productive than some of them are today and supported organisms that require more calcium (lime) and other bases than are present in the lakes today. Thus, early sediments contain assemblages of diatoms that prefer alkaline (limy) conditions.

This was true also of the surrounding land. The same early sediments contain pollen grains of two flowering plants, Jacob's Ladder, Palemonium caeruleum and the Hoary Rock Rose, Helianthemum canum, both of which require limy soil. The explanation is not far to seek. The glaciers ground up the rocks into a fine powder so that their salts were readily released. Although very hard, the Borrowdale Volcanic rocks in particular contain considerable amounts of calcium carbonate — sometimes visible as veins of white calcite. However, this is only accessible if the rocks are broken or crushed. Because the ice did just this, the young lakes were, for a time, richer in salts, and more productive, than they were to be as they became older. An influx of salts continued for many years, but gradually this capital was used up and youthful exuberance gradually gave way to a less productive phase. The diatoms tended to respond by changing to assemblages dominated by species indifferent to lime or which prefer acidic, lime-free waters.

Lakes and tarns age at different rates depending on their depth and the nature of the silt burden of the streams that feed them. One sign of old age is an encroaching alluvial flat at the head of the lake. Long, narrow lakes are not only susceptible to the deposition of silt at their head, but are particularly vulnerable to deposition by side streams. Deltas so formed sometimes extend into the lake and in some cases even build a barrier across it. Derwent Water and Bassenthwaite Lake are derivatives of a single lake. They were separated by material brought in by the River Greta and Newlands Beck. Buttermere and Crummock Water were also formerly continuous, as probably were Ullswater and Brothers Water.

There is no good example of a senile (senescent) lake in the Lake District though Elterwater, a heavily silted remnant of a once larger lake, must have shown signs of senility before its surrounding marshland was drained in the 19th century. On a smaller scale, however, Harrop Tarn, above Thirlmere, provides a good example of a senescent tarn. Senility is perhaps an unkind term to apply to this tarn. In due season its displays of Yellow Water-lily

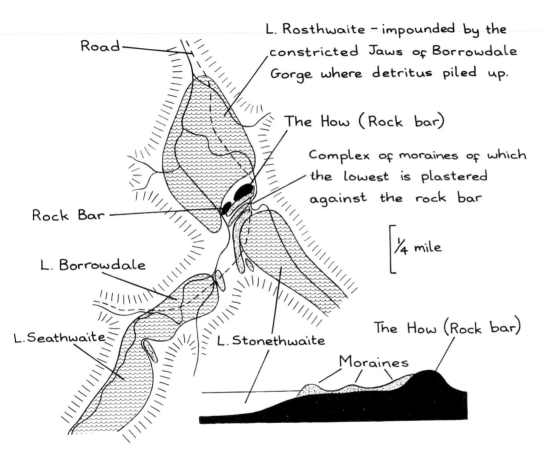

Road —

L. Rosthwaite – impounded by the constricted Jaws of Borrowdale Gorge where detritus piled up.

The How (Rock bar)

Complex of moraines of which the lowest is plastered against the rock bar

Rock Bar —

¼ mile

L. Borrowdale

The How (Rock bar)

L. Seathwaite

L. Stonethwaite

Moraines

Former lakes in Borrowdale and the rock bars and moraines that dammed them (Moraines stippled)

Nuphar lutea, Many-headed Cotton-grass, *Eriophorum augustifolium*, and Bog Bean, *Menyanthes trifoliata*, among the encroaching vegetation are very beautiful and it may be said to be growing old gracefully.

Several lakes have already died. Examples are to be found in Borrowdale and in Long Sleddale, where some of the moraines that helped to make them are to be seen.

The lowest of the extinct Borrowdale lakes (L. Rosthwaite) lies above the gorge known as the Jaws of Borrowdale. It was impounded by the debris that accumulated at this constriction in the valley. Above it was another lake (L. Stonethwaite). This was held up near the present Rosthwaite village by a combination of a rock bar — The How — and a further rock bar to the west of it and three terminal moraines where the snout of a glacier briefly halted. The uppermost

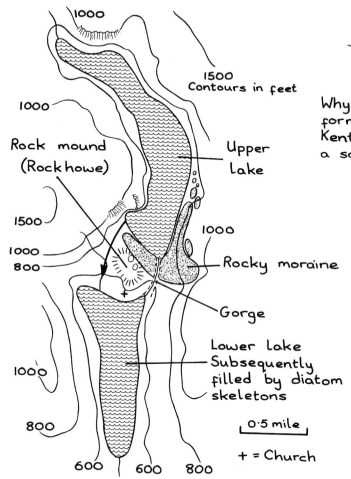

Former lakes in the Kentmere Valley.
Arrow shows original overflow of upper lake.

1000
1500
Contours in feet
1000
Rock mound (Rock howe)
Upper Lake
1500
1000
800
1000
Rocky moraine
Gorge
Lower lake Subsequently filled by diatom skeletons
1000
800
0.5 mile
600 600 800
+ = Church

Silt trap   Clear silt-free water
Diatoms flourishing

Why the lower of the two former lakes in the Kentmere Valley became a source of diatomite.

Diatomite (eventually almost filling the basin.)

moraine is the largest.   A public footpath runs along the summit ridge of its southern arm, affording a splendid opportunity to observe its shape and the way it rises above the valley floor. Other moraines impounded what may have been two lakes (Lakes Borrowdale and Seathwaite) in the Seathwaite valley, though at one time these may have been confluent.

There are two extinct lakes in the Kentmere Valley.   The upper, north of the church, collected the sediment borne by the river, so the lower, south of it, received clear, detritus-free water, and its sediments consisted to a large extent of the skeletons of the diatoms that flourished there.   These eventually filled in the basin, which was finally drained by man when the R. Kent was deepened.   Before it was drained this must have been a good example of a senile lake.   Subsequently the deposits of this dead lake were dug out over many years as a source of diatomite — and a new lake was created.   The upper lake committed suicide when the R. Kent gradually cut through an originally minor overflow in the supporting moraine and drained the basin.

Certain other lakes apparently cut their own throats when their effluent streams deepened their exit channels to such an extent that they were eventually drained.   Many tarns did likewise.   One such existed beneath Wolf Crags (Matterdale) where it was held up by a crescentic moraine.   This has been cut through by a stream, Mother Syke, and is now a soggy morass.

Where death has not ensued the process of ageing has in several cases been speeded up as the lake level has been lowered by this process.   Such level-lowering, as well as silting, contributed to the senility of Elterwater.

In Longsleddale there was a chain of four lakes, one above the other, along the length of the valley.   The demise of all these robbed the Lake District of a good example of what are sometimes called Paternoster lakes — a name given to such a series from a fancied resemblance to the string of beads that make up a rosary.

The influence of man on the history of lakes.

Although the date is uncertain, man probably settled in the Lake District, particularly on its fringes, about 6000 years ago, but may have frequented the adjacent coast, where the forest was probably thinner and the sea afforded food, 1000 years earlier than this. Sites adjacent to former tarns on the coastal plain proved attractive for settlement.   By about 3000 BC, Neolithic (New Stone Age) Man had already begun to affect the vegetation of the Lake District by felling trees, making clearances by burning, and by practising primitive agriculture.   He grew crops of early types of cereals and raised stock. Axes were made of local stone such as the fine-grained tuffs of Borrowdale Volcanic rocks obtained in Great Langdale and elsewhere.   His activities affected the run-off of water from the land, and therefore the sediments entering lakes.

About 5000 years ago, as indicated by a decline in the amount of pollen found in lake deposits, Elm trees of the area (and elsewhere) suffered a sudden set-back.   Some have blamed man for this, alleging that his collection of leaves and branches of Elm to feed his stock was responsible.   This is implausible.   Millions of trees were involved, the

44

human population was very sparse, and the very need to collect such fodder is questionable. An outbreak of Dutch Elm disease or something akin, is a more likely explanation.

Man's impact increased as his technology improved and his population grew. Stone implements gave way first to those of bronze, then to those of iron and ultimately to the use of modern materials, and became increasingly effective. Manpower was eventually replaced, at first partly by oxen and horses, in very recent times by machinery. Today's mechanised agriculture, forestry, land drainage and quarrying operations affect the material entering lakes. Some such activities have influenced the lakes for many years. Thus, about 1000 years ago, at the time of the Viking settlement in the area, much deforestation took place — as is indicated by the pollen record of lake sediments. This led to increased erosion of material from the land, and increased deposition in the lakes. Thus, from that time on, sediment has been accumulating in Blelham Tarn at an annual rate two to four times greater than before.

Populations, sparse at first, gradually increased to an estimated 70-80,000 for the entire Lake District in A.D. 1500. In 1986 the population of Cumbria (a somewhat larger area) was almost 484,000. Settlement occurred in areas conducive to agriculture. Land around Wastwater, Ennerdale Water, Buttermere and Crummock Water was unattractive in this respect and remains sparsely settled to this day. These lakes are therefore but little affected by man's activities. Land in the vicinity of Esthwaite Water was attractive to farmers and much of it has long been used and settled. Nutrients from the dung and fertilizers applied to the land find their way into the lake and enrich it, increasing the growth of plants just as they do on the land. Man also produces his own dung and domestic wastes. These too have long found their way into Esthwaite and do so via a plant treating the domestic sewage of Hawkshead which adds nitrates, phosphates and other nutrients to the lake. Similar sewage plants enrich Grasmere, Windermere and other lakes. Such enrichment has increased greatly in recent years. For example, in Windermere the average maximum phosphate phosphorus content of the water was more than six times as great during the seven year period 1966-73 as it was during the comparable seven year period 1945-52. This change has been accompanied by a decrease in the abundance of desmids (page 119) and an increase in the abundance of certain Blue-Green Algae (page 128).

Mining activities have also affected certain lakes. High lead levels in the sediments of Ullswater bear witness to former lead mining in its drainage area. A fish, the Char, which

formerly occurred there, may have been exterminated by lead poisoning as all Swans that settle there are reputed to be.   Copper was formerly mined in the Coniston area and this activity put much copper into Coniston Water.   The sediments show that, before mining began, about 0.045 gm of copper was deposited on each square metre of the lake bed each year.   This reflects natural leaching from copper-bearing rocks.   At the peak of activity of the mining industry, around 1850, the amount increased to 1.8 gm per square metre per year.   Much copper is locked up in the deposits of Coniston Water.   With the demise of the mining industry, deposition rates subsequently declined.
   Even in lakes unaffected by mining, atmospheric pollution has increased the amounts of

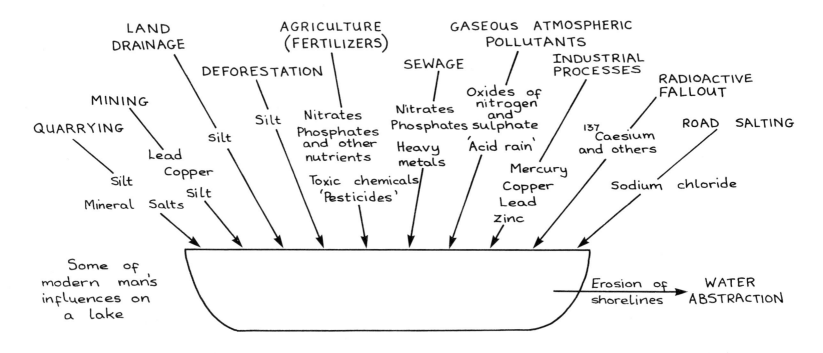

copper deposited each year. In the past copper was deposited in Blelham Tarn at the rate of about 0·002 gm per square metre per annum. This can be called the background rate. In recent times the rate has increased ten-fold, to about 0·02 gm per square metre per annum. Levels of lead and zinc have similarly increased in Windermere.

Man's activities also put mercury into the environment. Recent sediments of Windermere show that five or six times as much mercury is now finding its way into the deposits as was the case in A.D. 500, but the amount is still small.

Another source of certain chemicals, especially of common salt (NaCl), is salt used for de-icing roads in winter, many thousands of tonnes of which are scattered annually in the drainage areas of lakes. Such salt began to be used extensively on the relevant roads in the 1960s and 70s. During the 1981-2 winter, about 2,000 tonnes of it were scattered in the Windermere drainage area. Much of this eventually finds its way into the lake. It has been calculated that over a 20 year period (between 1956 and 1976) such salt has increased the chloride (Cl^-) content of the South Basin of Windermere by about 27%.

Industrial pollutants other than heavy metals also find their way into lakes via wind and rain. A much discussed recent phenomenon is that of acid rain. Oxides of sulphur and nitrogen resulting from the combustion of fossil fuels (coal and oil) acidify water droplets in the atmosphere which fall as acid rain. This has a deleterious influence on vegetation and on the animal life of certain kinds of lakes.

Agricultural pollutants (the toxic chemicals used as herbicides and pesticides) also find their way into lakes, and into the organisms that live there.

Fallout of radio-active materials put into the atmosphere by man is also incorporated in lake sediments. For example the testing of nuclear weapons in the early 1960s is faithfully recorded by increased amounts of ^{137}caesium in the deposits of Windermere and other investigated lakes. A peak in 1963 is clearly recorded.

Like weapon testing, the 1986 Chernobyl incident showed how radio-active material can be dispersed over vast distances. Because of its heavy rainfall as the radio-active 'cloud' covered the area, the Lake District received more fallout of radio-active iodine and caesium than most parts of Britain. These materials, especially caesium which remains active for long periods, are inevitably washed from the land into lakes, where their fate can be followed for many years by the use of appropriate techniques.

Modifications of lakes for the collection and abstraction of water are dealt with on page 94.

The development of shorelines

The lakes which came into existence as the ice retreated from the Lake District had barren, rocky shorelines. In some of those that lie on the hard Borrowdale Volcanic and igneous rocks the shorelines have not altered greatly, though boulders may have accumulated and become rounded as a result of wave action. Such shorelines may be said to have remained in a primitive state (A). Wastwater is a classic example of a lake with such a shoreline.

Where the rocks are softer, wave action has often been able to cut a terrace by breaking up the material just above and just below the water level and depositing the gravel, sand and silt so formed in deeper water. The finer the material the deeper it lies. Lakes on the softer rocks — the Skiddaw Slates and Bannisdale Slates — also lie in regions where the surrounding terrain often has a better soil cover than exists on the Borrowdale Volcanic rocks. In part this is because glacial activity transported debris from the centre of the district to its periphery. This soil contributes silt which is brought in by streams.

In some cases the gravel, sometimes with larger stones near the shore, is unstable and lacks vegetation. This is particularly so in the larger lakes where wave action is severe. Even here, however, the Quillwort, _Isoetes lacustris_ (page 134) can often establish itself

A — Bare rocky shoreline with boulders. No vegetation

B — Wave-cut terrace. Unstable gravel. Some plants on sand and silt. Gravel. Thin sand with _Isoetes_. Silt with _Nitella_

C — Sward of _Littorella_. Shore stabilized by plants which show zonation. Gravel. Sand with _Isoetes_. Sandy silt. Fine silt with _Potamogeton_ on the more sheltered sand, and what looks like a higher plant but is actually an alga, <u>Nitella opaca</u> (page 122), can do so on the silt (B).

A further development is the colonisation and stabilisation of the gravel terrace by the Shoreweed, <u>Littorella uniflora</u> (page 134), while on the sand there is often <u>Isoetes</u> and, in deeper water on the silt, often a luxuriant growth of vegetation among which Pondweeds, <u>Potamogeton</u> spp, are usually most conspicuous, but which may include other plants such as the Canadian Pondweed, <u>Elodea canadensis</u> (page 136). (C)

In Esthwaite Water such processes have resulted in the development of shores that are for the most part silt covered. Shorelines in this condition can be said to be evolved.

In the less exposed areas plant remains can accumulate above the gravel and sand and give rise to peaty deposits which can then support reed-swamp vegetation of which the characteristic plant is the tall Common Reed, <u>Phragmites communis</u> (page 131). Such reeds are not to be found around lakes with primitive shorelines such as Wastwater, Ennerdale and Buttermere, but make up a conspicuous fringe on parts of the shore of Bassenthwaite, Grasmere and Esthwaite Water, virtually encircle Blelham Tarn, and are present in some of the bays of Windermere (D). They are sometimes accompanied by Water-lilies but the deeper water offshore tends to have a sparse vegetation.

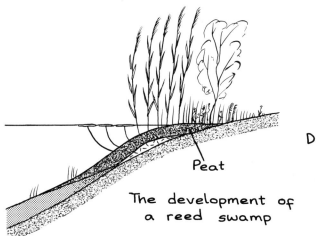

D

Peat

The development of a reed swamp

In some areas more extensive peaty deposits accumulate and become colonised by Willows and Birches and form localised patches of marsh. Marshes are not well developed around most Lake District lakes but the North Fen at Esthwaite (page 145) is an outstanding example, and is a National Nature Reserve.

The basic features that determine the development (or evolution) of a shoreline are the nature of the rocks—geology—and wave action—which is powered by the wind. In areas where accumulations of easily eroded glacial drift lay along the shore, wave action can have dramatic effects as can be seen in Derwentwater not far from the main road up Borrowdale.

49

Different types of shoreline attract different kinds of animals, and the faunas of bare rocky shores and the fringes of reed swamps are very different. Animals that inhabit exposed, vegetationless rocky shores require different adaptations from those useful to creatures that live in sheltered areas among stands of vegetation or on silty bottoms.

Shores can be modified locally by inflowing streams. Streams descending into a lake, may carry stones and gradually build up deltas at their mouths. Deltas tend to be unstable areas : heavy rain causes spates in streams which carry additional stones into the lake and sometimes move those already deposited. Such areas tend also to be well scoured and devoid of higher plants, not least near the shoreline, as there is little opportunity for finely particulate material to accumulate.

The major inflow of a lake, especially of valley lakes such as those of the Lake District, usually enters at its head. The smaller side streams that rapidly descend the steep walls of the valley sometimes build small stony deltas, but it is the larger, more slow-flowing, major inflow that usually carries the largest silt burden and deposits most material. The river often changes its course as it meanders through the level delta or alluvial flat so formed, and the shoreline at the head of the lake changes in sympathy. Because of these changes, and the frequent deposition of new material, the shore-lines of such flats tend to be unstable. Good examples of alluvial flats or deltas are to be seen at the heads of several Lake District lakes. The road to Watendlath passes near a splendid viewpoint from which to see the flat at the head of Derwentwater. Changes that have taken place at the head of Esthwaite Water since mid 19th Century are described in the section on vegetation (page 145).

The shapes, sizes and locations of the English lakes and tarns.

The sizes and shapes of lakes and tarns have many important consequences. Lake District lakes differ much in these respects. Windermere (area 14·76 km² : 5·7 sq miles) is England's largest lake — but is tiny on the world scale. It is also the largest lake in terms of volume. It holds about 315 million cubic metres of water — almost 70 billion gallons.

The deepest lake is Wastwater (76m : 249 ft). By comparison Esthwaite Water is very shallow — only 15·5m (50·8 ft) deep.

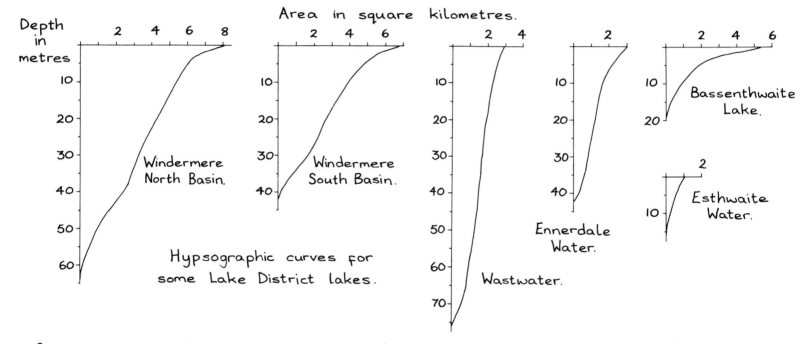

Hypsographic curves for some Lake District lakes.

Some lakes have been carefully surveyed for depth by echo-sounding. This enables depth contours to be plotted. Curves showing depths and areas — hypsographic curves — enable the area at any depth to be read off. Such curves strikingly reveal the differences between such lakes as Wastwater and the considerably larger Bassenthwaite Lake.

Because they lie in rather narrow valleys the English lakes tend to be long and narrow. This was even more the case in the past when lakes now separated from each other, such as Buttermere and Crummock Water, Derwentwater and Bassenthwaite, and probably Brotherswater and Ullswater, formed three long, narrow lakes (page 41). The heads of several lakes have also been encroached upon by deltas that have reduced their length while their widths have remained virtually unchanged.

It is because they lie in overdeepened valleys of this sort (page 12) that the English lakes are relatively deep for their size. Thus Windermere has almost exactly the same mean depth as Lake Victoria in Africa, a lake bigger than Switzerland, and their maximum depths differ but little.

Most of the valley lakes are more or less straight but Ullswater has kinks along its length. This is because it lies over a series of faults — places where massive dislocations of the rocks have occurred.

The valleys in which the lakes lie are sometimes steep-sided and flanked by high hills. Winds are therefore funnelled along their long axes, often producing rough conditions at the surface. This is also conducive to efficient mixing of the water at certain times of the year (page 71) and to the setting up of internal waves at others (page 76).

Tarns, many of which were formed in different ways from the lakes, are seldom elongate. Corrie tarns (page 14) especially tend to approach a circle in shape, and are often very deep in relation to their size. The most remarkable is Blea Water (above Haweswater). With an area of less than a fifth of a square kilometre it has a maximum depth of 63·1 m (207 ft) — almost the same as Windermere (64 m : 210 ft) which is more than 85 times as big. Such tarns, especially as they tend to be sheltered by crags, are less susceptible to mixing by winds than are many of the lakes.

Tarns generally lie at higher altitudes than valley-bottom lakes. The climate here is cooler, a coolness that is accentuated by the relatively sunless north- or east-facing aspect of many corrie tarns. These can remain cool well into spring. For example even after a mild spell, Red Tarn, Helvellyn (altitude 2356 ft : 718 m) was still partly frozen at the end of April 1984, and much snow lay in the gullies above it, so its inflows consisted of meltwater not much above freezing point. At this time the surface temperature of Windermere (altitude 129 ft : 39·3 m) was not much below 8°c in the North Basin and above 8°c in the South. These differences affect plants and animals. For example growth is usually retarded at low temperatures.

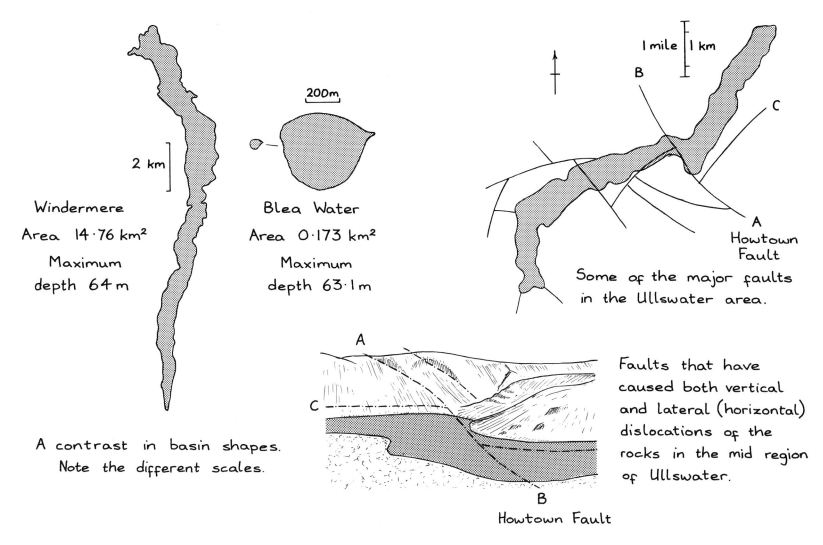

200m

2 km

Windermere
Area 14·76 km²
Maximum
depth 64 m

Blea Water
Area 0·173 km²
Maximum
depth 63·1 m

A contrast in basin shapes.
Note the different scales.

1 mile 1 km

B

C

A

Howtown
Fault

Some of the major faults
in the Ullswater area.

A

C

B

Howtown Fault

Faults that have
caused both vertical
and lateral (horizontal)
dislocations of the
rocks in the mid region
of Ullswater.

53

Vital statistics of the major lakes

For convenience of reference, information on the areas, depths and volumes of the major lakes is summarised here in tabular form. To facilitate comparisons, in each table the sequence is from the largest to the smallest value of the attribute considered.

AREAS	Km²	Square miles
Windermere	14·76	5·70
Ullswater	8·94	3·45
Derwentwater	5·35	2·07
Bassenthwaite Lake	5·28	2·04
Coniston Water	4·91	1·90
Haweswater (dammed)	3·91	1·51
Thirlmere (dammed)	3·27	1·26
Ennerdale Water	3·00	1·16
Wastwater	2·91	1·12
Crummock Water	2·52	0·97
Esthwaite Water	1·00	0·39
Buttermere	0·94	0·36
Grasmere	0·64	0·25
Loweswater	0·64	0·25

MAXIMUM DEPTHS	metres	feet
Wastwater	76	249
Windermere	64	210
Ullswater	62·5	205
Haweswater (dammed)	57	187
Coniston Water	56·1	184
Thirlmere (dammed)	46	151
Crummock Water	43·9	144
Ennerdale Water	42	138
Buttermere	28·6	93·8
Derwentwater	22	72·2
Grasmere	21·5	70·5
Bassenthwaite Lake	19	62·3
Loweswater	16	52·5
Esthwaite Water	15·5	50·8

54

	MEAN DEPTHS			VOLUMES
				millions of cubic metres $(m^3 \times 10^6)$
	metres	feet		
Wastwater	39·7	130·0	Windermere	314·55
Crummock Water	26·7	87·6	Ullswater	223·0
Ullswater	25·3	83·0	Wastwater	115·62
Coniston Water	24·1	79·1	Coniston Water	113·3
Haweswater (dammed)	23·4	76·9	Haweswater (dammed)	76·59
Windermere	21·3	69·9	Crummock Water	66·4
Ennerdale Water	17·8	58·3	Ennerdale Water	53·25
Buttermere	16·6	54·5	Thirlmere (dammed)	52·54
Thirlmere (dammed)	16·1	52·8	Derwentwater	29·0
Loweswater	8·4	27·5	Bassenthwaite Lake	27·9
Grasmere	7·7	25·4	Buttermere	15·2
Esthwaite Water	6·4	21·1	Esthwaite Water	6·44
Derwentwater	5·5	18·0	Loweswater	5·38
Bassenthwaite Lake	5·3	17·3	Grasmere	4·99

For those who prefer to think in gallons, one cubic metre is approximately 220 gallons.

The chemistry of lake waters

Although the waters of all Lake District lakes are unambiguously 'fresh' they contain dissolved substances of various kinds. These include salts and gases. The amounts and kinds of salts in any water body depend on a variety of factors including the nature of the rocks on which it lies, its geographical location and the prevailing climate. A more recent, and increasingly important, factor is the influence of man.

The diversity of dissolved substances in water is a reflection of its remarkable ability to act as a solvent. This is just one of the outstanding properties of water — a relatively simple chemical compound (H_2O) — which is, however, the basis of life.

Dissolved solids in water and where they come from

The geology of a lake basin, and of its catchment area, greatly influences the nature and amounts of the salts dissolved in its waters. Hard rocks, such as prevail in the Lake District, are very resistant to weathering. They dissolve and yield salts exceedingly slowly. The hardest rocks, the Borrowdale Volcanics and igneous intrusions, are the most reluctant to yield their contained salts. Although hard, the Bannisdale Slates are softer than these and yield salts more readily. The Skiddaw Slates do so less willingly than the Bannisdale Slates but more readily than the Borrowdale Volcanics. Thus lakes lying on the hardest rocks contain least salts.

Different kinds of rocks are of different chemical composition. Limestone contains an abundance of calcium compounds, especially calcium carbonate ($CaCO_3$) — 'lime'. By contrast, most Lake District rocks are either very poor in such compounds, or are so hard that any calcium carbonate locked within them cannot easily be dissolved — hence the 'soft' water of the area, for it is the carbonates of calcium that are largely responsible for making the waters of limestone areas 'hard'.

The calcium carbonate of limestone readily goes into solution as calcium bicarbonate — $Ca(HCO_3)_2$ — if it is 'attacked' by water that is at all acidic — as rain water generally is. Lakes and tarns in limestone areas therefore contain more dissolved salts than either the volcanic or sedimentary rocks of the central Lake District. For example, the waters of Cunswick Tarn, which lies on the Carboniferous Limestone at the fringe of the Lake District near Kendal, contain about 11 times as much dissolved material as those of Wastwater, and those of the calcareous Urswick Tarn, near Ulverston, just outside the Lake District, more than 15 times as much.

Even such apparently intractable substances as silica (SiO_2), which occurs as quartz and is the principal constituent of many rocks, can be slowly dissolved by water, particularly when acidic. The chemistry is complex, and the material finds its way into lake waters in various forms. Although not used as a nutrient in the usual sense by organisms, dissolved silica is important in lakes as it provides the material from which certain algae, the diatoms (page 124) manufacture their skeletons.

When salts dissolve they are broken into their constituent parts, called <u>ions</u>, each of which carries an electrical charge. This process is known as dissociation. Those ions with a positive charge are called cations, those with a negative charge anions. For example, the dissociation of common salt, sodium chloride (NaCl) can be shown as

$$NaCl + H_2O \; \nearrow \; Na^+ (aq) - \text{The cation} - \text{dissolved in water}$$
$$\searrow \; Cl^- (aq) - \text{The anion} - \text{dissolved in water}$$

Thus we can speak of sodium (Na^+), calcium (Ca^{2+}), chloride (Cl^-), sulphate (SO_4^{2-}) and other ions. This enables us to say succinctly that the ionic concentration of waters on the Borrowdale Volcanics is generally low, that of waters on the Bannisdale Slates higher, and of the waters of Cunswick Tarn higher still.

The size of its catchment area also helps to determine the quantity of salts washed into a lake. Most lakes have outlets so salts are also lost via the outflow. Only closed basins can accumulate salts and become 'salty' or saline. There are no such lakes in the Lake District.

Some salts come from the sea. Winds whip up spray which is carried inland before it falls to the ground or is washed out by rain. The predominant salt in the sea is sodium chloride (NaCl). Lakes not far from the sea tend to contain more Na^+ and Cl^- ions than those lying further inland. Each year about 2350 tonnes of sodium (and potassium) chloride is deposited in the Windermere catchment, which has an area of about 90 square miles (230 km²). The total weight of all chemical substances falling from the atmosphere in the catchment each year is over 7700 tonnes.

The remains of vegetation, such as dead leaves, sometimes even whole trees, also find their way into lakes where they rot down to give both organic (carbon based) and inorganic substances.   There are also small inputs from the faeces of animals, such

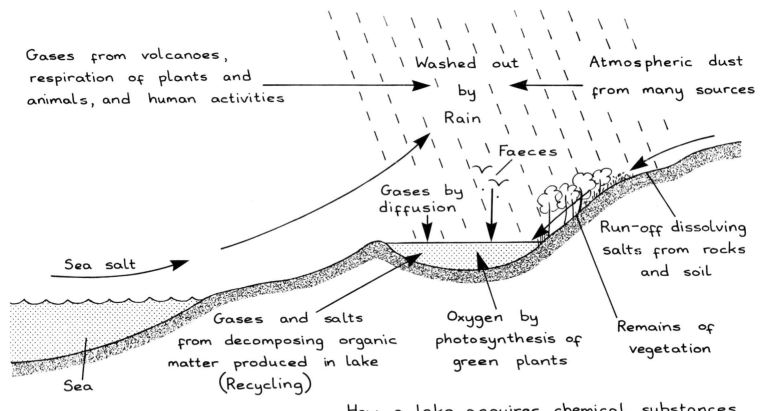

How a lake acquires chemical substances

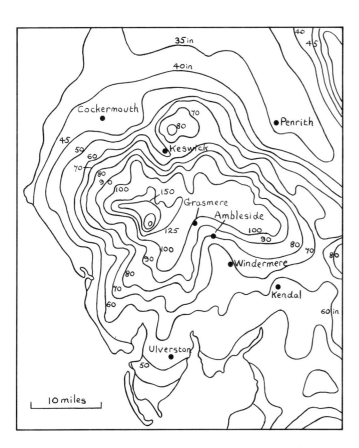

Annual precipitation in the Lake
District 1915 — 1960 (1 in = 2·54 cm)

as birds, that have fed on the land.

Both the dissolving of salts from the land and the transport of salts from the sea are influenced by climate. The heavier the rainfall, the greater the amount of salts washed from the rocks and soil is likely to be. Frost shatter of rocks facilitates the process. The Lake District is a wet place - much the wettest in England - so one might expect the dissolving of salts to be facilitated. In fact the heavy rainfall has tended to wash out (leach) most of the readily dissolved salts from the thin soils on hard rocks, so the amounts released are small. The substances leached from soils include nitrates (NO_3^-) and phosphates (PO_4^{3-}) that are important nutrients for plants. The 'best' soils, in the sense of the farmer or gardener, yield most salts. It is these soils that have long attracted human settlement. Man now adds fertilizers to them and his livestock manures them. These nutrients find their way into adjacent lakes.

Winds carry particles - solid or liquid. It is because prevailing winds in the Lake District come from the sea that they bring so much salt spray. They do so particularly during stormy weather in autumn and winter. They also bring other substances - such as oxides of sulphur and nitrogen put into the atmosphere by natural and, ever increasingly, by industrial and domestic processes.   These acidify the rain (page 69). Radio-active particles emanating from power plants or from nuclear test explosions are also brought by winds and, washed out of the atmosphere by rain, find their way into lakes just as they are deposited on the land.

Because it is such a good solvent, rain is not just 'pure' water — unadulterated H_2O. On the contrary it contains a variety of salts and gases in solution.   Thus each litre of uncontaminated Lake District rainwater usually contains about 3 mg of Na^+ and 5 mg of Cl^- and smaller amounts of various other ions.

An unusual source of salts is a salt spring at Manesty in Borrowdale.

Lake waters also contain <u>organic substances.</u>   These, of varied and often complex nature, are derived from, or produced by, living organisms.   Some occur in true solution, others as colloidal suspensions, a condition in which they are dispersed as exceedingly finely divided solids.   Sometimes they are present in relatively large amounts, but still only a few parts per million.   Their identification is often difficult. Many are brought into lakes as extracts from soils and peat.   These often give a yellowish colour to the water, and waters originating in peaty areas are often brown due to the presence of 'humic acids'.   Bassenthwaite Lake is rendered brownish by such substances.   The various odours that emanate at times from lakes are generally due to organic compounds.

Other organic compounds that occur in lake waters include <u>vitamins</u>, such as niacin (vitamin B) and thiamin (B_1), and <u>antibiotics</u> produced by algae.   The amounts are very small, but may be biologically important.

The amounts and kinds of salts in different lakes

The chemical composition of all lake waters is not the same (page 62).   Even within such a small area as the English Lake District there are considerable differences both in the concentrations of dissolved substances and in the proportions of those that are present in different lakes and tarns.   The map shows the salt content— the total ionic concentration — of a selection of lakes and tarns.   The bigger the circle the greater is the quantity of salts present.   The southern lakes and tarns that lie on sedimentary Silurian rocks are clearly seen to have higher salt contents

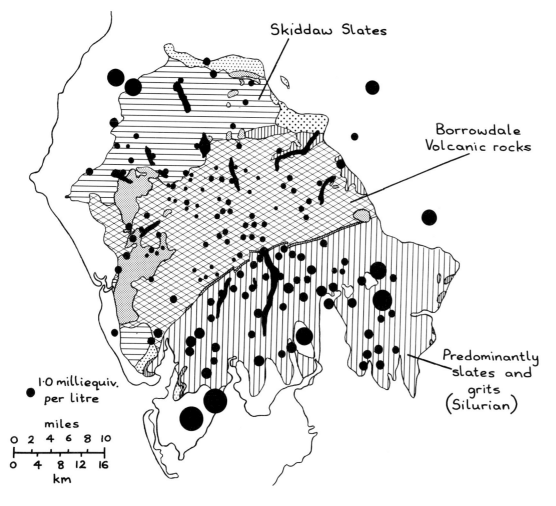

Skiddaw Slates

Borrowdale
Volcanic rocks

Predominantly
slates and
grits
(Silurian)

1·0 milliequiv.
per litre

miles
0 2 4 6 8 10

0 4 8 12 16
km

The total ionic concentration
(salt content) of Lake
District lakes and tarns.
The larger the circle the
greater the ionic
concentration.   The water
bodies with the highest
concentrations at the fringes
of the district lie on
Carboniferous Limestone.
For details of the geology
see map on page 1.

61

than water bodies located on the hard Borrowdale Volcanic rocks in the centre of the district. Where limestone is present in the catchment area the ionic concentration is higher still.

The proportions of the major ions, as well as their concentrations, are shown as pie diagrams for two very different water bodies, Wastwater which lies on, and receives its inflows from, hard volcanic and igneous rocks, and Cunswick Tarn which lies on the limestone.

If the concentrations of some of the major ions in a selection of lakes and tarns are listed in a table, the wide range that is found in the Lake District is easily seen and some interesting comparisons can be made. The values are given in micro-equivalents * (μ-equivalents) per litre; a measure of the quantity of dissolved charged particles in each litre of water, but for comparisons the nature of the units is unimportant.

The values are averages of many measurements. Ennerdale Water, which has a similar chemical composition to Wastwater, is a good example of a lake with a low salt content.

Major ions in Wastwater (slightly acidic) and Cunswick Tarn (alkaline). Diameters indicate total ionic concentrations: segments the contribution of individual ions.

* Micro-equivalents are units which give a measure of dissolved charge. To obtain the micro-equivalent concentration of an ion, one multiplies the micro molar concentration (1000 micromol = 1m mol) by the charge of the ion concerned i.e. by two for Ca^{2+}, Mg^{2+} and SO_4^{2-}. For Na^+, K^+, Cl^-, NO_3^- and Alkalinity μ-equivalents and μ-mol per litre are the same. Thus the total micro-equivalent concentration of all dissolved cations is equal to the total micro-equivalent concentration of all dissolved anions.

The average amounts of some major ions in certain Lake District lakes and tarns. Values in μ-equivalents per litre.

	Na$^+$	K$^+$	Ca^{2+}	Mg^{2+}	*Alk	Cl$^-$	SO$_4^{2-}$	NO$_3^-$	pH
Ennerdale Water	187	10	100	72	42	208	102	15	6·5
Windermere (N. Basin)	202	14	314	81	204	222	157	24	7·0
Windermere (S. Basin)	219	17	355	92	236	242	171	25	7·1
Esthwaite Water	249	25	526	123	386	282	231	31	7·1
Easedale Tarn	153	7	97	37	6	180	82	17	5·6
Urswick Tarn	535	65	3826	1097	4357	614	514	82	8·0

Na$^+$ = Sodium   K$^+$ = Potassium   Ca^{2+} = Calcium   Mg^{2+} = Magnesium
Alk = Alkalinity   Cl$^-$ = Chloride   SO$_4^{2-}$ = Sulphate   NO$_3^-$ = Nitrate

(For the significance of the last column see page 65).

* Alkalinity refers to bicarbonate, plus hydroxyl ions (see page 65), plus the anions of weak acids. At pH values above 6·0, bicarbonate ions (HCO_3^-) are usually the dominant component of Lake District waters. To show how μ-equivalents relate to weights, 100 μ-equivalents per litre of Na$^+$ is 2·3 mg per litre, whereas 100 μ-equivalents per litre of K$^+$ is 3·91 mg, and of Ca^{2+} 2·0 mg per litre; a difference reflecting the different masses and charges of these ions.

The North Basin of Windermere has higher levels of every ion than Ennerdale, and Esthwaite Water has higher levels of every ion than Windermere (North). The South Basin of Windermere has a higher salt content than the North, but a lower content than Esthwaite Water. This is partly a reflection of the fact that it receives the outflow of Esthwaite. It is also enriched by the discharge of a sewage works (page 96).

Two contrasting tarns are also compared. Easedale Tarn, an upland tarn in bleak surroundings on the Borrowdale Volcanic rocks, is poorer in salts than any of the lakes. By contrast, Urswick Tarn, which lies on the Carboniferous Limestone near Ulverston, just outside the Lake District, contains much larger amounts of dissolved substances than any of the lakes. In particular the calcium ion concentration and alkalinity (a measure of bicarbonate content) are enormously greater than in the lakes and tarns lying on non-limestone rocks.

Dissolved gases.

The waters of lakes also contain <u>dissolved gases</u>.

<u>Oxygen</u> (O_2) is obtained from the atmosphere by direct diffusion. This is a very slow process in still water but is greatly accelerated by wave action. It is also obtained from plants. As plants only produce oxygen in sunlight, which does not penetrate very deeply in lakes, this gas is added to the water only in the shallow marginal (littoral) regions and in a thin upper layer of the open water where microscopic algae flourish. Oxygen is taken to the bottom of lakes largely by the wind, by a mechanism explained in the section on 'Water movements' (page 71).

<u>Carbon dioxide</u> (CO_2) is also obtained from the atmosphere, but only in small amounts. Most of it comes from the decomposition of organic matter, which is always accumulating in lakes — as dead leaves, the remains of plants and animals that die there — and from the respiration of plants and animals.

<u>Methane</u> or marsh gas (CH_4) is another decomposition product of organic matter. It is produced only from muds at the bottom of lakes whose oxygen becomes depleted in summer (page 73) and from piles of decomposing vegetable matter that sometimes accumulate at the margins of lakes. It is an inflammable gas responsible for the phenomenon of 'Will-o'-the-Wisp' in swamps. This is the gas now supplied as 'natural gas' to domestic consumers.

64

Hydrogen sulphide (H_2S) is a decomposition product of organic matter that contains sulphur. Like methane it forms only in the absence of oxygen at the bottom of certain lakes in summer. It is a very toxic gas with a characteristic odour of bad eggs.

Nitrogen (N) is an inert gas usually present in abundance in lake waters.

Other gases occur in small amounts, the most important probably being ammonia (NH_4), another decomposition product of organic matter.

Acidity and alkalinity

Natural waters can be acidic, neutral, or alkaline. Acidity increases as the concentration of hydrogen ions (H^+) increases: alkalinity as that of hydroxyl ions (OH^-) increases. Water in which the H^+ and OH^- concentrations are equal is neutral. In practice acidity and alkalinity are expressed in pH units. For reasons of convenience acidity and alkalinity are measured on a scale ranging from 0 to 14, with the mid point at 7, representing neutrality. Below 7 indicates acidity; above it alkalinity. The scale does not follow a simple arithmetic progression but is logarithmic. This means that a shift of one pH unit, from say 6 to 5 or 5 to 4, indicates a 10-fold increase in the concentration of acid. Water at pH 4 is 10 times as acidic as at pH 5, and 100 times as acidic as at pH 6.

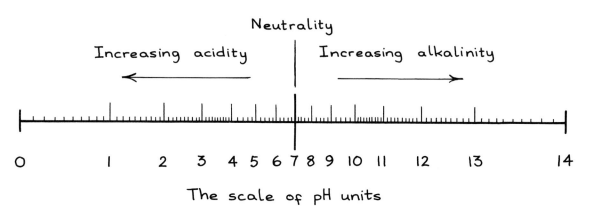

The scale of pH units

65

Most Lake District lakes do not stray far from neutrality, though most tend to be slightly acidic and changes occur that are related to seasonal events and the activity of organisms. Average pH values for Buttermere, Crummock Water, Ennerdale Water and Wastwater range from 6·2 to 6·7. The highest average values among the major lakes are about pH 7·1.

Upland tarns are often acidic. Easedale Tarn for example has an average pH of about 5·6. Levers Water is more acidic. Its average pH is about 4·7. By comparison tarns on limestone are alkaline. Urswick and Cunswick Tarns usually have a pH of about 8.

Streams rising in the calcium-poor, sometimes peaty, uplands are often acidic, sometimes below pH 5, but frequently become less so in their lower reaches where they are partially neutralised by flowing over alkaline (base yielding) rocks.

What the different dissolved substances are used for.

Although salts and gases are present only in small amounts -- usually in only a few parts per million in the English Lakes — without them the lakes would be lifeless.

Their rôles are various. For example calcium is an essential ingredient in the bones of fishes and the shells of snails, and silicon is equally important in the skeleton of the tiny plants called diatoms. As on land, plants require such nutrients as nitrates and phosphates as well as other substances in minute amounts — the so-called trace elements — to enable them to grow and build up proteins. Magnesium is required by all green plants, including the microscopic plants so important in lakes (page 117). At the centre of each molecule of the green colouring matter of plants (chlorophyll) is an atom of magnesium. Without this atom, chlorophyll, and therefore green plants, could not exist. Similarly iron is needed for the making of the blood of red-blooded animals, and the body fluids of freshwater animals require, among many others, sodium and chloride ions. Among the dissolved gases, carbon dioxide is essential to aquatic plants as the raw material of photosynthesis — the process which enables them to manufacture their own food and produce oxygen. All higher animals require oxygen. Many aquatic animals take it up in solution, for which purpose they frequently have special structures. The gills of fishes provide a familiar example.

The rôles of dissolved organic substances are difficult to elucidate. Some can certainly be taken up and utilized by certain microscopic plants (algae). Others perhaps protect the organisms producing them from being eaten by animals, and some are used by certain animals as a means of communication: chemical messages can be passed from one animal to another by various means. Migrating salmon returning from the sea can recognise the stream in which they formerly lived by its odour, which is imparted by dissolved organic compounds.

As material is continuously being taken out of circulation in a lake — some is washed out of the outflow, some is buried in the sediments, more is lost when a fisherman removes his catch or an insect emerges and dies on the land — constant renewal is necessary if fertility is to be maintained. In this, as in other ways, lakes are dynamic systems.

Chemical conditions as limiting factors for plants and animals

The concentration of particular ions in lake water is not constant. The amount entering from inflows varies with weather conditions; as organisms grow they tend to deplete the supply of the ions that they require; and some material becomes lost by incorporation in the bottom deposits. As dead organisms, mostly microscopic, fall to the bottom they decompose and much of the material of which they are made is eventually re-cycled, but some becomes lost to the bottom. The skeletons of diatoms and the animal fragments so useful in helping to elucidate lake history (pages 33, 34) provide examples. Seasonal changes also affect the way in which dissolved substances are distributed in different parts of a lake (page 73).

Sometimes populations of particular organisms increase to such an extent that their demand for a particular material exceeds supply. This is often the case in certain planktonic (open-water, drifting) diatoms. These so deplete the supply of silica, which they need to make their skeleton, that population growth comes to a halt. The growth of populations of other algae — which do not need silica — can be limited by a shortage of nitrates or phosphates.

The demand for particular ions is easily seen by measuring the amount present in the water throughout the year. Analyses from the South Basin of Windermere, for example, reveal a marked decline in nitrate concentration during the summer months,

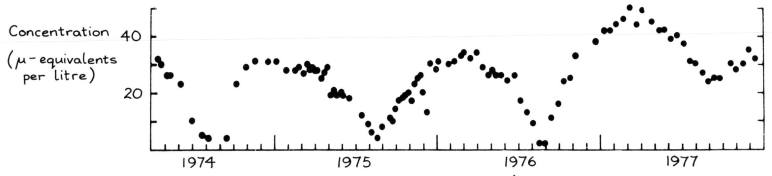

Seasonal changes in the concentration of the nitrate ion (NO_3^-) in the South Basin of Windermere, showing how supplies are reduced, and sometimes seriously depleted, by growing crops of algae during the summer months, and subsequently returned to circulation.

reaching a minimum by about August, by which time almost complete depletion has occurred in some years. The decline reflects uptake by growing algae living in the open waters, which, in some years, clearly find it difficult to obtain sufficient nitrate in late summer.

In some lakes there is never enough of a particular material to allow certain animals to colonise it. Some Lake District lakes do not contain sufficient calcium to enable certain snails to make their shells, so these snails are excluded.

Gases, or the lack of gases, can also limit the activity of organisms. In summer, a lack of dissolved oxygen frequently prevails in deep water in certain lakes (page 73). This effectively excludes most kinds of animals from these regions. Some gases, such as hydrogen sulphide are very poisonous to most organisms — but mostly occur in situations from which animals have in any case been excluded by lack of oxygen. Ironically an excess of oxygen can also be dangerous. Under certain circumstances — when algae are producing oxygen under exceptionally favourable conditions — water can become super-saturated with oxygen. It then comes out of solution as bubbles of gaseous oxygen. Such bubbles can coat the gills and lead to the death of fishes.

Oxygen is a vital necessity to most organisms, but to some bacteria it is a deadly toxin.

They can flourish only in its absence. They do so for example in the deep water of lakes such as Esthwaite Water when they become depleted of oxygen in summer.

For complex physiological reasons some animals cannot tolerate acidic water, and a few shun alkaline water. The inability of some animals — especially certain fishes — to tolerate acidic water has been forcibly brought to notice by the recent publicity given to acid rain. Industrial processes put oxides of nitrogen and sulphur into the atmosphere. All these gases can be dissolved in rainwater and convert it into dilute solutions of nitric (HNO_3) and sulphuric (H_2SO_4) acids.

Coal and oil contain much sulphur, and the combustion of these fuels, especially in power stations, causes the discharge of sulphur, mainly as sulphur dioxide (SO_2), into the atmosphere. Each year, in Britain alone, well over 2 million tonnes of sulphur, equivalent to more than 4 million tonnes of sulphur dioxide, are emitted to the atmosphere. This figure, for the mid 1980's, is less than it was at the beginning of the decade. Not all of this falls on the country, a considerable proportion of it being exported, much of it to Scandinavia, though in return we receive a smaller amount of sulphur from elsewhere. Some 750 tonnes of sulphuric acid and 500 tonnes of nitric acid are deposited in the Windermere catchment area each year.

The pH of rain in the southern part of the Lake District varies from 3·5 to 6·8. The mean is pH 4·4. When the wind blows from the west the pH of the rain is usually above 4·4. When it blows from the south and east, bringing acidic material from industrial areas, it falls.

The deposition of acids in rivers and lakes tends to increase their acidity — lowering their pH. Where the rocks and soils contain carbonates — especially limestones, though even veins of calcite may suffice — acid precipitation is rapidly neutralized. However, where soils are thin and derived from hard rocks that contain few bases (alkaline substances) this is not possible. In the hard rock areas of the central Lake District most such bases were in any case long ago leached out by the copious acidic rain.

Freshwater animals are sensitive to levels of acidity and alkalinity, and acidity can increase to a point beyond which they are unable to survive. Many invertebrate animals are intolerant of pH levels below about 5·7.

In spite of such limitations, many plants and animals can cope with a wide range of chemical conditions — their survival depends on such an ability.

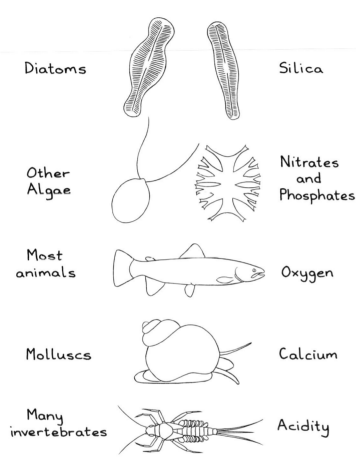

Diatoms — Silica

Other Algae — Nitrates and Phosphates

Most animals — Oxygen

Molluscs — Calcium

Many invertebrates — Acidity

Some of the chemical factors that can limit the occurrence, distribution or population size of plants and animals in Lake District waters.

The recycling of chemical substances in lakes.

Chemical substances incorporated into the bodies of plants and animals, or trapped in the surface layers of bottom muds, are usually only temporarily removed from the water. This applies even when they are built into the complex materials of animal bodies. There is a rapid exchange of some substances as animals respire, returning carbon dioxide to circulation. Animals also defaecate, releasing partly broken down waste products. These are further decomposed by bacteria (page 152) and the simple chemicals that are released become available for re-use. All animals and plants eventually die, often by being eaten, which merely delays the return of their component chemicals. Many bodies, however, fall to the bottom, break down and release simple materials that return to circulation. Microscopic plants and animals, which occur in countless millions, often break down very rapidly. The chemistry of a lake is indeed dynamic and ever changing. A further element of complexity is introduced by the fact that the water is continuously on the move. Some of these movements are strongly influenced by the cycle of the seasons and have profound repercussions on water chemistry. These matters are outlined in the section on water movements in lakes (page 71).

Water movements and their consequences
: the hydromechanics of lakes

The water in a lake is seldom still. Its movements are complex and of great biological significance. As some of the most important movements are related to seasonal changes that affect an important physical property of water this property should be understood. The density of water changes with temperature. As it cools it becomes denser until a temperature of 4°c is reached, at which it has its maximum density. Below 4°c it gets less dense (lighter) as it cools — which is why ice, which is the form assumed by water when it cools to 0°c, floats.

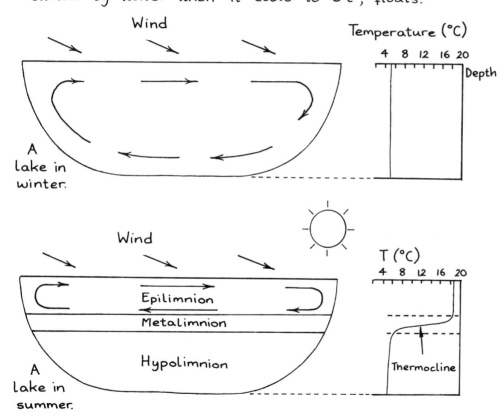

Wind

Temperature (°C)

4 8 12 16 20

Depth

A lake in winter.

Wind

T (°C)

4 8 12 16 20

Epilimnion

Metalimnion

Hypolimnion

Thermocline

A lake in summer.

The seasonal cycle in a Lake District lake.

In spring any residual ice melts and the entire lake becomes more or less the same temperature from top to bottom. It is then said to be <u>homothermal</u>. When the wind blows persistently from one direction it can set the entire lake in circulation. This mixes all the dissolved salts and gases, which are thus uniformly distributed in the water. Lakes in which such complete mixing takes place are said to be <u>holomictic</u>.

As the season advances the lake warms up. At first the warming is slight but, given a few calm days, the sun warms the surface waters whose density is therefore reduced. They become lighter. Because water is a poor conductor of heat, a temperature gradient is established, and as the warming of the surface waters continues, a distinct upper layer of

71

warm water becomes established, which sits on a deeper, cooler layer. The lake is now said to be stratified. The upper layer is called the epilimnion, the lower the hypolimnion. The zone of rapid change in temperature is called the thermocline. Somewhat confusingly the region in which the temperature gradient is steep is also often called the metalimnion.

The wind can now mix the epilimnion, which circulates independently of the hypolimnion. This is facilitated by the fact that as the temperature of water increases, its viscosity decreases. The less viscous epilimnion thus moves on the more viscous hypolimnion. Friction is small and the thermocline acts as a slippery surface. While the epilimnion behaves largely as a separate entity there is some turbulence at the interface between it and the hypolimnion. This induces certain smaller movements in the hypolimnion which are mentioned later (page 76).

In a warm summer, even though the temperature of the epilimnion may occasionally rise to over 20°c, the lower part of the hypolimnion remains much cooler, generally below 10°c, in the larger Lake District lakes and well below this in deep lakes such as Wastwater and Windermere North Basin. In a shallow lake, such as Esthwaite Water, the hypolimnion becomes warmer and its temperature may rise to 10°c, or even a little higher.

In autumn the epilimnion gradually cools until its temperature, and therefore its density, differ but little from those of the hypolimnion. A strong wind — gales are prevalent at this season — eventually overcomes the small residual density difference and mixes the entire lake. This is the autumnal overturn. The lake is now once more homothermal. Although there may be occasional periods of ice cover, the lake is generally well mixed in winter.

When a lake is frozen the wind cannot mix its waters, so if there is a long period of ice cover in winter (seldom the case in the Lake District except perhaps in certain high tarns) there are two periods of mixing, in autumn and again in spring. For obvious reasons such lakes are said to be dimictic.

Some consequences of the seasonal cycle in lakes of different kinds.

Because green plants need light, and because light cannot penetrate very far into water (page 82), most of the microscopic plants of the open water of a lake, which comprise the phytoplankton (page 117), live in the epilimnion during the summer. Their activities, and turbulent mixing at the surface, ensure that the epilimnion is well supplied with oxygen. No such supplies of oxygen are available to the deeper-lying hypolimnion, which has to rely on the store of oxygen carried down during the period when the lake was well mixed from autumn to spring. As the summer proceeds, demands are made on this store of oxygen. Decomposition in the mud consumes it and there is a continuous rain of dead bodies, mostly minute but sometimes exceedingly numerous, from the epilimnion, whose decomposition also uses up oxygen. If the demands are high, as in a 'rich', productive lake such as Esthwaite Water, the store of oxygen in the hypolimnion can become depleted and a layer of oxygenless water can build up at the bottom of the lake. This is a serious matter for most animals which are forced to leave this zone in summer.

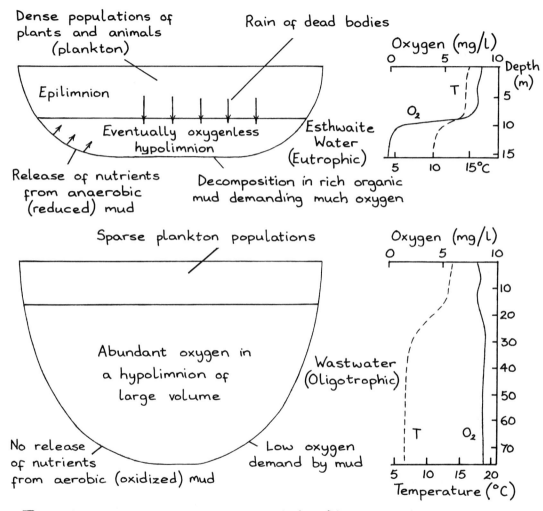

The situation in summer in two Lake District lakes.

In some cases the entire store of oxygen in the hypolimnion can be used up, as it is every summer in Esthwaite Water.

By contrast the demands made on the store of oxygen in the depths of a 'poor', unproductive lake, such as Wastwater, are much less — and because it is a deeper lake, the volume of the hypolimnion is much greater — so there is ample oxygen to last throughout the summer. No oxygenless layer therefore develops.

This is a fundamental difference between a rich lake and a poor lake, and provides the means whereby a technical definition can be framed to distinguish the two. A 'poor', unproductive lake in which the hypolimnion retains its oxygen all summer is said to be <u>oligotrophic</u> — which mearly means 'poor in food'. A 'rich' productive lake in which the oxygen of the hypolimnion is partially or completely used up is said to be <u>eutrophic</u> — which means 'rich in nutrients'.

Because material falls from the epilimnion to the hypolimnion in summer, and does not return, the epilimnion becomes depleted of nutrients and the hypolimnion enriched. Another mechanism also enriches the hypolimnion of eutrophic lakes, such as Esthwaite, in summer. When the oxygen is used up, conditions at the mud surface are said to become anaerobic — which merely means 'without oxygen'. Under such conditions the mud releases nutrients to the water which is thereby enriched. No such release takes place from the aerobic muds of Wastwater.

When the autumnal overturn mixes the lake it takes oxygen to the depths and replenishes the upper layers with nutrients from the deep water. In Esthwaite these include those released from the bottom muds. In winter, temperatures are low and there is not much sunshine. As on land, production of plant and most animal life is at a low ebb, though some algae flourish at this time of the year.

Surface waves

Surface waves are the most obvious of water movements in lakes. While important, they are of less biological significance than movements that cannot be observed directly. The speed of waves is related to wind speed but can be modified by things like the configuration of the shore-line and the relative proportions of deep and shallow water over which they pass. In general the greater the amount of open water, the greater is the length, height and velocity of a wave likely to be.

74

Waves exert much influence on shore lines, in whose evolution they play a major part (page 48). Especially in the larger lakes some shores may be more exposed to wave action than others. This is so for example in Windermere where in general, the eastern shore is more exposed to the prevailing south-west winds than is the western shore.

At lake margins sedimentation is prevented by persistent wave action. However while things like the size of the water body and local topography make generalisation dangerous, it is doubtful whether waves exert much influence below a depth of about a metre in any English lake.

Surface waves affect the behaviour of birds that rest on water surfaces. Violent storms can inhibit the activities of ducks, grebes and coots and induce local movements. Thus aggregations of Coots and of such open-water ducks as the Pochard and Tufted Duck are a familar sight in the sheltered bays of Windermere when winter storms render the open lake inhospitable by creating large waves, and sometimes 'white horses'. A 'white horse' is a wave whose crest has been blown over by the wind.

Surface seiches (or surface standing waves)

When a wind blows persistently in one direction over a lake, water piles up at one end. If it suddenly stops a current flows from that end towards the other until the surface levels out. As the current still has energy at this point it continues to flow and piles up water at the formerly depressed end. The process is then again reversed and continues with ever diminishing amplitude until, if not interupted by wind, the lake levels out. Such an oscillation is called a seiche. The kind described, a uninodal seiche — which means rocking about one point — is basically simple but, depending on the shape of the basin, seiches can be very complex and, as winds are variable, so too is the amplitude of such seiches.

Although surface seiches are usually set up by winds, earthquakes can do likewise, and there are interesting historical records of such events in Britain. In November 1755 Lisbon was devastated by an earthquake which caused many water bodies in England and Scotland to oscillate, sometimes dramatically. Loch Lomond, which is bigger than any English lake, did so with an amplitude of 2½ ft (c. 75cm) every 10 minutes or so.

Internal waves or internal seiches

Stratification makes possible the setting up of internal waves or internal seiches. When a strong wind blows persistently in one direction over a stratified lake it not only circulates water in the epilimnion but causes the end opposite to that from which it comes to be pushed down. This depression of the thermocline lifts the other end. The epilimnion is now wedge-shaped. When the wind drops, the depressed end returns to the horizontal but, such is its momentum, it overshoots and rises. The other end is therefore depressed.

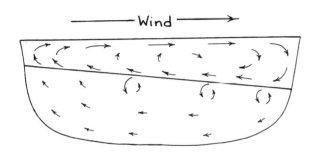

Depression of the thermocline by a strong, sustained wind blowing along the axis of a stratified lake. Arrows give some idea of the motion induced, including turbulence at the interface.

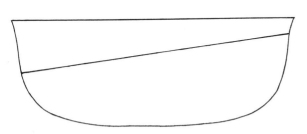

Wind stopped. The thermocline swings back, but momentum carries it past the horizontal.

An internal wave or seiche

A rocking action is thus set up which is gradually damped out by friction, or interfered with by wind. The time taken for a seiche to complete one cycle of events is called its period. In Windermere, which is composed of two basins — it is almost divided near Belle Isle — each basin has its own internal seiche. Periods of 12 to 15 hours have been recorded in the North Basin; of almost 24 hours in the South. Periodicity is related to the size of the lake. In a lake like Loch Ness (length about 38 km : nearly 24 miles) the period is more than 2 days : in Lake Baikal (Siberia) (length 636 km : c. 395 miles) something approaching 40 days.

Differences in the depth of the thermocline between its highest and lowest points at the end of a basin in Windermere during a seiche

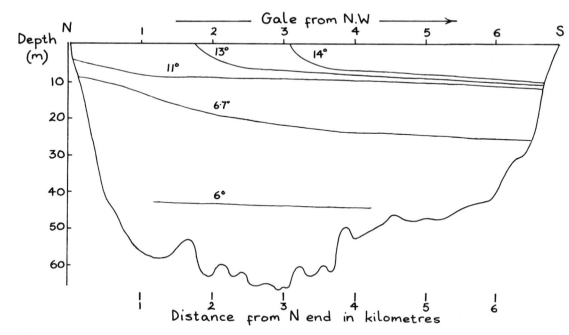

Gale from N.W

The pattern of temperature as seen in a longitudinal section of the North Basin of Windermere after a 12 hour gale.

can be of the order of 10m (c.33ft). In large lakes outside the Lake District the amplitude can be several times as great as this.

Winds not only tilt the thermocline but induce flows of water in the epilimnion. There is a flow near the surface in the same direction as the wind and an inevitable return current in the opposite direction in the lower part of the epilimnion along the top of the thermocline. Because of the density difference between the water in the epilimnion and hypolimnion there is little mixing across the thermocline so long as flow remains stable. However, various conditions can lead to instability and give rise to turbulence in this region, which leads to some stirring and mixing as indicated by arrows in the figure. (page 76).

Seiches are best followed by temperature measurements. An example from the North Basin of Windermere shows the situation after a gale had blown for 12 hours. The piling up of the warm epilimnion at the south end is clearly shown. In the ensuing days of calm weather a seiche was set up. The striking effect of this in deep water is shown by changes in the depth at which a temperature of 6.7°c was measured at a point near the head of the lake over a period of three days of calm weather following the gale.

Even moderate winds can set large volumes of water in motion. This motion, although not apparent to the land-based observer, continues during succeeding calm periods. It is dramatically revealed by temperature measurements taken at a fixed point at an appropriate depth. The diagram shows such a continuous temperature record made at a depth of 9.5m (c.12 ft) near the north end of Windermere. It was made over several days at the end of June. The marked changes that it displays

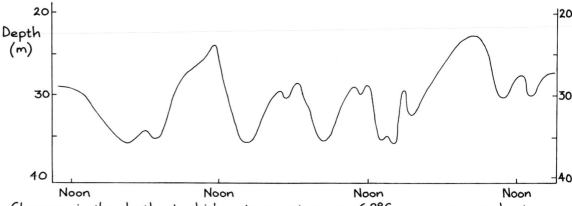

Changes in the depth at which a temperature of 6.2°C was measured at a fixed point near the head of Windermere in the calm that followed the gale illustrated on page 77.

show that the water was never at rest.

It is easy to appreciate how, as autumn advances and temperatures fall, and as gales begin to blow, tilting of the thermocline brings cool water to the surface — and drives warmer water deeper at the opposite end. This, combined with turbulent mixing in the vicinity of the thermocline, gradually breaks down the

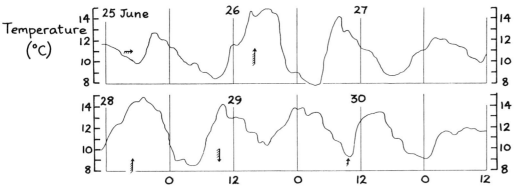

Changes in temperature at 9.5m near the north end of Windermere over a 6 day period. Arrows indicate wind direction and strength.

stratification of the lake and leads eventually to the autumnal overturn and complete mixing. The sort of situation that precedes this event is graphically revealed by the conditions that prevailed on a specific occasion in late October in the North Basin of Windermere as a force 7 to 8 gale blew from the north.

Although they cannot be seen, internal seiches are dramatic physical events which move enormous volumes of water through considerable distances in relatively short periods of time. One consequence of such movements is that material in the otherwise isolated hypolimnion is, to some degree at least, mixed. At times of exceptionally strong winds water from the hypolimnion can even be brought to the surface during summer.

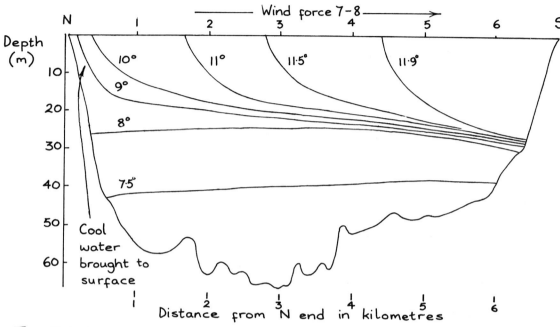

The distribution of temperature in the North Basin of Windermere in late October as a force 7-8 gale blew from the north

Currents and complications

A note of complexity is added to internal seiches and the flow of currents by the rotation of the earth. In the deep valley lakes of the Lake District, winds tend to be channelled along their long axes. These set up a surface current in the direction in which they blow, and a deeper return (counter) current flows in the opposite

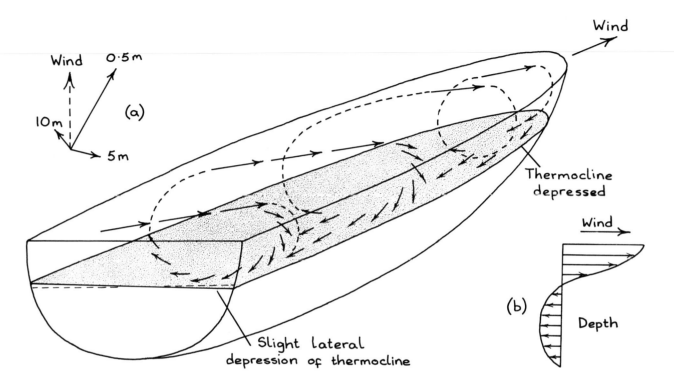

Wind

0.5 m

10 m

5 m

(a)

Wind

Thermocline
depressed

Wind

(b)

Depth

Slight lateral
depression of thermocline

A diagrammatic representation of the situation in a basin of a lake like Windermere as a moderate wind blows along its axis. The thermocline is slightly tilted transversely, as well as being depressed at the down-wind end of the lake, and the flow of the currents takes on a helical configuration. Surface currents are indicated by long solid arrows: deeper counter currents by short solid arrows or dashed lines.

Inset (a) gives an example of the change in direction and velocity of currents with depth based on a day when the thermocline lay at a depth of 13 m. The longer the line the greater the speed. Inset (b) presents similar information in a two-dimensional profile.

direction — like an endless belt.   The rotation of the earth causes the surface current to be deflected to the right.   (It is deflected to the left in the Southern Hemisphere.)   This has the effect of tilting the thermocline in the transverse plane as it rocks in the longitudinal.   This effect is slight in small lakes : more important in large.   Windermere is sufficiently large for this force — the Coriolis force — to be significant.   As well as tilting the thermocline transversely it causes a progressive rotation of the wind-induced current with depth so that a significant part of the deep counter current flows not in the opposite direction to the surface current but obliquely across it.   Thus a simplified general picture of current flow in Windermere when a moderate wind is blowing along its long axis is of a helical system with the surface currents deflected to the right and the deep counter currents flowing to the left of the wind.

As a very rough approximation, (see the inset to the diagram) the uppermost one third of the epilimnion is moving with the wind and relatively rapidly, the lower two thirds against the wind and more slowly.   The total amount moved in each direction must of course be equal though, for a time, depression of the thermocline enables water in the epilimnion to pile up at the down-wind end of a stratified lake.   The situation is more complex near the margins where bays break up the shoreline, and at the ends of long lakes.

While it is the rocking of the thermocline that is responsible for much of the movement of water in the isolated hypolimnion, movements in the epilimnion are predominantly direct responses to the wind.   These movements (which involve other complexities!) can have a marked influence on the movements and distribution of the drifting organisms that make up the plankton of open water.

Underwater Light

Like glass, water is a relatively good transmitter of light — but a very much poorer transmitter than air. Thus the water near the surface of a lake is well illuminated : the deeper lying waters are dark. Clear water transmits light better than turbid water. Thus light penetrates deeper into a clear-water lake than into a lake that is turbid.

An adequate amount of light is essential for the existence of green (chlorophyll-containing) plants. It is equally essential to the many microscopic algae that have pigments of other colours (page 117). As all animals ultimately depend on plants, light is essential to all life.

Light is less easily obtained in aquatic than in terrestial systems. Some of that which strikes the surface of a lake is reflected back (about 10 to 15% under an overcast sky) so the light intensity beneath the surface is always lower than in the air above it. The intensity of the light that penetrates the water diminishes rapidly with depth. It tends to do so in a near-logarithmic manner. This means that, if the amount has been reduced to 1% of surface illumination at a depth of 10m (c. 33 ft) — which would be the case in a not particularly turbid lake such as Windermere — it will be reduced to about 1% of <u>that</u> amount in the next 10m, that is to 0.01% of the intensity at the surface — $\frac{1}{10,000}$ of surface illumination.

Light penetration in the English Lakes

While there are seasonal differences, in general a white disc (a Secchi Disc) 20cm (8 ins.)* in diameter disappears at a depth of about 3m (c.10ft) in Esthwaite Water but can be seen down to about 9m (almost 30ft), and sometimes even to 12m (c.40 ft), in Wastwater. The transparency of other lakes lies between these values. Light penetration can be measured very precisely by use of a photocell, but Secchi Disc readings provide a simple and convenient means of comparing transparencies. Esthwaite is less transparent than Wastwater because its waters are rendered turbid by their crop of suspended microscopic plants (planktonic algae — page 117), whose presence reflects its greater nutrient content than that of Wastwater. It is the nutrient-poor lakes on hard rocks that are most transparent.

* A 30cm disc is sometimes used.

	Metres	Feet
Wastwater	9·0	29·5
Ennerdale Water	8·3	27·2
Buttermere	8·0	26·2
Crummock Water	8·0	26·2
Haweswater	5·8	19·0
Derwentwater	5·5	18·0
Windermere	5·5	18·0
Ullswater	5·4	17·7
Coniston Water	5·4	17·7
Esthwaite Water	3·1	10·2
Bassenthwaite Lake	2·2 †	7·2

Relative transparency of the major lakes — based on the depth at which a white disc 20cm in diameter disappears from sight.
† Peat-stained

Light penetration in three contrasting lakes

The colour of underwater light.

White light is a mixture of several colours — most of which can be seen in a rainbow or when white light is similarly split into its component colours by a prism. The different colours have different wavelengths. Different wavelengths (colours) of light penetrate lakes to different depths. If a lake were full of distilled water with no particles in suspension, light towards the blue end of the spectrum, which is of

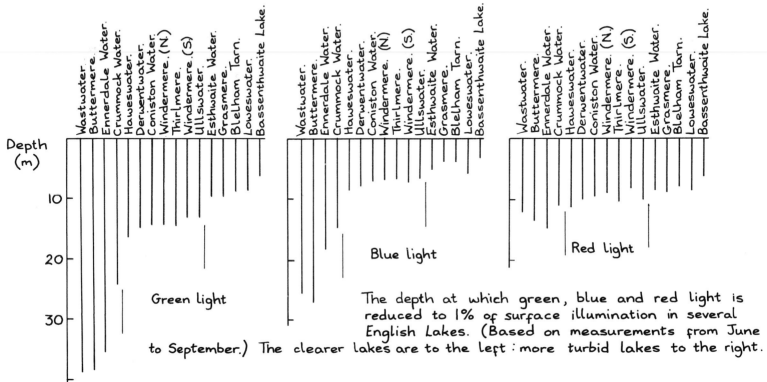

Green light

Blue light

Red light

The depth at which green, blue and red light is reduced to 1% of surface illumination in several English Lakes. (Based on measurements from June to September.) The clearer lakes are to the left: more turbid lakes to the right.

short wavelength and high energy, would penetrate deeper than long wavelength, low energy, light at the red end.   There is a strong tendency for this pattern to prevail in clear-water lakes.   Many lakes, however, contain considerable amounts of suspended and dissolved material of various kinds, and in these the wavelength (colour) showing the deepest penetration is often pushed towards the red end of the spectrum.

   The diagram shows how, in terms of the penetration of light, the lakes fall into three distinct groups.   In the clear-water lakes — Wastwater, Ennerdale, Buttermere and Crummock Water — green light not only penetrates deepest but does

84

so to a much greater extent than in the rest of the lakes.   Haweswater, Derwentwater, Coniston Water, Windermere, Thirlmere and Ullswater are very similar to each other in the depth to which green light penetrates.   Here, while it penetrates less deeply than in the four clearest lakes, it does so more effectively than in the relatively turbid Esthwaite Water, Grasmere, Bassenthwaite Lake, Loweswater and Blelham Tarn, which make up a third group.

The same grouping is evident with respect to blue light, which again penetrates deepest in the four clear-water lakes — though less deeply than green light.   It penetrates less effectively in the second group where however, it does so to somewhat greater depths than in the third group.

Red light behaves differently.   It is more effective at penetrating the turbid lakes than is blue light, and not much different in this respect from green light. It is also more effective than blue light at penetrating the waters of the second group of lakes, but less so than green.   While it actually penetrates somewhat deeper into clear-water than into turbid lakes, its abilities in this respect are much inferior to either blue or, especially, green light.

Light in the life of aquatic plants

Without light chlorophyll-containing plants, whether forest trees or minute algae, cannot carry out photosynthesis.   This is the process whereby they use the energy of sunlight to build up complex organic substances from carbon dioxide and water — giving off oxygen as they do so.   Photosynthesis means 'putting things together in the light.'   Thus, provided conditions for rooting or attachment are suitable, the depth to which light penetrates determines the depth to which rooted plants and attached algae can grow in a lake.   The zone within which growth is possible is called the euphotic zone.   Its lower limit is effectively that at which 1% of the incident surface light remains.   Its thickness is greater in clear-water than in turbid lakes.

The depth to which light can penetrate also to a large extent determines the thickness of the layer of water in which suspended algae can grow.   For reasons that have nothing to do with differences in the abilities of such algae and higher plants to flourish in dim light, the inhabited zone is not necessarily the same for these two types of plants.   Drifting algae are mobile but rooted plants and

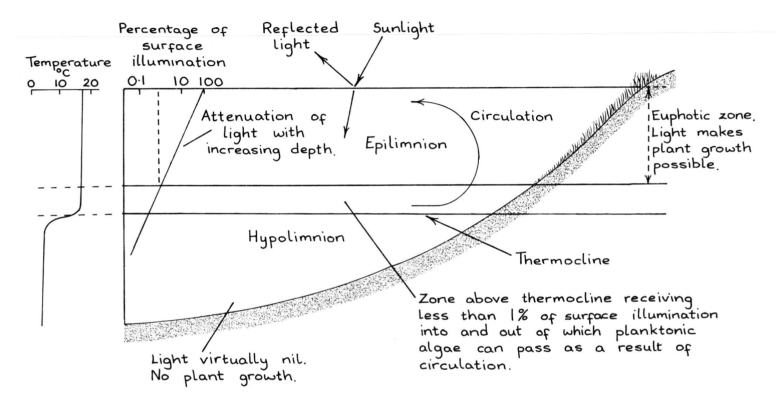

Temperature °C
0 10 20

Percentage of surface illumination
0·1 10 100

Reflected light

Sunlight

Attenuation of light with increasing depth.

Circulation

Epilimnion

Euphotic zone. Light makes plant growth possible.

Hypolimnion

Thermocline

Zone above thermocline receiving less than 1% of surface illumination into and out of which planktonic algae can pass as a result of circulation.

Light virtually nil. No plant growth.

Light penetration into a stratified lake. Note how circulation in the epilimnion enables planktonic algae to inhabit a thicker layer than can rooted plants.

attatched algae are sedentary. In summer the water in the epilimnion of a lake circulates (page 71) and carries suspended algae with it. At times they will be near the surface where there is plenty of light: at other times they may be carried into deeper, darker, regions, where the light is inadequate. However, circulation is

86

likely eventually to bring them back into the light. In practice the well-populated zone for such algae is usually synonymous with the epilimnion.

In the clear waters of Wastwater, however, the depth at which light intensities fall to 1% of surface illumination is often <u>below</u> the thermocline. At such times, therefore, all the algae in the epilimnion have sufficient light to flourish. In Buttermere, which is both clear and relatively shallow, there is often more than 1% of the surface illumination right down to the bottom.

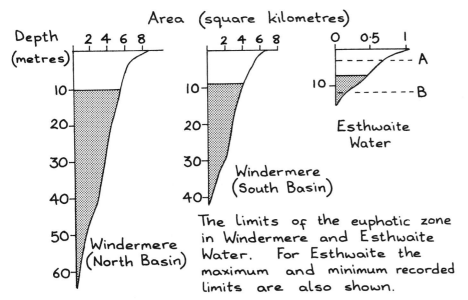

The limits of the euphotic zone in Windermere and Esthwaite Water. For Esthwaite the maximum and minimum recorded limits are also shown.

Some idea of the thickness and volume of the euphotic zone and of the deeper ill-lit waters of Windermere and Esthwaite is given in the form of hypsographic curves (see Lake shapes and sizes, page 51, for explanation). These show the situation in April which happens to be roughly representative of average conditions.

In Esthwaite Water the euphotic zone is generally only about 5m (16 or 17 ft) thick. Occasionally it is less. Ironically a major factor reducing its thickness is the presence of dense populations of suspended algae which screen out the light. Circulation of the epilimnion, however, effectively increases its thickness to about 10m (33 ft) so far as planktonic algae are concerned.

Because, as they penetrate water, different wavelengths of light are absorbed to different extents, the spectral composition (colour) of light changes with depth. Although light may penetrate relatively deeply in clear water, in many lakes it is the green component that does so most effectively — and this happens to be the least effective in photosynthesis. So, from the point of view of green plants, deeper water is sometimes poorer, not only in the quantity, but in the quality, of the light that it receives.

Green plants not only produce oxygen, they use it in respiration. That which is liberated is the excess of the amount produced, the <u>gross production</u>, over that required for respiration, and represents the <u>net production</u>. The depth to which planktonic algae can flourish is determined by the depth to which sufficient light penetrates to allow some net production to be achieved. The point where the amount of oxygen produced is the same as that required for respiration is called the <u>compensation point</u>. It is the position of the compensation point that determines the thickness of the zone of growth potential.

The diagram gives a generalised picture of the situation in a lake. No values are shown for oxygen production as these vary widely from lake to lake, and the picture changes from day to day and throughout a day as light intensities change. Net production has to take account of the hours of darkness during which photosynthesis ceases but respiration continues.

On bright days maximum production often occurs some distance below the surface. Close to the surface photosynthesis is partially inhibited by the intensity of the light that prevails there. As some light is reflected from the surface, and more is rapidly absorbed as it penetrates the water, this is an indication that algae are generally adapted to the dimmer light regimes that prevail under water than on land.

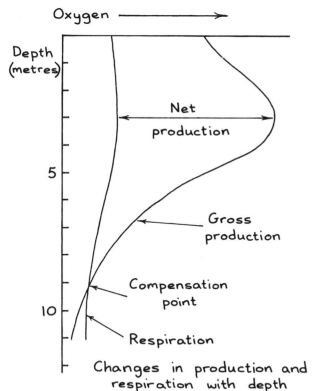

Changes in production and respiration with depth

Some biological consequences of dim light in deep water.

The most obvious consequence of the rapid extinction of light as it passes through water is the inability of photosynthesising plants to penetrate to more than modest depths.

Animals need light in order to see. As they penetrate deeper in lakes it gets darker and seeing becomes more difficult. In Windermere the depth at which the amount of light is reduced to 1% of that at the surface is usually about 10m (c. 33ft). In the next 10 metres or so this amount of light is again reduced to 1% so at 20m there is about 0·01% (one ten-thousandth) of surface illumination. This may seem very dark, and it is even darker in yet deeper water, but conditions are put into perspective if we consider nocturnal terrestrial animals. Sunlight, whose intensity of course varies much, is often as much as 200,000 times as bright as a full moon, yet many nocturnal animals that use vision can operate successfully on dark nights, though they may not rely entirely on this sense. Even a man can see quite well at quarter moon. We just don't know how well the fishes of Windermere can see in deep water, but certainly Char have been netted at 60m. Other species penetrate less deeply. The Perch, for example, seems seldom to venture below about 10m. These depths are much less than those frequented by some freshwater fishes — and of course trivial when compared with deep-sea fishes. In Lake Baikal, Siberia, fishes occur regularly at 500m and often penetrate deeper.

It is not known to what extent the other senses available to them are utilised by deep-penetrating freshwater fishes, or whether their eyes are adapted to seeing in dim light. Some deep-sea fishes have specialisations that render them up to 120 times as sensitive to dim light as the human eye, so it would not be surprising if fishes that penetrate the depths of lakes were also at least somewhat more sensitive, but we know very little about most of them in this respect.

The eyes of some, but not all, freshwater invertebrates are less important sense organs than are those of most fishes, and some of them lack eyes altogether. Such animals are not likely to be inconvenienced by dim light in deep water.

Some deep temperate-zone lakes, whose waters are always oxygenated to the greatest depths are inhabited by specialised deep-water animals. Lake Baikal in particular has a diverse and spectacular deep-water fauna of both invertebrates and fishes. No Lake District lake harbours such animals. None is particularly deep, nor have any of them existed sufficiently long to enable such animals to evolve there. Dispersal of deep-water animals is difficult, so many of them tend to be confined to a single lake.

Rich and poor : the worldly standing of the various lakes

The lakes of the English Lake District can be arranged in a series according to a variety of criteria. In each case an essentially similar trend is revealed though, as natural systems are involved, there is not always perfect agreement. At one end of the scale are the 'poor' lakes, exemplified by Wastwater and Ennerdale Water ; at the other the 'rich' Esthwaite Water and Blelham Tarn. The 'level of wealth' can be measured in various ways. Poor lakes tend to have considerable expanses of barren, rocky shorelines, clear water, and only a small percentage of the drainage area suitable for cultivation. Rocky shores, clear water and lack of cultivation are indices of poverty. Rich lakes have less rocky, often reed-fringed, shorelines — in

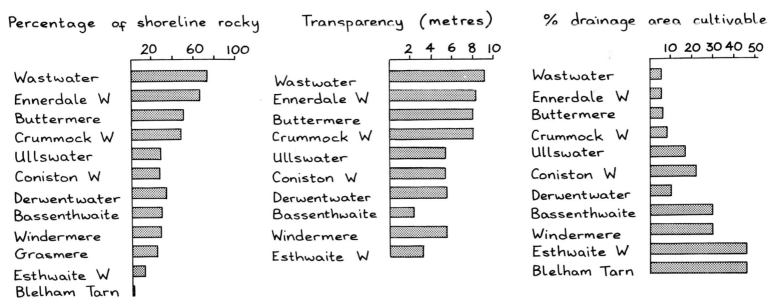

Three indices of wealth, or poverty, among the English Lakes. The poor lakes are at the top of the diagrams, the rich at the bottom. Note how, with minor discrepancies, similar trends are shown by each index. In the first two a high level, like a <u>high</u> level of unemployment, is an indicator of poverty.

general the 'wealthier' a lake the greater the extent of its reed beds — have less clear water, and are set in drainage areas more suitable for cultivation.

Wealth can be measured in terms of crop production, just as it can in a field. In lakes important crops are those of minute algae suspended in the water — the phytoplankton. The richest lakes produce the biggest crops of algae. These colour the water green, render it turbid and therefore reduce its transparency, which is why a low transparency is usually an indicator of wealth. (Turbidity can also be due to silt, but not to any great extent in the Lake District, and transparency can be reduced by peat staining, as in Bassenthwaite Lake.) The green colouring matter of algae (chlorophyll) can be extracted and the amount in a given volume of water measured, so absolute average values can be used as a real measure of wealth — like the number of pounds in a bank account.

These values in large part reflect the amounts of those substances dissolved in the water that are needed by the plants (algae). These too can be measured to give further numerical measures of wealth or poverty. Electrical conductivity gives an indication of the total salt content. The more salts present, the better the water conducts electricity or, put the other way round, the lower its resistance. Calcium is just one of the elements that show the kind of trend illustrated. Though present in very small amounts (those shown in the diagram are measured in millionths of a gramme per litre only) phosphorus is an important plant nutrient, taken up as phosphates. Phosphatase activity — processes that take place in micro-organisms (bacteria and algae) and release phosphates — gives an indication of the numbers of micro-organisms present and is a further measure of wealth. The richer the lake the greater the phosphatase activity.

Just as a rich man can afford more possessions than a poor man, a rich lake can, in general, support a greater variety of animals than a poor lake, and more of them. Thus Esthwaite Water boasts more species of flatworms, leeches, snails, copepods and corixid bugs than the larger Wastwater and Ennerdale, and produces heavier crops of midges.

Thus rich and poor lakes differ both _qualitatively_, that is in their different kinds of possessions, and _quantitatively_, that is in the differing degrees to which they enjoy the same kinds of 'income', such as amounts of phosphorus. Other examples of qualitative

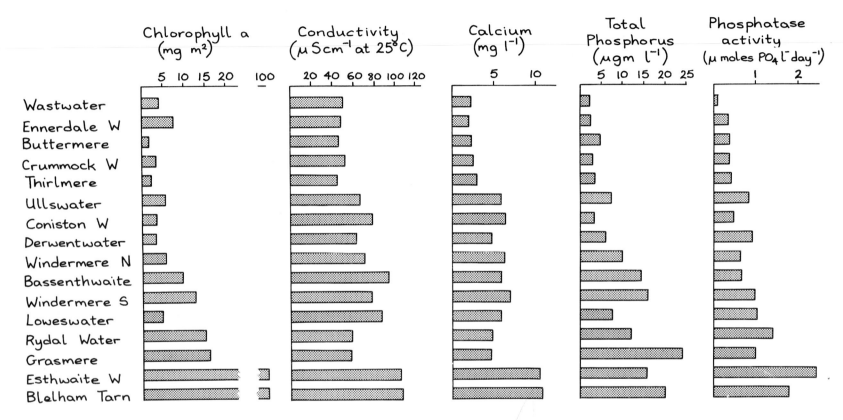

The average amount of chlorophyll <u>a</u> (a green plant pigment) and of various dissolved substan--ces in the waters of different lakes. The north and south basins of Windermere are treated separately. The south basin is richer than the north.

differences are provided by organisms as diverse as algae and fishes. Poor lakes tend to support more kinds of that group of algae called desmids (page 119) than do rich lakes, which in turn support more blue-green algae (page 128) including species unknown in lakes such

92

as Wastwater and Ennerdale. Although Windermere is an exception, it is the poorer lakes that support populations of Char, while Pike and Perch favour the richer lakes and are unknown in Wastwater and Ennerdale.

Wealth is not without drawbacks or obligations. The greater the production, the greater the amount of dead material that has to be broken down. A tax is levied on this process, payable in oxygen, and is heaviest in the richest lakes (page 90). With their low incomes, poor lakes incur no such crippling tax demand for oxygen. This is why, for all its wealth, a lake like Esthwaite can become bankrupt of oxygen in deep water in summer, and run up an overdraft that has to be repaid at the overturn. The poverty-stricken Wastwater, though less well endowed in other respects, enjoys a plenitude of oxygen in deep water throughout the summer.

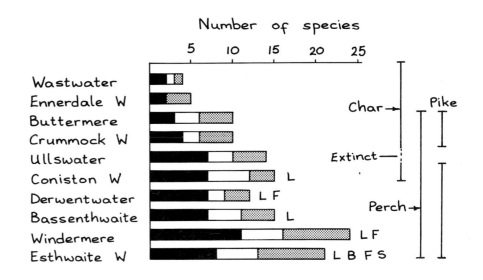

Number of species

Number of species of snails (black), triclad turbellarians —flatworms— (white) and leeches (stipple) in different lakes. The distribution of certain fishes is also shown. Other animals present in the richer lakes, indicated by code letters are — L the copepod Mesocyclops leuckarti, B the cladoceran Bosmina longirostris, F and S the corixid bugs Sigara falleni and S. semistriata.

Wealth can be accumulated in such quantities that it is difficult to manage. Esthwaite produces such heavy crops of planktonic algae that they greatly curtail the penetration of light. They do so to such an extent that algae lying at even very modest depths receive less light than they could utilise. By such 'self-shading' they reduce the level of production of which such a population is potentially capable. Nevertheless, the algae of its relatively narrow euphotic zone (page 85) produce heavier crops than do those of the much thicker equivalent zone of Wastwater.

Water supplies

The value of lakes as a source of enjoyment to man cannot be measured in terms of cash. To many the scenic beauty of the English lakes and tarns is a source of deep and lasting pleasure. Others derive aesthetic or scientific satisfaction (or both!) from the plants and animals associated with them. Uplift of the spirit is, however, not the concern of the waterworks engineer. His job is to supply water. Water is a prime necessity of life, and a lake is a valuable natural resource. The annual revenue of the United Kingdom Water Authorities exceeded £2 billion in the mid 1980s, so water is big business. The presence of so much water in the Lake District has not escaped the attention of the water industry. Not only is there plenty of it, but its quality is mostly excellant. Scarcely polluted, most lakes are relatively unproductive (page 90). They produce relatively small crops of algae and therefore present fewer treatment problems than rich lowland lakes. Oligotrophic lakes like Wastwater and Ennerdale are the most desirable to the seeker of pure water.

While abstraction of water and the preservation of natural beauty and biological diversity are not entirely incompatible, they present severe problems, as the devastating effects of drawdown in Thirlmere and Haweswater make plain. Sometimes there is a clash of interests. Several lakes and tarns are now used as sources of water. Thirlmere, and later Haweswater, increased in size by damming, have been major suppliers of Manchester and other Lancashire towns for many years.

Work to enlarge Thirlmere — then two lakes — began in 1890, and the lake, now with a capacity of about 9000 million gallons, supplied its first water to Manchester — via a 96-mile aqueduct and entirely by gravity — in 1894. Up to 50 million gallons (227 megalitres) per day are provided by this route. Preliminary treatment — straining to remove detritus, chlorination, and reduction of acidity by adding caustic soda (sodium hydroxide) — is done as the water leaves the lake: final treatment at Manchester, or at intermediate supply points en route.

Haweswater supplied its first water to Manchester in 1941. An aqueduct, including 5 miles of tunnel, linked it to the Thirlmere aqueduct. This Haweswater aqueduct was extended as a second supply line to Manchester, and was in use by 1955. Subsequently a new pipeline, the Shap aqueduct, along which water is pumped to a modern treatment plant at Watchgate, near Kendal, was completed in 1978. The capacity of Haweswater

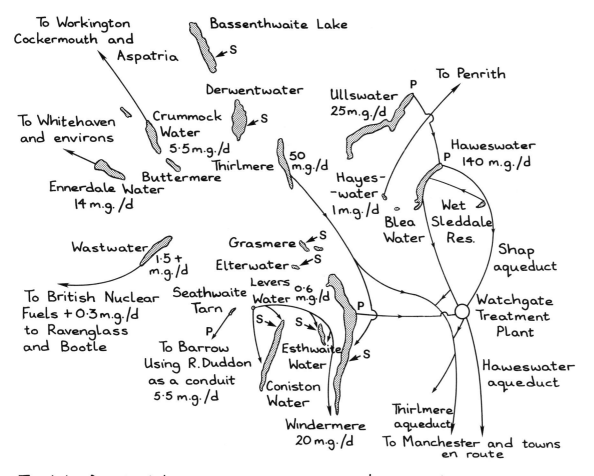

To Workington Cockermouth and Aspatria

Bassenthwaite Lake
S

To Penrith

Derwentwater
S

Ullswater
25 m.g./d
P

Crummock Water
5.5 m.g./d

To Whitehaven and environs

Haweswater
140 m.g./d
P

Thirlmere 50 m.g./d

Buttermere

Ennerdale Water
14 m.g./d

Hayes- water
1 m.g./d

Blea Water

Wet Sleddale Res.

Shap aqueduct

Wastwater
1.5 + m.g./d

Grasmere S
Elterwater S

To British Nuclear Fuels + 0.3 m.g./d to Ravenglass and Bootle

Seathwaite Tarn
P

Levers Water 0.6 m.g./d

S   S

P

Watchgate Treatment Plant

To Barrow Using R. Duddon as a conduit
5.5 m.g./d

Esthwaite Water
S

Haweswater aqueduct

Coniston Water

Windermere
20 m.g./d

Thirlmere aqueduct

To Manchester and towns en route

P = Pumping station
S indicates lakes that receive sewage

Blea Water is used for local supplies. Any excess flows into Haweswater.

For those wishing to convert these figures to metric equivalents one million gallons = 4.546 megalitres.

The Lake District lakes as sources of water and receptacles for sewage. The supply lines are indicated diagrammatically and do not represent the exact routes followed. Amounts supplied are indicated in millions of gallons per day. These figures are the usual permitted average maximum. Compensation water to maintain river flows is also supplied.

is about 18,600 million gallons and it can supply up to 140 million gallons per day. Its inflows are supplemented by water from a reservoir at Wet Sleddale (capacity 500 million gallons) and by water diverted from Heltondale, Swindale and the Naddle Valley. Since 1971 it has also been possible to supplement its inflow by pumping excess water from Ullswater at a permitted average of 25 million gallons a day. The pumps can pump 80 million gallons a day if necessary.

When needed, water can now be pumped from Windermere at a permitted average of 20 million gallons a day to an underground storage reservoir, whence it flows by gravity to the Watchgate treatment plant. The inlet is in deep water in the North Basin. This avoids the plankton of the upper layers — and the sewage (treated) of Windermere township that enters the South Basin. The underground, sound-proofed and landscaped pumping station (like that of Ullswater) is a model of how to site such a unit without harming the environment. Other lakes and tarns are also used as water sources, as indicated in the diagram, as are several small, man-made reservoirs (not shown).

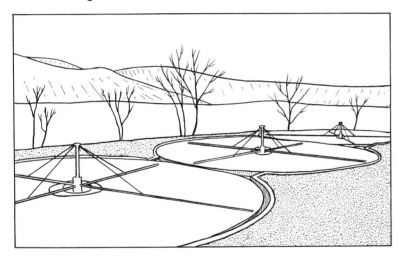

The Windermere sewage works with the lake beyond

Sewage disposal

That a lake serves as a source of drinking water is not incompatible with its use as a receptacle for sewage. Several Lake District lakes receive sewage. This is a cheap method of disposal. It can save expenditure on pipes, pumps and maintenance. The sewage of Ambleside is discharged into the South. In addition water is received from Grasmere that has absorbed the effluent of Grasmere village, from Elterwater that has a small sewage plant, and from Esthwaite Water that has received the sewage of Hawkshead. All this sewage is treated and is bacteriologically

The greatest load is borne by Windermere. Its North Basin: that of Bowness and Windermere township into the South. In addition water is received from Grasmere that has absorbed the effluent of Grasmere village, from Elterwater that has a small sewage plant, and from Esthwaite Water that has received the sewage of Hawkshead. All this sewage is treated and is bacteriologically acceptable.   That the sewage — garnished water of Windermere is deemed safe to drink after treatment reveals the nonsense of excluding the public from reservoirs on the alleged grounds that access may constitute a health hazard.

Treated sewage may be no threat to health but it contains such plant nutrients as nitrates and phosphates.   In the mid 1980s the Ambleside and Windermere sewage works put almost 2000 Kg (2 tonnes) and about 6000 Kg (6 tonnes) of soluble reactive phosphorus respectively into Windermere each year — being much the largest source of phosphorus for the lake.   In a world run for the benefit of society as a whole and not simply for economic gain, this material would be recovered.   As it is such nutrients encourage the growth of algae, often of undesirable kinds (page 130).   Lakes elsewhere have been rendered foul — or have even been 'killed' by such enrichment.   At present no Lake District lake is seriously threatened, but none of them has an infinite capacity for dealing with man's wastes and readily measurable changes have already taken place as a result of the input of sewage.   The dangers are now sufficiently apparent that a phosphate stripping plant was commissioned for the Esthwaite sewage works in the late 1980s.

Fishes and fisheries

The most exploited biological products of Lake District lakes are fishes.   Several lakes have a long history of commercial netting.   The earliest reference to fishing in Windermere goes back to 1223 at which date the Abbot of Furness complained that William de Lancaster, Baron of Kendal, had deprived the monks of their fishery and broken their boat.   By 1246 the baron must have had a change of heart for he granted the monks two boats, one on Windermere, the other on Thurstanwater (Coniston Water), each with 20 nets 'for continual fishing'.   What sort of nets these were is not known.

Fisheries in Windermere are referred to in several later, but still ancient, documents relating to the Barony of Kendal, which was divided in 1246, after which fishing rights in different parts of the lake resided in various hands.   For example, a chantry with two chaplains was founded in the 13th century on an island, Lady Holme, which in 1354 evidently had the right to operate a boat with 10 nets at all times of the year.

By the 16th century the lake was divided into 12 fisheries whose owners could sell or let them.   Rent was due to the Lord of the Fee and it is recorded in 1574 that

Queen Elizabeth I received £6 yearly for 'the Fishery and ferrying of the water of Windermere'.

Trout

Char

Perch

Pike

Fishes formerly netted for food in Windermere; now caught only by rod and line.

From the 16th century, or even earlier, commercial fishing took place with seine (or draw) nets. No figures for yields are recorded but what is known of present-day populations suggests that a steady yield of about 3 tons of Char, 1 ton of Trout, 2 tons of Pike, 5 tons of Perch and 2 tons of Eels could have been removed each year.

Protection of the fisheries was not ignored. In 1670 reference was made to the mesh size, apparently of some kind of gill net — a net set like a fence into which fishes stick their heads and are unable to get them out, being caught behind the gills. (It is actually the opercular bones that prevent the fish from extricating its head.) Small meshes catch small fishes, large meshes only large fishes. In 1768 the capture of Char spawning in the River Brathay was banned for 7 years as a means of protecting the stock and a minimum mesh size was imposed. By about 1840, however, fishing pressure on the Char — a delicacy and always a prime target — was intense and small-meshed nets were in use. Furthermore, rod fishing by means of an 'otter' that allowed several hooks to be deployed simultaneously, had come into use and was very effective. This method was made illegal in 1884.

The census returns of 1841 and 1851 show that 12 or 13 individuals gave their occupation as 'fisherman' and in 1861 a dozen were recorded either as fishermen or 'boatman and fisherman', which gives some indication of the size and importance of the industry. By 1862, however, the fisheries were so depleted that the then proprietors, acting in concert, stopped all netting from the autumn of 1863. It was restarted in 1869. Fishery Acts imposed close seasons for Trout in 1865 and Char in 1873, and a bye-law of 1884 imposed restrictions on mesh sizes and on the lengths of the nets set. These actions evidently had some effect for the average value of the Char caught over several years in the 1890s has been estimated at about £1,200 per annum, and there was evidently an increase in the size of the population of this species, and in the average size of fishes caught. It is difficult to ascertain the weight of Char removed, but between 1893 and 1914 the major netter caught about 1 ton per year. Other fisheries and anglers removed additional Char. Perch were important until the end of the 19th century. In 1899 Perch fishing was described as the main industry of Bowness! Thereafter commercial fishing for 'coarse' fishes became uneconomic.

By 1915 all the Windermere fisheries had passed into the hands of a Board of Conservators which ceased to net the lake in 1921, since when no commercial fishing has taken place. During and immediately after the 1939-45 war, however, Perch were trapped and some 90 tons were canned in tomato sauce and sold under the name of 'Perchines' as a contribution to the nation's larder.

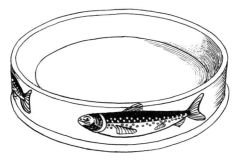

A 17th century Char dish

Although there is now no commercial fishing, angling for sport is a major recreational activity on the lakes, and supplies a small amount of fish for human consumption. The Char has always been favourite prey. Long esteemed locally, during the 17th, 18th and 19th centuries Windermere Char in particular became famous and were shipped as pies or in special Char pots to London. and elsewhere. Still a sought-after delicacy, the Char is now often caught by trolling — trailing lures from two rods in a rowing boat — any captures finding a ready sale.

A more recent development has been the commercial production of trout in cages in Esthwaite Water using the American Rainbow Trout, <u>Salmo gairdneri</u>. This is essentially a kind of farming, or ranching. Supplementary feeding is necessary to stimulate sufficient growth to ensure an economically viable enterprise. While a useful means of exploiting lakes and producing food, such ventures are open to similar criticisms as are levelled at 'factory farming' and are a source of potential danger to the environment.　　Enrichment of the water by uneaten food particles and by the excretory products of dense fish populations is inevitable and leads to increased oxygen demand, a situation that has to be carefully watched, especially in an already rich lake like Esthwaite Water.

Mineral exploitation.

For some years Windermere was used as a source of gravel which was dredged from certain areas of the lake bed.　This activity has now ceased.

Diatomite — consisting of the skeletons of diatoms that have accumulated on the lake bed — was for many years dug from an extinct lake in Kentmere (page 43).　This operation too has now come to an end.

Transport

The major lakes have long been used as highways.　Water transport must always have been attractive in the difficult terrain of the Lake District.　The Romans evidently had dock facilities at their fort (Galava) at Ambleside and vessels of many kinds must have plied the waters of Windermere since those times.　The Baron of Kendal not only granted fishing rights to the monks of Furness Abbey in 1246 but also "granted to the same abbot and monks in perpetuity two suitable boats" one on Windermere the other on Coniston Water "to carry their wood and timber and whatever else they need."　Several centuries later the successors of these boats were carrying slate down the lakes.　In the 18th and 19th centuries thousands of tons of it were transported from Coniston down the full length of the lake to Nibthwaite, thence by road to Greenodd or Ulverston from where it went by sea to London, Bristol and elsewhere. Windermere was similarly used to carry slate quarried in the Troutbeck Valley.　The railway that reached Coniston in 1859 put an end to the lake-borne traffic.

Boats had been used for industrial transport much earlier than this on Derwent-water.　In this area copper mining, long practised on a small scale, was rapidly developed in Elizabethan times following the setting up of the Society for the Mines Royal in 1561.　Ore was brought by packhorse from the Goldscope Mine in the Newlands Valley to a place on the western side of the lake that came to be known as Copperheap Hill, and was shipped from the adjacent Copperheap Bay across the lake en route to a smelter at Brigham on the River Greta, near Keswick.   Other mines in the Borrowdale area shipped ore down the length of the lake to the same destination, and trees for the furnaces were similarly transported.   The vessels used were evidently barge—like constructions with square sails.

Regular carriage of goods and passengers by lake must have taken place for centuries — there has been a public ferry across Windermere for more than 500 years — but details are obscure.   However, a well established service evidently existed in 1793, when the cost of carrying goods from Newby Bridge to Bowness, and to the head of the lake, was 9d and 1/7d, per ton respectively.   Lime is specifically listed.   It cost 1½d to carry a bushel from Newby Bridge to Bowness.   Barges with both oars and sails operated regular passenger services on Windermere from about 1836, and the first steamship —a paddle-ship— came into service in 1845.   Others quickly followed as did steamboats on Coniston Water and Ullswater.   On Coniston Water the 'Gondola', launched in 1859, operated for almost 80 years.   After subsequent use as a houseboat, then lying derelict for some years, this vessel was restored and now again plies the lake as a passenger vessel.

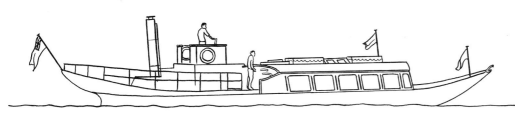

The steam yacht 'Gondola' — launched 1859

In Victorian times wealthy businessmen regularly travelled in their own boats from Bowness to Lakeside, there to take the train to Manchester and elsewhere. 'Pleasure boats' were mentioned in 1793 but the tourist boom of recent years has seen an upsurge in the number of visitors and the 'steamers' of Windermere and Ullswater carry thousands of passengers each summer.   Several of the major lakes also provide pleasure to cruising, sailing, rowing and canoeing enthusiasts — activities that also provide work of various kinds both locally and further afield.

Lake District rivers and streams

There are no large rivers in the Lake District proper. Even the largest are little more than overgrown streams. Of streams, locally called becks, there is an abundance. Most are stony, with clear, often briskly-flowing water, and largely weed-free. The contrast between these and their more sluggish, meandering, often weedy counterparts of many lowland areas is very striking. Many Lake District streams arise high in the fells. Some of the seepages that supply them are boggy but the streams themselves have cut down to the rocks over which they flow and therefore have hard, stony beds. Bare in some fast-flowing reaches, these are more usually strewn with boulders and pebbles, often rounded by erosion, and with smaller pebbles and occasionally sand in quieter parts, as near the bank or in the lee of large boulders. Muddy bottoms, such as characterise some lowland streams, are alien to the area. These streams are characterised by erosion rather than deposition.

The difference between Lake District streams and those of the lowlands is dramatically revealed by comparing the profiles of two Lakeland becks with that of the River Hull, a lowland stream in Yorkshire. In the figure the vertical scales are the same in all cases but the River Hull is about 20 times as long as Sour Milk Gill and 10 times as long as Tongue Gill. Sour Milk Gill (page 20) arises in the Buttermere Fells, drops steeply into Bleaberry Tarn, then out of the hanging combe in which the tarn lies, and falls precipitously into Buttermere. Tongue Gill, which is typical of many Lakeland becks, arises on Fairfield and descends steeply to join the River Rothay — an affluent of Grasmere,

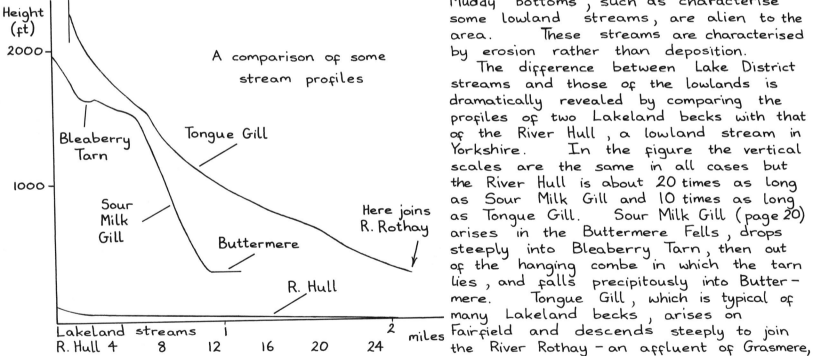

A comparison of some stream profiles

Rydal Water, and ultimately, Windermere.   Longer streams of course tend to fall less steeply in their lower reaches.

Currents in Lakeland streams vary much in velocity.   They depend in part on the slope of the ground — very steep in places, waterfalls being not uncommon — and on the width of the stream at any given point: in part on the amount of incoming water. Input is subject to much change in rainy and dry periods.   Currents are also influenced by differences in topography within the stream.   They swirl round rocks in a complicated way.   Furthermore, velocities are less near the bottom than at the surface and, because of friction, fall rapidly as the surface of a stone or the stream bed is approached.   Thus, flattened animals that keep a low profile are not merely streamlined to cope with fast-flowing water but actually live in a layer that is flowing much less quickly than water near the surface.   Even in fast-flowing streams there are quiet areas where even small, delicate organisms can live.

Turbulent streams are well oxygenated.   Animals that live in them have few problems concerned with respiration except at times of drought.

Extreme conditions are experienced at times.   Heavy flooding can not only scour out sand and pebbles but move large rocks.   This is dramatically revealed for example by the array of boulders to be seen near the road on the ascent from Great Langdale to Blea Tarn.   All these rocks were displaced by what at most times is a very modest stream less than a mile in length.   The effect of such spates on animals living in the streams is obviously severe.   Invertebrates are swept away or crushed. So far as fishes, such as the Trout, are concerned it is the young especially that suffer from such spates.   Such floods also break and grind rocks, releasing the calcareous material present even in the hard volcanic rocks.   This, for a short time, reduces the acidity of the water.

At the other extreme, some streams, even in the wet Lake District, dry out during droughts.   At such times some animals can take refuge in subsurface water which persists for some time among gravel or at the margin, even when the stream appears to be dry.   Such water of course is less well oxygenated than that of a turbulent stream and may be unsuitable for some animals.   Severe droughts have a marked effect on Trout populations.   Not only do they greatly reduce numbers, they retard the growth of the survivors.   Instability and fluctuating conditions are therefore typical of many Lakeland streams.

At high altitudes the stones in streams are often bare. Sometimes a few bryophytes (mosses and liverworts) are present ; sometimes not even these. Even in apparently bare streams, however, the stones often support a film of algae — one of the sources of food for animals in upland reaches. Another source is the debris of terrestrial plants, which is usually sparse in such places. Lower down this is supplemented by the dead leaves of trees.

Even at low altitudes, streams often remain rocky and fast-flowing, but where they are shaded, as in woodland, the exposed rocks are sometimes covered by a carpet of bryophytes. These include the beautiful, arborescent and easily recognised moss <u>Thamnium alopecurum</u> (which has the curious habit of growing also in calcareous woods!). Sometimes submerged bryophytes such as the moss <u>Eurhynchium riparioides</u> and the liverwort <u>Scapania undulata</u> are present and provide additional habitats for invertebrate animals, as do the occasional forests of the long-fronded, dark green moss <u>Fontinalis</u> which develop on stones or tree roots.

There is no sharp distinction between rivers and streams. Lake District rivers are generally stony, though as some of them enter the lowlands, where they are often enriched by drainage from fertilized fields or by other inputs of man, they tend to assume the character of other English lowland rivers. But by then they have left the Lake District.

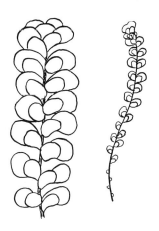

<u>Scapania undulata</u>
- a liverwort

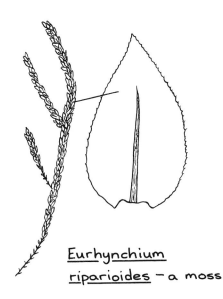

<u>Eurhynchium riparioides</u> - a moss

Two bryophytes of Lake District streams

The River Duddon and its animal life

Many Lake District streams arise on the hard Borrowdale Volcanic rocks and, in their upper reaches, often have a low salt content and tend to be markedly acidic. Adjacent streams can, however, differ according to local differences in the composition of the underlying rocks. As they descend to lower, often more fertile, ground, not only does their speed diminish, but they receive additional salt inputs, and become less acidic. This is particularly the case when their lower reaches lie on the Skiddaw Slates or on Silurian slates, grits and flags in the southern part of the district, but it is true also of the River Duddon which, apart from a very short stretch near its mouth, lies entirely on Borrowdale Volcanic rocks.

As streams descend, the diversity of their faunas (that is the number of species present) tends to increase. While other factors play a part, this seems to be associated particularly with the reduced acidity of their lower reaches. Several of the tributary streams of the Upper Duddon are permanently acidic with a pH always below 5·7 (category 1). Other tributary streams are less acidic, being above pH 5·7 in summer and below in winter, fluctuating between pH 4·8 and 7·0 (category 2). All the tributaries of the Lower Duddon are less acidic than either of these categories. Their pH is above 5·7 throughout the year and can rise as high as 7·3, which is alkaline, at times (category 3). A few tributaries of the Upper Duddon are also category 3 streams. As Upper Duddon streams of all three categories are similar in other respects, any differences in their faunas probably reflect differences in acidity.

The most acidic streams (category 1) have very impoverished faunas. The larger invertebrate animals present are mostly nymphs of stoneflies (page 248) — 10 species —, caddis larvae (page 272) — 4 species — the larvae of a few Diptera (page 298) — 3 or more species, and a few worms. Category 2 streams have a somewhat richer fauna, having all the species of the most acidic streams, and 4 additional species, 3 stoneflies and a mayfly (page 252). Category 3 streams in the Upper Duddon have much more diverse faunas, having at least 17 species not present in their more acidic associates. These include mayflies, stoneflies, caddis — flies, beetles, the amphipod Gammarus pulex (page 227) and the limpet Ancylus fluviatilis (page 212). However, 4 species of stoneflies are absent. These evidently prefer more acidic water.

The Lower Duddon has a similar, but slightly wider, assemblage than the

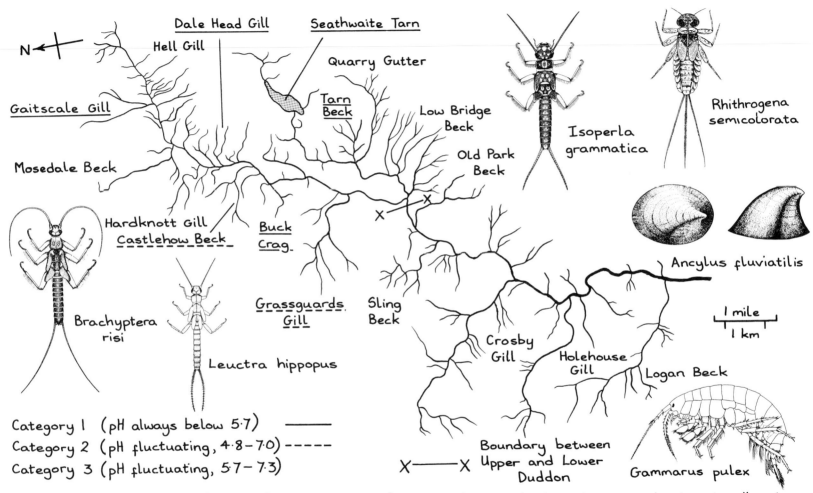

N

Dale Head Gill

Hell Gill

Seathwaite Tarn

Quarry Gutter

Gaitscale Gill

Tarn Beck

Low Bridge Beck

Old Park Beck

Isoperla grammatica

Rhithrogena semicolorata

Mosedale Beck

Hardknott Gill
Castlehow Beck

Buck Crag

Ancylus fluviatilis

Brachyptera risi

Grassguards Gill

Sling Beck

1 mile
1 km

Leuctra hippopus

Crosby Gill

Holehouse Gill

Logan Beck

Category 1 (pH always below 5·7) ————
Category 2 (pH fluctuating, 4·8 – 7·0) -----
Category 3 (pH fluctuating, 5·7 – 7·3)

Boundary between Upper and Lower Duddon

X———X

Gammarus pulex

The R. Duddon, a typical Lake District river with many short inflowing streams, showing the differing acidities of its tributaries, and a few representative invertebrates of the most and least acidic.

least acidic streams of the Upper Duddon, but 2 stoneflies drop out. The situation can be summarised in a table.

	Lower Duddon		Upper Duddon	
	(Category 3) Always $>$ pH 5·7	(Category 3) Always $>$ pH 5·7	(Category 2) $\pm$ pH 5·7	(Category 1) Always $<$ pH 5·7
Number of species	31 + (8)	27 + (8)	16 + (6)	13 + (6)

The number of species of animals in streams of different levels of acidity in the River Duddon. Numbers in parentheses are entities (taxa) not identified to species, that sometimes include two or more species.

Salmon and Sea Trout run up the River Duddon and there is a resident population of Brown Trout. It is known from other streams that Trout grow better and to a larger size in alkaline than in acidic water, though how much this is a direct effect or a reflection of food supply is difficult to elucidate. In the Duddon, Trout are most numerous in the least acidic streams of its lower reaches where aquatic food organisms are most numerous and whose temperatures are slightly higher than those of upland becks.

Springs

Some Lake District streams arise as springs, which are common at various altitudes. The surrounding area is often wet and provides a good habitat for byrophytes (mosses and liverworts) of which there are often attractive displays around such springs. Very characteristic and easily recognisable is the bright yellowish — green moss <u>Philonotis fontana</u> whose upright shoots stand out conspicuously. Equally characteristic are the brilliant golden — or yellow — green <u>Dicranella palustris</u> and the also golden green <u>Brachythecium rivulare</u>, while <u>Bryum pseudotriquetrum</u>, whose shoots are green towards their tips and purplish brown below, is also often present. The liverworts <u>Scapania undulata</u>, found also in streams, and <u>Solenostoma cordifolium</u> are other typical members of this bryophyte community. Added visual attractiveness is added to such sites by moisture — loving flowering plants, which may include the beautiful Starry Saxifrage, <u>Saxifraga stellaris</u>, the Golden Saxifrage, <u>Chrysosplenium oppositifolium</u> (found at all altitudes in the Lake District) and several others. Such places, both in the main flow and in the constant trickle of water among the bryophytes, provide habitats for a variety of small invertebrate animals.

Starry Saxifrage
<u>Saxifraga stellaris</u>

Golden Saxifrage
<u>Chrysosplenium oppositifolium</u>

Two saxifrages associated with springs and wet places

Freshwater is in some ways a good medium in which to live; but it has its drawbacks. Water is essential for life and to be surrounded by it can be very convenient. There is then no risk of water loss and desiccation — a constant hazard to terrestrial organisms, especially if they be small. Water offers support: tiny plants and animals can float suspended in it, submerged leafy plants can expand in it without the need to produce woody tissues, or their leaves can float on the surface, and even large fishes, if they have a swim bladder, can become effectively weightless and move around with ease. These advantages enable many kinds of soft-bodied animals, or animals with delicate cuticles, that would find life on land impossible or extremely difficult, to flourish in freshwater. Others have exploited the properties of the surface film, on which they walk or skate.

Water is a good medium for offering support, but because it is more viscous than air, aquatic animals cannot move as quickly as terrestrial creatures. Even a fast-swimming fish is very slow compared with many terrestrial birds and mammals of comparable size. This can be a liability, for example to a fish trying to escape from a stabbing Heron whose beak accelerates before entering the water. It doesn't matter so much if one's enemy or competitor suffers from the same handicap as oneself. However, the smaller the organism, the more viscous is the water in relation to it. Life to a small animal is akin to that of a man swimming in treacle. This imposes all sorts of constraints on small animals. There can be no aquatic equivalent of a leaping flea. A flea-sized animal can have virtually no momentum in water. Whereas a giant oil tanker can travel for miles under its own momentum if it stops its engines, if a flea-sized aquatic animal stops its engine it comes to an abrupt halt. Such animals can, however, easily hang suspended in the open water of lakes, and find it easy to clamber about in vegetation.

Viscosity is not constant: it changes with temperature. Warm water is less viscous than cold so tiny open water animals (which comprise the plankton) sink faster in summer than in winter. Some of them have devized devices to counteract these changes. Cold water can be very viscous as a fall on a frozen pond makes plain.

One of the drawbacks of freshwater is that it has a very low salt content.

Animal tissues, including blood, need a certain level of common salt, sodium chloride ($NaCl$). In freshwater animals this is obtained partly via the food, partly by direct uptake through the skin. Especially in very dilute waters, such as some of those in the Lake District, it can be difficult to get enough salt. Furthermore there is a tendency for salt to leak out of freshwater animals and (by a process called osmosis) for water to seep in. Unless special precautions are taken, either salt loss or waterlogging can prove fatal. Tiny animals can literally burst if the regulatory mechanism breaks down. The difficulty of getting enough salt is increased if the water is acidic, as it is in upland tarns and in the upper reaches of many Lake District streams. These difficulties are sufficient in themselves to prevent certain animals that live for example in Windermere or in the lower reaches of Lakeland streams from colonising, and surviving in, upland sites.

Some animals, such as snails and mussels, require lime, calcium carbonate ($CaCO_3$), in order to make a shell, or, like the crayfish, to impregnate and strengthen their skeleton. While freshwater animals are very good at getting chemical substances from very dilute solutions (a very few parts per million is often ample) there is a limit beyond which they cannot go. So far as lime is concerned, for many snails and mussels, and for the crayfish, that limit is reached, and exceeded, in many Lake District lakes, tarns and streams.

Some chemical substances that are readily available at times can be in short supply at others. The tiny algae called diatoms, that often abound in lakes, have a skeleton made of silicon (SiO_2). Silicon is the most abundant substance on earth, but it doesn't dissolve very readily. Nevertheless it is often available in sufficient amounts to allow enormous crops of diatoms — in astronomical numbers — to develop in the open waters of lakes. Often they deplete silicon levels to such an extent as to bring an end to their increase, and sometimes, as in Windermere, there is a population crash when diatoms die in billions.

Algae, like terrestrial plants, also require phosphates (PO_4^{3-}) and nitrates (NO_3^-), and these too can be depleted and lead to mass deaths. The way in which the nitrate content of the waters of Windermere are reduced in late summer is described on page 68.

Most freshwater organisms require oxygen, which dissolves in water. Except

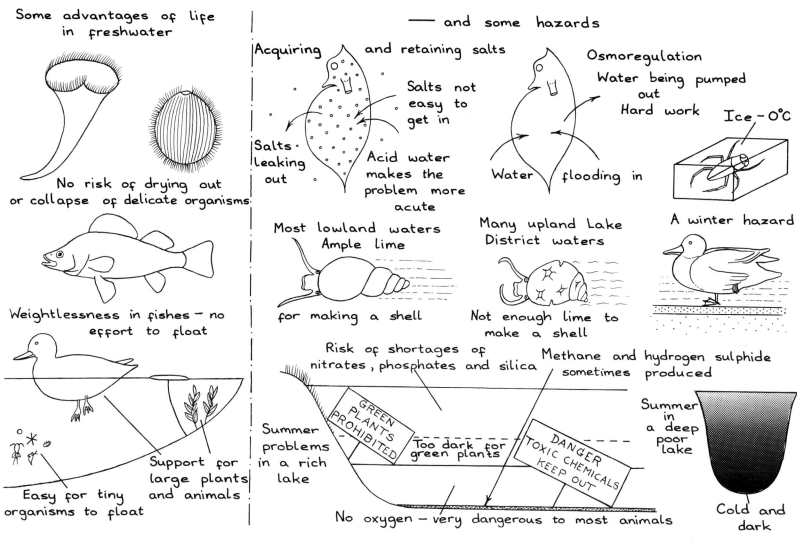

Some advantages of life in freshwater

No risk of drying out or collapse of delicate organisms

Weightlessness in fishes — no effort to float

Easy for tiny organisms to float

Support for large plants and animals

— and some hazards

Acquiring and retaining salts

Salts not easy to get in

Salts leaking out

Acid water makes the problem more acute

Osmoregulation

Water being pumped out
Hard work

Water flooding in

Ice—0°C

A winter hazard

Most lowland waters
Ample lime

for making a shell

Many upland Lake District waters

Not enough lime to make a shell

Risk of shortages of nitrates, phosphates and silica

Methane and hydrogen sulphide sometimes produced

Summer problems in a rich lake

GREEN PLANTS PROHIBITED

Too dark for green plants

DANGER TOXIC CHEMICALS KEEP OUT

Summer in a deep poor lake

No oxygen — very dangerous to most animals

Cold and dark

111

on high mountains and a few other unusual situations there is always an adequate supply of oxygen for terrestrial (and indeed for marine) animals. In freshwater the deeper parts of 'rich' (eutrophic) lakes, such as Esthwaite Water, became depleted of oxygen in summer (page 73) and become uninhabitable to most animals. Poisonous gases — hydrogen sulphide (H_2S) and methane (CH_4) sometimes accumulate here.

In temperate latitudes water is subject to considerable fluctuations in temperature, and when its temperature drops to zero (0°c) it turns to ice. Shallow waters can freeze solid and lake margins suffer likewise. Although air may become even colder it doesn't solidify. In summer some water bodies dry out, even in the wet Lake District, so ice and drought are sometimes hazards to be faced by freshwater animals. Special adaptations, such as an ability to encyst or produce drought-resistant eggs, have been necessary in some species in order to combat such hazards.

Warm-blooded animals lose heat more rapidly in water than on land, as the outdoor swimmer soon realises. Birds and mammals living in water therefore require to be well insulated or enveloped in a waterproof envelope of feathers or hair. Both these waterproofing agents are also excellent insulators. Ice can be a serious hazard to aquatic birds and mammals by shutting off their source of livelihood.

Green plants need light. This is less easy to get underwater than on land because some of the light striking the water surface is reflected, and that which enters is rapidly absorbed. Thus limits are set to the depth to which plants can penetrate by the depth to which light can do so. Furthermore the quality as well as the availability of light changes with depth. In some circumstances the most useful wavelengths for photosynthesis are absorbed quickly, so algae and rooted aquatic plants are at a disadvantage light-wise as compared with terrestrial plants. In clear-water lakes, such as Wastwater, green plants can live at greater depths than is possible in the more murky Esthwaite Water.

In the depths of lakes it is dark and, in temperate latitudes, persistently cold (about 4°c in really deep lakes) and, even when oxygen is plentiful, these conditions are shunned by many animals. These are just not comfortable places in which to live. (Other reasons why animals don't live in deep water are

112

secondary — food is scarce, the bottom deposits are unsuited to many ways of life, and the sheer distance from the shore is sometimes an obstacle to insects that need to pupate there).

Running water presents certain advantages that some animals have exploited. For example, provided the means of catching it are available, it can bring some kinds of food to an animal and obviate the need to go and look for it. On the other hand there is the ever present danger of being swept away. In turbulent, fast-flowing, upland streams in the Lake District, the stony bottom can be unstable and subject to dangerous movement at times of heavy rain, and small streams can become dry in summer.

In spite of all these hazards and problems, the waters of the Lake District have been colonised by a rich diversity of organisms that have exploited the wide range of situations (<u>habitats</u>) that present themselves. Within these habitats, by virtue of many remarkable and beautiful adaptations, they have been able to occupy many different <u>niches</u>. The animals that occupy these niches make up <u>communities</u> whose members interact in various ways. Different habitats support different communities.

The freshwater plants and animals of the Lake District : an introduction.

The plants (the _flora_) and the animals (the _fauna_) — together with the bacteria, which are neither — make up what it is convenient to refer to as the _biota_ ('bios' means 'life') of these waters. The number of different kinds (species) of plants and animals in the freshwater biota of the Lake District cannot be specified with exactitude. Complete inventories of groups such as the flowering plants and fishes can be compiled, but this is still not possible for some of the less well known groups of organisms whose representatives are small, often microscopic, and sometimes rich in species. Certainly, however, the freshwater biota of the Lake District includes over 2000 species. Totals or estimates for various groups are given where appropriate in the sections that follow.

Here the modest objective is to introduce the various groups of these organisms, give some indication of their structure, diversity and ways of life, and indicate their roles in the economy of nature, especially in the local context.

A word about classification.

Plants and animals are arranged into groups that are deemed to be related, a concept based on common sense, similarity, and the idea of evolution. That the Trout, Perch and Pike are all fishes, and ducks, swans and herons are birds is apparent to all. They share the attributes of fishes and birds respectively. This is an example of classification. The grouping together of certain other organisms is less obvious but the principles are the same.

Groups, like ranks in an army, are arranged in hierarchies. Every animal or plant has two names. For example the Trout is called _Salmo trutta_. The first, or generic, name, tells us that the Trout belongs to the genus _Salmo_, the second, or specific, name, that it belongs to the species _trutta_ which is included in that genus. The Salmon is called _Salmo salar_, which tells us that it is more similar to the Trout than to the Pike, _Esox lucius_, because it and the Trout are put in the same genus, which the Pike is not. Similar genera (plural of genus) are put together in families. _Salmo_ and _Salvelinus_ (which includes the Char, _Salvelinus alpinus_) belong to the family Salmonidae. Related families are grouped into orders, orders into classes, and classes into phyla. Thus in the case of the Salmon and Trout, the family Salmonidae belongs to the order Isospondyli of the class

114

Pisces, (the fishes) of the phylum Chordata (the backboned animals). These categories are all that are necessary here though there are various convenient subdivisions. Categories of less than specific rank are also sometimes required. These will be met when we consider the Lake District fishes. If a generic name has to be used more than once it is convenient to abbreviate it so long as this leaves no room for ambiguity. Thus <u>Salmo trutta</u> can be abbreviated as <u>S. trutta</u>.

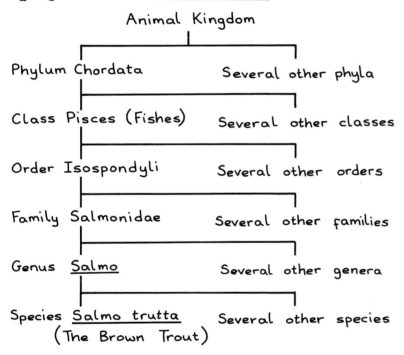

How the Brown Trout is classified

Note that different authorities favour different systems! Some employ additional categories (taxa) in the hierarchy. For example, some regard the Isospondyli as a sub order of the order Teleostei. This does not affect the <u>principles</u> employed, or one's understanding of the position of the Brown Trout in the scheme of things

It is easy to separate a fish and a bird, but in some parts of the animal and plant kingdoms such separation is not always easy. Indeed there is even a sort of no-man's land between the plants and the animals. Many one-celled organisms occur in lakes and some of them are difficult to place : it is a matter of debate whether they are plants or animals. The baffled biologist therefore conjures up a name — Protista — to embrace all such enigmatic organisms, which enables him to refer to them without committing himself.

There are other problems of classification, of which it is useful at least to be aware. For example the Blue Green Algae make up a group of pigment-containing organisms long regarded as algae, as their common name indicates. On the basis of how their nuclear material is arranged, it is now recognised that these organisms are more closely related to bacteria (as which some regard them) than to algae. Their organisation is more simple than that of the algae. As these names are now in common usage it can be noted that bacteria and Blue Green Algae are called prokaryotes : all the other organisms eukaryotes. Fungi also present problems. Here they are treated as plants : by others they are regarded as a group in their own right.

One-celled and many-celled organisms

The basic building block of plants and animals is the cell — a little box of life. There are many single-celled (unicellular) plants — algae (though not all algae are single-celled) — and animals — protozoans. That such organisms consist of one cell only doesn't necessarily mean they are simple. A many-celled animal can use some cells for one purpose — say making a shell or an eye, others for digesting food and so on, or a multi-cellular plant can use some cells to make roots, others to make leaves or seeds, but a one-celled organism has to do everything with its one cell. If it needs to move, catch food and digest it, or manufacture it from basic ingredients, to make offspring, or perform any other activity, it has to do so with its single cell, so it can hardly be called simple. One-celled organisms are particularly abundant in freshwater. A watery medium affords support not available in air, and dessication is avoided. While it is true that many-celled organisms are derived from single-celled ancestors, not all the latter have, as it were, striven to become multicellular. Many have become specialised in ways that not only fit them admirably for their own lifestyles but which effectively preclude them from developing along routes that would enable them to embark on a multicellular existence.

116

The Algae : The plant life of the Lakes

The most obvious plants of the English lakes are those large forms, conveniently called macrophytes — which just means 'big plants' — that grow around their margins or, in certain sheltered areas, extend as splendid expanses of yellow or white water-lilies over their surfaces.   From the point of view of the economy of lakes, however, the most important plants are often invisible, or barely visible, to the naked eye.   These, the algae, abound in countless millions in the open waters and form living coatings on stones and the submerged leaves of higher plants at the margins.   Open water drifting organisms constitute the plankton.   The planktonic algae make up the phytoplankton (Greek — phuton — plant): drifting animals, the zooplankton.   Planktonic algae are sometimes so abundant — millions of cells per litre — as to make a rich lake appear greenish.

Algae belong to several different groups.   While specialists recognise finer divisions, it is sufficient here to regard those found in the Lake District as belonging to the Green, Yellow-Green, Blue-Green and Red Algae, with the stoneworts, euglenaphytes, cryptophytes and diatoms as additional groups.   Strictly speaking the Blue Greens are not algae but have closer affinities to bacteria, but, partly for traditional (if unscientific!) reasons, and partly for convenience, they are treated with the true algae here.

Many Green Algae (the Chlorophyceae) are unicellular.   Some, such as the several species of Chlorella, are no more than tiny spheres of cytoplasm (only about 5 to 10 microns (μm) in diameter) enclosed within a tough cell wall and provided with a green chloroplast — a packet of chlorophyll.   This is the same substance as that which makes grass and the leaves of trees green.   As in higher plants four pigments are involved, but 'chlorophyll' serves to embrace them all.   Whether the cell wall of Chlorella is made of cellulose — a typical plant product — is uncertain. In some algae it is not, but in many it is.

There are many other tiny one-celled green algae of diverse shapes that occur in many situations in fresh water, and even on wet rocks and damp tree trunks. These forms are non-motile.   Like higher plants they stay put or, in some cases, drift at the mercy of currents in the water.   Other unicellular Green Algae, however, are motile, being provided with a pair of whiplash-like flagella (Compare the one-celled animals — Protozoa, page 157) with which they drive themselves through the water.

117

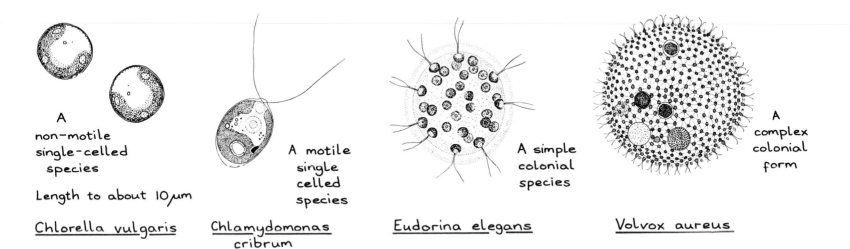

A non-motile single-celled species

Length to about 10μm

<u>Chlorella vulgaris</u>

A motile single celled species

<u>Chlamydomonas cribrum</u>

A simple colonial species

<u>Eudorina elegans</u>

A complex colonial form

<u>Volvox aureus</u>

(Some other green algae, believed to be of different ancestry, and with a single flagellum are mentioned later, page 123).

Very similar algal cells associate in groups and form simple colonies. Such are species of <u>Pandorina</u> and <u>Eudorina</u>. More complex colonies, involving more cells, are formed by species of <u>Volvox</u>. These beautiful organisms, that with practice can easily be recognised with the naked eye, roll majestically through the water, propelled by their array of flagella. Several species occur in the lakes and tarns of the Lake District, sometimes in large numbers.

Other Green Algae are multi-cellular, their cells being firmly united, end to end, to form long filaments. Of these there are many kinds. Species of <u>Oedogonium</u>, <u>Zygnema</u>, <u>Spirogyra</u> and many others are often abundant in a variety of waters in the Lake District. <u>Cladophora</u> is a genus with coarse filaments that, especially in richer waters than are found in the Lake District, sometimes develops in such quantities as to form a blanket-like mass near the shore. This has earned it a common name, a distinction unusual for an alga — Blanket Weed. A non-aquatic

118

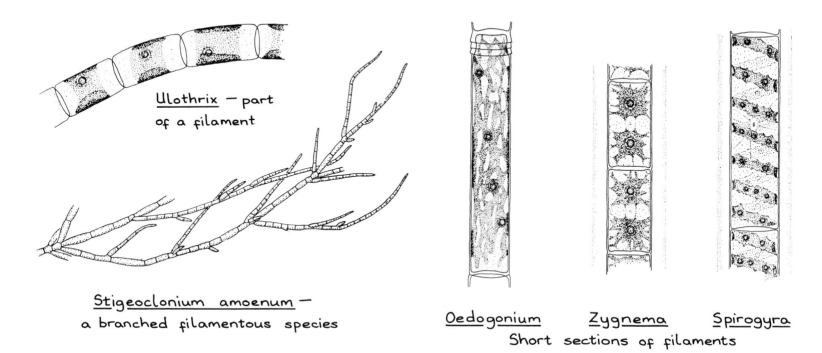

Ulothrix — part of a filament

Stigeoclonium amoenum — a branched filamentous species

Oedogonium   Zygnema   Spirogyra
Short sections of filaments

Some of the many filamentous Green Algae of the Lake District

filamentous form, Trentepohlia, is worthy of mention as it grows commonly on damp rocks in the Lake District, imparting to them a beautiful golden orange hue that is sometimes sufficiently intense to add colour to the landscape.   It owes its colour to the presence in its cells of orange oil.

Desmids make up a distinctive group of unicellular Green Algae that, having a preference for acidic, and a dislike for calcareous, alkaline, waters, is particularly well represented in the Lake District.   Here they abound in the weedy margins of lakes and tarns and in bogs — and in profusion of species.   A single collection

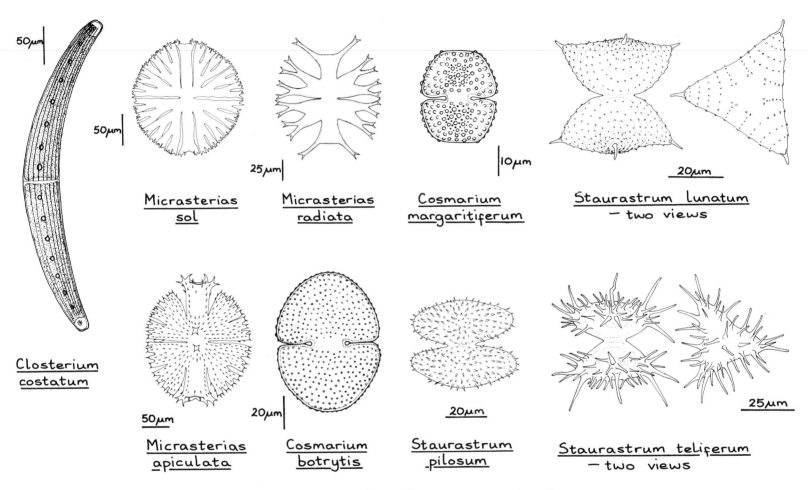

50μm

Closterium
costatum

50μm

Micrasterias
sol

25μm

Micrasterias
radiata

10μm

Cosmarium
margaritiferum

20μm

Staurastrum Lunatum
— two views

50μm

Micrasterias
apiculata

20μm

Cosmarium
botrytis

20μm

Staurastrum
pilosum

25μm

Staurastrum teliferum
— two views

Some of the many desmids of the Lake District

from one site sometimes yields more than 50 species.   Desmids, which are often bright green in colour, are of diverse shapes, many of them having a deep median incision that virtually divides them into two symmetrical halves.   Some of them are flat and conveniently lie in such a way as to display their shape.   Aesthetically

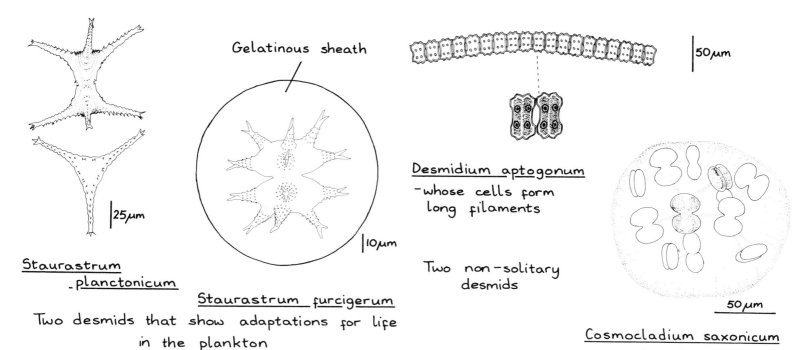

Gelatinous sheath

|50μm

|25μm

|10μm

Staurastrum
-planctonicum

Staurastrum furcigerum

Two desmids that show adaptations for life
in the plankton

Desmidium aptogonum
-whose cells form
long filaments

Two non-solitary
desmids

50μm

Cosmocladium saxonicum
-a colonial species

they are among the most attractive of the algae.
    Some species are members of the plankton.   These have adaptations that facilitate flotation, or at least impede sinking.   Some, like Staurastrum planctonicum, have long prolongations at the angles of the cell which, by providing resistance to the water, delay sinking.   Others, such as Staurastrum furcigerum, are surrounded by a gelatinous

secretion of low density that acts as a kind of life-buoy.

Most desmids are solitary but in a few species a number of cells join end to end to form filaments, sometimes enclosed in a gelatinous sheath. Two genera are colonial. One of these is <u>Cosmocladium</u>. Here several cells are united by bands of gelatinous material and the whole colony is surrounded by a spherical or ellipsoidal gelatinous sheath.

A curious feature of members of the genus <u>Closterium</u>, that are elongate, often lunate (crescent-moon shaped) in form, is that towards each end there is a fluid-filled cavity (a vacuole). These vacuoles contain from a few to several hundred minute vibrating crystals of barium sulphate. Why <u>Closterium</u> should accumulate barium in this way is a mystery, all the more so since this element is usually present in extremely small amounts in the water in which desmids live.

Looking superficially like desmids but belonging to another group of the Green Algae, and in fact forming colonies consisting of a small number of cells, are algae such as <u>Pediastrum</u>. This forms flat disc-shaped colonies of from 2 to 128 cells, the marginal members of which often have processes that give the colony a serrated appearance. Species of <u>Scenedesmus</u> also produce flat colonies of from 2 to 8 cells in a row, some species having spines at the corners of the colony. Several species of <u>Scenedesmus</u> are common in the Lake District.

Very different from any other algae are the <u>stoneworts</u> or charophytes. These could easily be taken for higher plants, for this is what they look like at a casual glance. However, their reproductive habits (deliberately not dealt with here for most algae) reveal their true affinities. Nevertheless, so different are they from other algae that they are perhaps best regarded as a distinct, well-defined group, though derived from the Green Algae.

Stoneworts have a long stem with nodes at intervals from which arise whorls of branches that look like the leaves of certain aquatic flowering plants, and even more like those of horsetails. They are anchored to the bottom by root-like rhizoids and often form dense swards in suitable places. Many species flourish best in 'hard' calcareous waters where some of them become encrusted with lime and feel rough to the touch. As a group they are not very well represented in the soft waters of the Lake District, but one species, <u>Nitella opaca</u> favours such waters and is abundant on soft bottoms in many lakes, penetrating to at least 7m (23 ft) in some places. Luxuriant growths have stems more than a foot (30 cm) long.

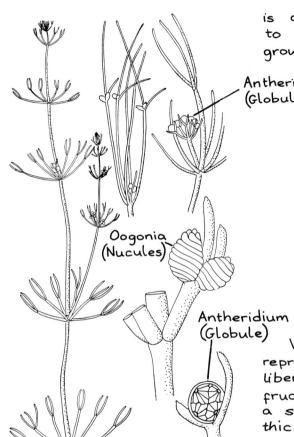

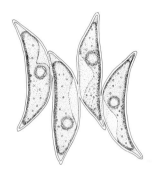

Pediastrum

Two species of <u>Scenedesmus</u>
S. acutus and a spinous species

<u>Nitella opaca</u> a common stonewort of the Lake District

Vegetative spreading takes place as does sexual reproduction. Male fructifications (antheridia or globules) liberate motile antherozooids that swim to the female fructifications (oogonia or nucules) each of which contains a single egg. Fertilized eggs (zygotes) secrete a thick wall, fall to the bottom, and there eventually germinate.

The <u>euglenophytes</u>, although generally green, are deemed distinct from the Chlorophyceae (true Green Algae). These are single-celled algae with a single flagellum. The group includes species that lack pigment and behave as animals and is, as it were, on the borderline

123

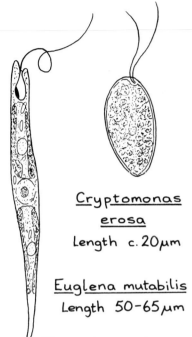

Cryptomonas
erosa
Length c. 20μm

Euglena mutabilis
Length 50-65μm

Two algae that
belong to groups not
far removed from the
animal kingdom

between the plant and animal kingdoms. An example from the Lake District is Euglena mutabilis.

Other algae that produce difficulties of this sort are the cryptophytes — which some regard as having strong affinities with the dinoflagellates, here treated among the Protozoa as animals! These have brownish packets of pigment (chromatophores). Species of Cryptomonas, such as C. erosa, are often abundant in Lake District lakes.

The chrysophytes include algae that can be called the Yellow Greens and the Golden Yellows (or Golden Browns). Regarded as two separate groups by some, all are treated together here. As their names suggest, these algae have a preponderance of yellowish or brownish pigments.

Two of the true chrysophytes represented in the Lake District give some idea of what these algae are like. Mallomonas longiseta is a unicellular species whose cell wall consists of a thin pectic sheath containing many tiny overlapping scales of silica. It also has long spines also made of silica. It swims by means of a flagellum.

Species of Dinobryon are either solitary or colonial. Arborescent colonies are often abundant in the plankton of Lake District lakes. Each cell is enclosed within a clear or yellowish brown sheath or lorica and is provided with two flagella, one long, one short.

Related to the chrysophytes are the diatoms, an important group of algae with well over 5000 known species, some freshwater, others marine. Some are known only as fossils. Diatoms have walls of pectic materials impregnated with silica. The wall, sometimes called the frustule, consists of two overlapping halves like the halves of a tin of boot polish. The halves are called valves. Their upper and lower surfaces are perforated by many tiny holes, often arranged in complex, but regular, and often aesthetically pleasing, patterns.

124

Mallomonas longiseta

Length generally 30 – 40 µm

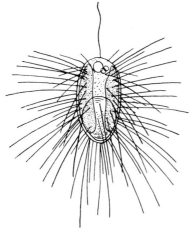

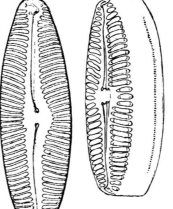

Pinnularia alpina

— seen here from two aspects — gives some idea of the structure of many common diatoms.

Two Lake District chrysophytes

Dinobryon divergens

A colony and a single individual

Length of the lorica of the single cell about 25 µm

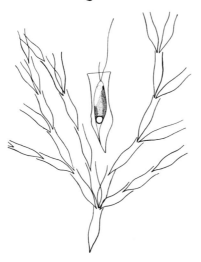

Solitary and colonial diatoms

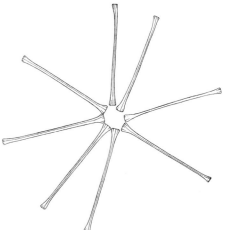

Asterionella formosa — a common and abundant planktonic diatom
Each cell is about 100 µm long

Diatoms occur in a wide spectrum of habitats. Some are free floating in the plankton, others live on the bottom and some form epiphytic growths on the surfaces of submerged plants. Many are solitary : some form loose colonies. Some are attached in various ways to the objects on which they grow, but many can move over surfaces by means of a complex and much discussed process involving streaming of the cytoplasm and the setting up of frictional currents in the water. It is the

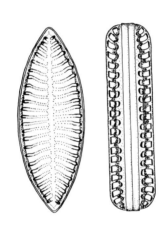  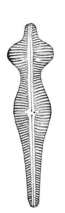 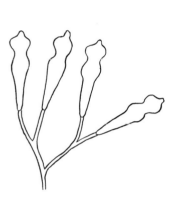 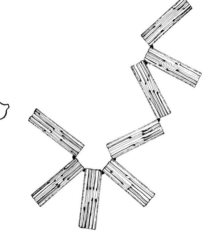

Surirella — in valve
and girdle views

Cymbella
helvetica

Gomphonema acuminata
A single cell and a group of
cells on gelatinous stalks

Tabellaria fenestrata

frustules of diatoms that, dissolving with reluctance, accumulate on the bottom of lakes and sometimes form deposits of diatomite, as in Kentmere (page 43). Diatomite is used in fine industrial filters, insulators and building materials and as very gentle abrasive in polishes and tooth-paste.

Among the dominant planktonic diatoms of Windermere and Esthwaite is Asterionella formosa. Individual cells form loosely attached colonies, usually of about 8 cells. The number of cells that may be present at any one time is impressive. In

126

Esthwaite at the time of the spring maximum of A. formosa, the average number of cells throughout the entire volume of the lake is some-times about 17 million per litre. As the volume of Esthwaite is about 6·4 million cubic metres, the number of cells is prodigous.   In the North Basin of Windermere A. formosa reaches a maximum abundance of about 3×10^{17} cells, there being about 21 tonnes of silica in suspension.   To give some idea of what this huge number means, although these tiny cells are only about 100 μm (a tenth of a millimetre) long, joined end to end they would stretch to the sun — and back — about 17 times!

Other common Lake District diatoms include species of Surirella, Cymbella and Gomphonema.   Species of Gomphonema are usually anchored on stalks of mucilage, either long or short, but when not so anchored they can glide over surfaces like many other diatoms.   Tabellaria fenestrata is another species that forms loose colonies.

Other diatoms are referred to as centric species.   These have cylindrical cells that unite together, end to end to form filament-like colonies.   In some species the end of the cell that abuts its neighbour has a ring of beautiful siliceous spines that embrace the adjoining cell to ensure firm union.   Some of the centric diatoms, such as species of Melosira, are often important constituents of the plankton in the English Lakes.

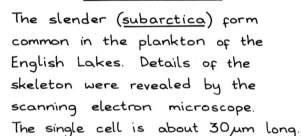

Melosira italica

Melosira arenaria seen in valve (face) view

The slender (subarctica) form common in the plankton of the English Lakes. Details of the skeleton were revealed by the scanning electron microscope. The single cell is about 30 μm long.

Centric diatoms

127

Diatoms are important dead and alive. Notwithstanding their siliceous skeletons they are readily digested by small animals.   Even if swallowed by a small animal, such as a crustacean, algae completely enclosed by a cellulose cell wall often pass through the gut unharmed, presumably because their devourer was unable to rupture the wall and lacks the enzyme (cellulase) necessary to digest it. Diatoms have pores through which the digestive juices of animals that swallow them can pass and gain access to the 'meat' within.   Diatoms often occur in the encrusting layer that frequently covers aquatic plants and submerged stones and is utilised by various small animals that browse upon it or scrape it off as food.

When dead they sometimes form deposits of diatomite. Red Algae (the Rhodophyceae) are mostly marine but a few species occur in freshwater.   As well as chlorophyll they contain a red pigment, phycoerythrin. The unicellular, almost spherical Porphyridium, which is sometimes found growing on rocks, is indeed bright red, but the Red alga most likely to be encountered in the Lake District — Batrachospermum — is brownish or greenish in colour.   This is a distinctive alga that can be recognised by the naked eye.   It grows in tufts of filaments, that may be several centimetres long, attached to stones, usually in streams, but sometimes in tarns.   In the common species, B. moniliforme there is a central axis with whorls of side branches at intervals along it.

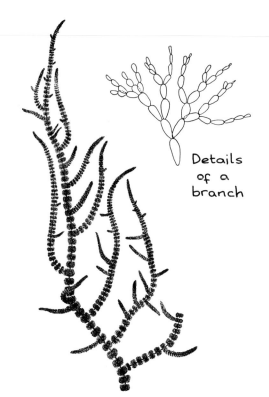

Details of a branch

Batrachospermum

The Blue Green Algae (variously called the Cyanophyceae, Myxophyceae or, perhaps most correct, the Cyanobacteria) are prokaryotes (page 116) and therefore really belong to the bacteria rather than to the true algae.   Like other bacteria they lack true nuclei and plastids, display an apparent lack of sexual reproduction, and have cell walls that contain a typical bacterial cell-wall polymer called peptidoglycan.

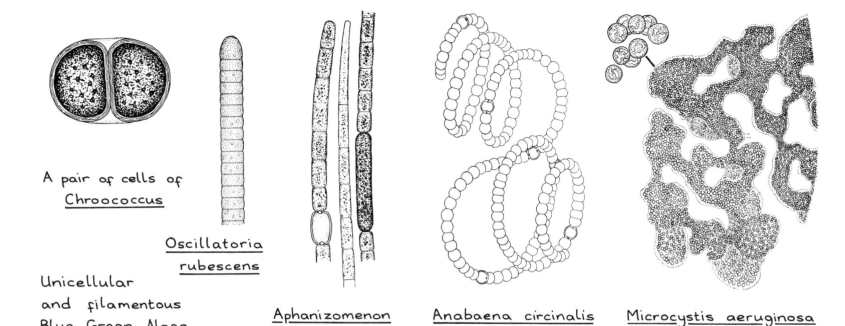

A pair of cells of
<u>Chroococcus</u>

<u>Oscillatoria</u>
<u>rubescens</u>

Unicellular
and filamentous
Blue Green Algae

<u>Aphanizomenon</u>   <u>Anabaena circinalis</u>   <u>Microcystis aeruginosa</u>

Blue Green Algae that cause 'water blooms' in 'rich' eutrophic lakes

They contain not only chlorophyll and carotenoid pigments, but a blue pigment, phycocyanin.
    Like the Green Algae they include single-celled forms, such as <u>Chroococcus turgidus</u>, which grows in many places — such as wet rock faces — in the Lake District.   <u>Gloeocapsa</u> is also unicellular but grows in groups surrounded by thick mucilaginous sheaths that sometimes form conspicuous slimy excrescences on rocks, or stony ground.
    Other species form colonies or filaments.   <u>Oscillatoria</u> is a common filamentous genus. Its unbranched filaments grow in a variety of situations, often on bottom deposits, but sometimes in suspension as components of the plankton.   Filaments of <u>Nostoc</u> become closely aggregated and form dark green lumpy colonies, sometimes an inch (2·5 cm) across, that grow on stones in rivers and streams.   Some filamentous forms are specialized members

129

of the plankton.   Such are <u>Aphanizomenon</u> and <u>Anabaena</u>.   Filaments of the former occur in bundles that float at the surface.   Both these algae have flotation devices whose mechanisms are still a source of debate.   Gas vacuoles are involved.   A common colonial form in the plankton is <u>Microcystis</u>.   Colonies consist of vast numbers of minute cells embedded in mucilage that form irregular masses, often punctured by holes.

Blue Green Algae are found most abundantly in eutrophic lakes.   Here they often 'bloom' in late summer or autumn.   During a bloom they float to the surface and, driven by the wind, form accumulations in bays and backwaters.   Such accumulations, looking like a film of green paint, are a familiar sight each year in Windermere.

Blue Green Algae are a frequent source of inconvenience to waterworks engineers. Not only do they clog filters but they sometimes impart unpleasant tastes and odours to the water.   These effects are sometimes accentuated when the algae die and release even more obnoxious substances.

In confined, shallow ponds, decaying Blue Green Algae can deplete the oxygen in the water at night, which leads to fish deaths, and some of them produce dangerous toxins. <u>Microcystis aeruginosa</u> produces a toxin that is one of the most potent liver poisons known.   It also causes cellular degeneration in other organs, especially the heart and kidneys.   In South Africa several thousand sheep and cows died after grazing on the banks of a reservoir in which <u>Microcystis</u> was abundant.   Less dramatically, in the warm autumn of 1989 about 20 sheep and 15 dogs died after wading in a green scum of <u>Microcystis</u> at the margin of the large reservoir, Rutland Water, and two young men became seriously ill after a training exercise on another English reservoir which had a similar scum.   Such events are more likely to occur in nutrient-rich lowland reservoirs than in Lake District lakes.   The best safeguard against such happenings, which are most likely to occur when warm weather continues longer than usual in autumn, is to prevent the enrichment of lakes by sewage and farmland fertilizers.   The phosphate stripper at the Esthwaite sewage works is a step in the right direction.

The Higher Plants

As a descriptive term 'higher' plants, as used here, embraces the flowering plants (angiosperms), the conifers and their allies (gymnosperms) that do not concern us here, the ferns and their allies (pteridophytes) and the bryophytes, made up of the mosses (Musci) and liverworts (Hepaticae). The higher plants of lakes and their margins are aquatic to varying degrees. Some merely like damp or marshy places; others prefer to keep their roots in water and have either emergent or floating leaves; others are completely submerged. A few, like the duckweeds, Lemna, are free-floating. Marsh plants and emergent aquatics can only advance for a short distance into the water. How far depends on the steepness of the slope and on the degrees of development of the shoreline (page 48). Even a robust plant like the Common Reed, Phragmites communis, cannot penetrate water more than about 1m (3ft) deep, and penetration is usually less than this in the Lake District. Floating leaved plants with flexible stalks, such as water-lilies and some of the pondweeds, Potamogeton, can extend further out — to depths of about 3m (10ft) in the case of water-lilies. Submerged — completely aquatic — plants can penetrate deeper. The depth to which light penetrates is the ultimate limiting factor here. This is greatest in clear, oligotrophic lakes such as Wastwater and Ennerdale Water; least in eutrophic lakes such as Esthwaite Water. Bassenthwaite Lake is anomalous in that, although it is less productive than Esthwaite, vegetation does not penetrate so deeply. This is because humic substances colour the water and reduce its transparency.

Of the marginal, 'marsh', plants, none is more striking than the Common Reed — a grass that often grows to a height of

	Metres	Feet
Wastwater	7·7	25
Ennerdale Water	8·3	27
Crummock Water	7·1	23
Ullswater	6·2	20
Coniston Water	5·5	18
Derwentwater	6·5	21
Bassenthwaite Lake	3·0	10
Windermere	6·5	21
Esthwaite Water	4·0	13

The depth to which vegetation penetrates in some Lake District lakes.

well over 3m (10ft).   It occurs in many places on the shores of the richer, but not the barren oligotrophic, lakes (page 8).   When present it generally forms pure stands — reed beds.   Phragmites is essentially a lowland plant and is not found around most high level tarns.   Its highest recorded altitude in the Lake District is 403m (1322 ft) at Dock Tarn (not far from Watendlath).   It also occurs at Seathwaite Tarn (366m : 1210ft) and Skeggles Water (314m : 1010ft).   Otherwise it scarcely ascends higher than about 240m (800ft).   Intolerant of wave action, and therefore restricted to sheltered situations, Phragmites can grow on a variety of soils, but coarse substrata usually lack nutrients and are exposed, and are therefore unsuitable.   Seed germination is very poor but vegetative propagation is effective and a single plant can spread and maintain itself for hundreds of years.   It is possible that some reed beds are the products of plants as much as 1000 years old.   Green in summer — it grows taller in warm than in cool seasons — its pale brown stalks persist throughout winter, and generally throughout the next season as well.

Another grass, the Reed Grass, Phalaris arundinacea, is present in almost all the lakes.   Smaller than Phragmites it forms similar, but smaller, beds at the margin. Clumps can be seen from the Windermere ferry as it approaches either landing. Like Phragmites, Phalaris is a lowland species.   Although it grows alongside such rocky lakes as Wastwater and Ennerdale it is found by relatively few tarns and seems not to ascend even to 1000 ft (305m).   Tewit Tarn (298m : 977ft) and Watendlath Tarn (258m : 847ft) appear to be its highest stations in the Lake District.

By contrast the commonest fringing sedge in the Lake District (sedges look rather like grasses but have stiff, usually triangular, stems), the Bottle Sedge, Carex rostrata , is characteristic of, but not confined to, upland tarns.   Present in most of the lakes and many tarns, it ascends to 2000ft (610m) at Scales Tarn.

In the lakes the distribution of truly aquatic vegetation is influenced by several factors as well as light penetration.   As a general rule, because the prevailing wind is south-west, south and west shores are comparatively silted.   North and east shores tend to be silt-free, and have less vegetation, but this pattern is modified by local configurations of the shoreline.

Because of the exposed conditions, floating-leaved plants are of restricted occurrence in most lakes.   Only Esthwaite Water has relatively large areas of

132

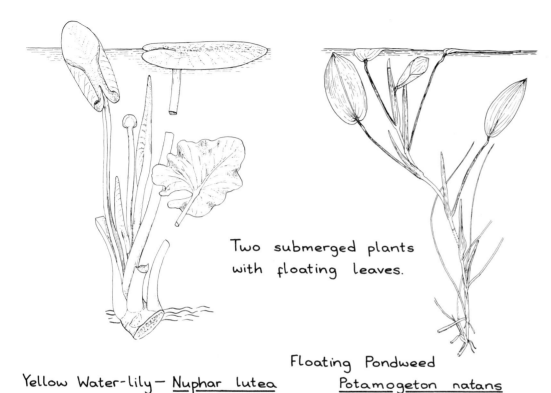

Two submerged plants
with floating leaves.

Floating Pondweed

Yellow Water-lily— Nuphar lutea   Potamogeton natans

water-lilies, yellow and white and even here these are confined to a few sheltered regions.   Neither the White Water-lily, Nymphaea alba, nor the Yellow, Nuphar lutea, is to be found in the exposed, rocky lakes Wastwater, Ennerdale, Buttermere and Crummock Water.

Derwentwater, a relatively broad lake, has plenty of sheltered bays.   Here, however, the dominant floating-leaved plant is the Floating Pondweed, Potamogeton natans. This is because silts, on which water-lilies grow, are relatively scarce.

Much indeed depends on the nature of the substratum — soil conditions.   Unlike algae which obtain nutrients from the water, higher plants obtain most of theirs from the substratum.   Lake District waters are in fact poor in nutrients (page 56).   To this the almost complete absence of free-floating plants is to be attributed.   Even the Common Duckweed, Lemna minor, so abundant in lowland ponds that it sometimes carpets their surfaces, is recorded only from Bassenthwaite.   The Ivy-leaved Duckweed, Lemna trisulca, occurs, but not commonly, in Windermere and Esthwaite Water, two of the 'richest' lakes.

Nutrients are most abundant where silting is taking place, and vegetation is only luxuriant in such places.   Silt is brought in by streams.   It is also removed from

133

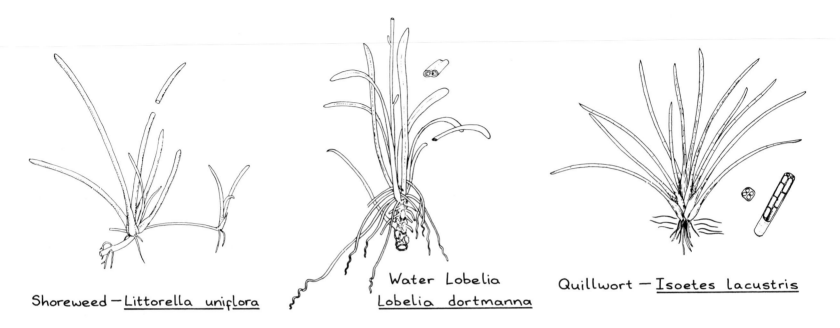

Shoreweed — <u>Littorella uniflora</u>

Water Lobelia
<u>Lobelia dortmanna</u>

Quillwort — <u>Isoetes lacustris</u>

Three plants that look deceptively similar. The Quillwort, however, is not even a flowering plant.

the shore by wave action and deposited in deeper water (page 48). The most inshore waters therefore tend to support sparse vegetation. Very characteristic of gravelly, but not boulder-strewn, shores is the Shoreweed, <u>Littorella uniflora</u>, which also colonises sandy regions. Such situations have a low organic content. By vegetative propagation <u>Littorella</u> forms a continuous sward. An ability to live out of water for a time enables it to cope with fluctuations in lake level. If detritus and silt accumulate in the sward the organic content of the soil is increased and the Water Lobelia, <u>Lobelia dortmanna</u>, is able to colonise such places. Where the organic content rises it tends to replace <u>Littorella.</u>

A third species of similar appearance is the Quillwort, <u>Isoetes lacustris</u>, but this is

134

not a flowering plant.   It is a spore-bearer probably derived from relatives of the ancient lycopods that flourished in Carboniferous times some 300 million years ago. Such resemblance in form in unrelated plants is an interesting case of convergent evolution.   <u>Isoetes</u> has two kinds of spores, large and small, secreted near the bases of its leaves.   The large megaspores give rise to a minute prothallus that bears the female sex organs; the microspores to the male gametes — antherozooids ('sperms').   <u>Isoetes</u> sometimes occurs close inshore, but often a little further out than <u>Littorella</u> and <u>Lobelia</u>.   It can colonise coarse, or stony, nutrient-poor substrata.   In deeper water it occurs on thin muds where silting is slow.

All three of these lake-shore plants are found particularly in northern and western Britain and <u>Isoetes</u> in particular is something of a Lake District speciality, though it occurs in Welsh lakes and Scottish lochs.   All three ascend to the higher tarns, e.g all occur in Sprinkling Crag Tarn at 617 m (2025 ft).   <u>Isoetes echinospora</u>, a rarer relative of the common Quillwort, occurs in Derwentwater.

Another plant of inshore regions, with even more thread-like (filiform) leaves, is the Bulbous Rush, <u>Juncus bulbosus</u>. The form of this plant differs according to its habitat. It can grow at the margins, when it looks more rush-like than the aquatic form — sometimes designated as the <u>fluitans</u> form.   The latter occurs particularly where rapid silting is taking place, as near the entrance of a stream. Here there is an abundance of coarse silt or sand.   It also occurs, however, on peaty deposits.   These share with silts a paucity of bases (alkaline substances) which it appears to shun.

Further offshore, where conditions are more stable, and where silts accumulate, one of the water milfoils, the Alternate-flowered, <u>Myriophyllum alterniflorum</u>, various pondweeds, <u>Potamogeton</u>, and either one or two species of

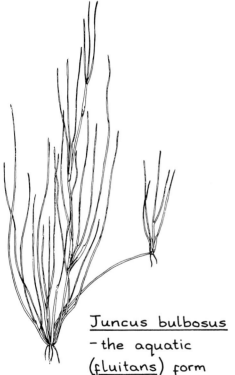

<u>Juncus bulbosus</u>
- the aquatic
(<u>fluitans</u>) form

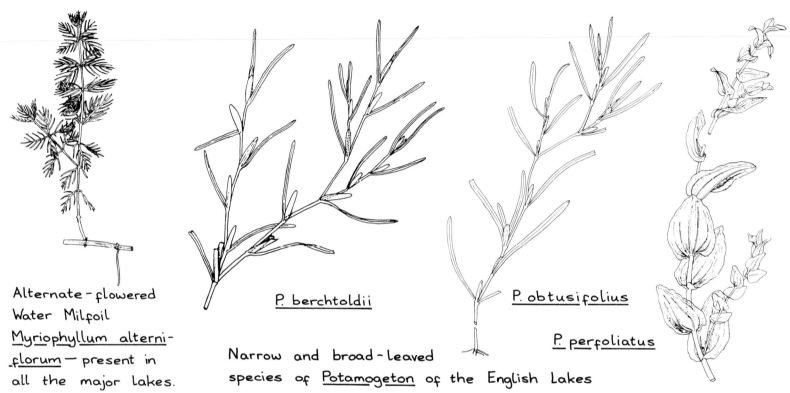

Alternate-flowered
Water Milfoil
Myriophyllum alterni-
florum — present in
all the major lakes.

P. berchtoldii

P. obtusifolius

P. perfoliatus

Narrow and broad-leaved
species of Potamogeton of the English Lakes

Elodea are likely to be present.   Both species of Elodea are invaders, E. canadensis,
the Canadian Pondweed, having arrived towards the end of the 19th century, E. nuttalli
more recently.   Both now occur in several of the richer lakes but it is interesting that
neither has yet colonised the four most oligotrophic lakes, Wastwater, Ennerdale,
Buttermere and Crummock Water.   In general the species of Potamogeton grow on the
finer silts, especially those rich in potash.   Ten species, and two different hybrids are
recorded from the lakes as a whole but the barren Wastwater, Ennerdale, Buttermere
and Crummock Water only have one or two species each.   Richer lakes have more
136

	P. polygonifolius	P. obtusifolius	P. alpinus	P. gramineus	P. natans	P. crispus	P. berchtoldii	P. praelongus	P. perfoliatus	P. pusillus
Wastwater	X	X								
Ennerdale Water	X	X								
Buttermere	X									
Crummock Water	X						X			
Ullswater		X	X	X	X	X	X	X	X	X
Coniston Water		X		X			X		X	
Derwentwater		X	X		X		X			
Bassenthwaite Lake		X	X	X	X	X	X		X	X
Windermere		X	X		X			X	X	X
Esthwaite Water		X	X	X	X	X	?			X

The recorded distribution of pondweeds (Potamogeton) in the English Lakes

Based on their general preferences — not just in the Lake District — the species are roughly arranged in 4 groups from left to right :- oligotrophic/acid loving (one species only): indifferent and tolerant : tolerant but with a preference for richer conditions : with a preference for richer conditions (Two hybrids omitted)

species but none has all of them. Many of the Lake District species have narrow leaves. The most widespread is the Small Pondweed, Potamogeton berchtoldii. The Blunt-leaved Pondweed, P. obtusifolius, is also common and widespread. An example of a broad leaved species is the Perfoliate Pondweed, P. perfoliatus, which forms dense weed beds just offshore in parts of Windermere. The Bog Pondweed, P. polygonifolius, has different habits and preferences from the rest. Rather than forming dense weed beds in the lakes it occurs in tarns, bog pools, oozing streams and seepages, where conditions are often acidic, and is found in some of the higher tarns. It has both floating and submerged leaves. It is significant that this is one of the species found in, and apparently only in, the four most oligotrophic lakes.

Also in deeper water, and tending to penetrate even deeper than the pondweeds, occur the stoneworts. These are algae (page 122) but in form and habits resemble higher plants. Of the few Lake District species, Nitella opaca is the most common. Stoneworts demand silted situations where there are accumulations of material into which they can easily penetrate. They form large

137

beds in Esthwaite Water and in parts of Windermere.

An unusual situation prevails in Esthwaite Water where the moss <u>Fontinalis antipyretica</u> forms extensive beds down to about 3m. While it is found in lakes — it can be seen growing attached to rocks at the margin of Windermere.— it is particularly a moss of rivers and streams, and the Esthwaite habitat is not the usual one. Here it grows on mud with a relatively high organic content. Its distribution is perhaps to some extent influenced by inflowing streams. Its long, dark green, leafy branches sometimes exceed 60cm (2 ft) in length. Other plants of local importance sometimes penetrate the lakes. The Water Horsetail, <u>Equisetum fluviatilis</u> — another non-flowering plant that is an ancient survivor from the past — does so in several lakes, and the true Bulrush, <u>Schoenoplectus lacustris</u>, sometimes forms a marginal fringe, as at the north end of Esthwaite Water. The Great Reedmace, <u>Typha latifolia</u>, is rare in the Lake District. It is plentiful in a small area where Black Beck enters the north end of Esthwaite Water and occurs elsewhere in the adjoining marsh. Small amounts are to be seen at certain places on Windermere and Rydal Water. Rydal Water is unusual in having both this species and the Lesser Reedmace, <u>Typha angustifolia</u>. Where much of the <u>T. latifolia</u> occurs at Esthwaite there is lots of methane (marsh gas) in the mud, which indicates rapid decay of organic material. This is facilitated by the abundant silt brought down by the stream.

All four of the British Bur-reeds occur in one or other of the lakes, but none of them has been recorded from either Wastwater or Ennerdale. Buttermere and Crummock Water have only the Floating Bur-reed, <u>Sparganium angustifolium</u>, a species characteristic of nutrient-poor often acidic waters in the highland regions of Britain.

<u>Plant communities in lakes and tarns.</u>

As on land the higher plants of lakes and tarns make up distinctive communities. Because different plants have different requirements they occur in different places even within a relatively small water body. Factors that influence the distribution of the various species include depth and the transparency of the water (which are inter-related), the nature of the soil or other substratum, the degree of exposure to wave action, and the presence of competing species. Some plants also have chemical requirements, such as the need for limy, alkaline water, that are not met in

138

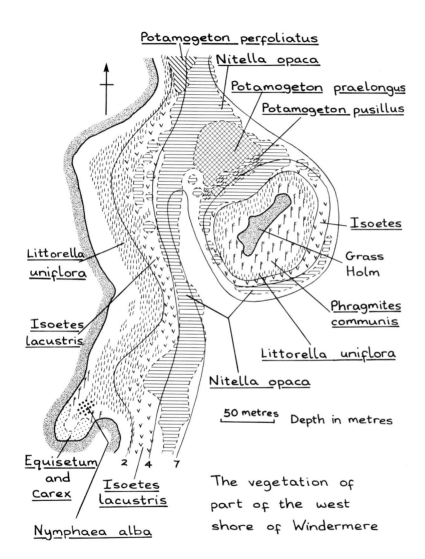

Potamogeton perfoliatus
Nitella opaca
Potamogeton praelongus
Potamogeton pusillus
Isoetes
Grass Holm
Littorella uniflora
Isoetes lacustris
Phragmites communis
Littorella uniflora
Nitella opaca

50 metres   Depth in metres

Equisetum and Carex
Isoetes lacustris
2   4   7
Nymphaea alba

The vegetation of part of the west shore of Windermere

the English Lakes.

While generalisation is possible, no two areas are exactly alike vegetation-wise. Furthermore the situation is dynamic, not static. Habitats change as they become silted, or as silt is removed, as they are invaded by other species, or altered in other ways. Thus, while we can speak of the communities of lakes, this is possible only in a rather general sense as each situation is unique — and subject to change with time.

As conditions differ much in several respects within a lake, several distinct communities are often recognisable. Specific examples, one from Windermere, another from Ullswater, give some idea of the kinds of communities of higher plants (the alga Nitella being included for convenience) to be found in the lakes. The Windermere example refers to the situation as mapped in the 1920s. It illustrates a common feature of the larger lakes, namely a plantless zone between the margin and the upper limit of submerged vegetation. This reflects wave action that inhibits plant growth. There is no such zone in the sheltered bay at the south end of the area shown. A bay of this sort is particularly sheltered as the prevailing wind comes from the south west. The map also

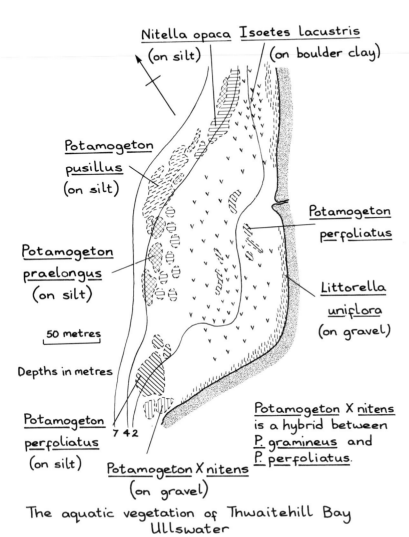

Nitella opaca (on silt)

Isoetes lacustris (on boulder clay)

Potamogeton pusillus (on silt)

Potamogeton praelongus (on silt)

50 metres

Depths in metres

Potamogeton perfoliatus (on silt)

Potamogeton X nitens (on gravel)

7 4 2

Potamogeton perfoliatus

Littorella uniflora (on gravel)

Potamogeton X nitens is a hybrid between P. gramineus and P. perfoliatus.

The aquatic vegetation of Thwaitehill Bay Ullswater

clearly reveals the zonation of the vegetation with depth. In general, as depth increases conditions become less disturbed, the bottom consists of finer material, and light intensity decreases. These changes are reflected by changes in the vegetation, which in turn reflect the preferences and requirements of individual species. That 'pure stands' of one particular species often occupy large areas is also clearly revealed. There are some places where several species jostle together, but large tracts of suitable terrain are dominated by single species.

The area illustrated demonstrates very nicely that vegetation in lakes is not static but subject to change. Marked changes occurred there during the first 60 years or so that elapsed since it was mapped. In 1980 Nitella and two of the species of Potamogeton were markedly reduced in abundance. Indeed they had virtually disappeared. The area covered by vegetation was now only about half the size of that occupied in the 1920s, the depth to which plants penetrated having been reduced by about 3m. On the other hand Littorella had extended its range. In the early and mid 1980s the western shore of Windermere also began to be invaded by a newcomer to the lake, Elodea nutalli, which rapidly established itself

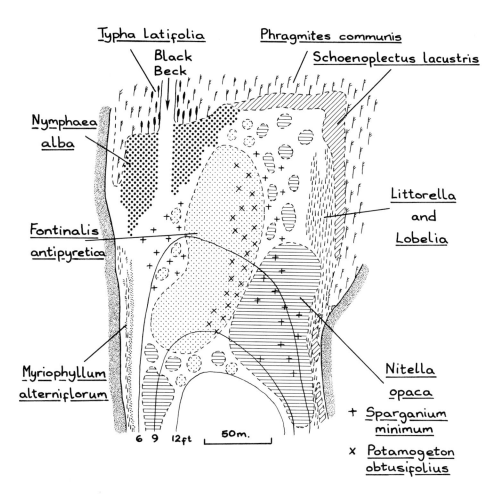

Typha Latifolia

Black Beck

Phragmites communis

Schoenoplectus lacustris

Nymphaea alba

Littorella and Lobelia

Fontinalis antipyretica

Myriophyllum alterniflorum

Nitella opaca

6   9   12ft   50m.

+ Sparganium minimum

x Potamogeton obtusifolius

The vegetation at the north end of Esthwaite Water

and spread so the picture is still one of change.

Clearly an area such as that illustrated provides an array of different habitats for animals. Equally the changes to which it has been subject affect the animals living there.

The example from Ullswater, which involves many of the same species as are present in Windermere, shows a different pattern of distribution and relates this, in part, to the kinds of substratum available.

The north end of Esthwaite Water is well vegetated.   It is relatively shallow, not too exposed, is near a source of incoming nutrients, and provides an example of the transition from aquatic to marsh vegetation.   This transition — seen here in space — also occurs in time and is discussed in the next section.

By no means all the species found in Esthwaite Water are represented in the illustration. For example, in water between about 1·5 and 2·5 m (c. 5 – 8 ft) deep, and where the mud has an organic content of less than

141

15%, there occurs in many parts a characteristic assemblage of a dozen or so species (several of them being species of <u>Potamogeton</u>) that tend to have long linear leaves. Such plants are fragile and their rich development reflects the sheltered nature of the habitat. Their form contrasts strongly with the rosette-like habit of <u>Isoetes</u>, which is particularly associated with stony substrata. It is interesting that stands of this species occur only at the south end of the lake where, as the flow is north to south, silt deposition is minimal. <u>Littorella</u> and <u>Lobelia</u> have a similar rosette form (page 134) and occur in shallow, and therefore often turbulent, water here and in many other lakes.

Floating-leaved communities, notably of the White Water-lily, <u>Nymphaea alba</u>, are able to develop at the sheltered north-west corner of Esthwaite, as they are in certain sheltered areas on the west shore (the east is more exposed). <u>Phragmites</u> and, to its lakeward side, <u>Schoenoplectus</u>, also flourish at the north end of Esthwaite, where the reedswamp that they comprise merges into the North Fen (page 145).

One member of the linear leaved association of Esthwaite Water merits special mention. This is <u>Hydrilla lithuanica</u>. This plant, very rare in Europe, is known no-where else in Britain, but has been found in Ireland. Formerly thought to be the same as the Asiatic, largely tropical, <u>H. verticillata</u>, it is now believed to be distinct.

Two lakes whose vegetation has been drastically altered by man's activities are Thirlmere and Haweswater, both of which are used as reservoirs. The over-riding factor here is the variable water level. Apart from exposing aquatic plants to the air, lowering the level leads to scouring of the shoreline by wave action at levels lower than would be effected by natural fluctuations. This removal of silt is very evident to the traveller alongside Thirlmere during dry periods when the reservoir is drawn down. Its barren bed, stripped of all silt, and therefore of plant nutrients and of a substratum for rooting, is then exposed. Nor can plants develop in deep water. Subject to fluctuations of several metres, plants established at depths of 5 or 6 m at times of draw-down would be covered to depths below which sufficient light to maintain life could not penetrate at times of high water level. As weed beds are the home of many of the animals of lakes, the consequences of large fluctuations in level — for this reason alone — are obvious.

Rocky, mountain tarns with their scanty, poor quality, soils, have very sparse

142

vegetation.　　Few species of higher plants can tolerate the conditions that prevail there.　　Typically <u>Littorella</u> can be expected near the shore, sometimes with <u>Lobelia</u>, and often with <u>Isoetes</u> further offshore, and perhaps <u>Myriophyllum alterniflorum</u> and <u>Nitella opaca</u> in deeper water.　　Stickle Tarn (altitude 469m : 1540 ft) provides an easily accessible example of such a tarn. All the species mentioned save <u>Nitella</u> are present as are <u>Juncus fluitans</u>, <u>Potamogeton polygonifolius</u>, one of the Water starworts, <u>Callitriche hamulata</u>, and the Floating Bur-reed, <u>Sparganium angustifolium</u>.　　All the last four species, especially the last three, are associated with oligotrophic (low nutrient), often acidic, situations.　　Stickle Tarn is also distinguished by the presence of a curious, rather rare, fern, the Pillwort, <u>Pilularia globulifera</u>, which here possibly reaches its highest altitude in Britain

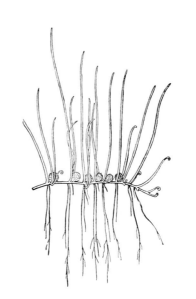

Pillwort, <u>Pilularia globulifera</u>
An aquatic fern

<u>Callitriche hamulata</u>

where it otherwise usually occurs below 400m (1300 ft).　　<u>Pilularia</u> has an un-fern-like appearance and looks rather like bright new grass, the fronds seldom being more than 6 or 7 cm (c. 2½ in.) long.　　Located on the rootstock near the base of the leaves are rough brown capsules (sporocarps).　　These contain a few large megaspores and many tiny microspores (as in <u>Isoetes</u>).　　Each megaspore grows into a prothallus on which the female sex organ, the archegonium, develops.　　Each microspore gives rise to an antherozoid.　　The latter enter the archegonium and fertilize it.　　From the fertilized ovum a new spore-bearing plant (the sporophyte) develops.
　　Not all upland tarns have as many truly aquatic macrophytes as does Stickle Tarn.

Thus the only species recorded from Bleawater is <u>Callitriche hamulata</u>. Dense forests of this attractive light green plant can be seen growing just offshore in this clear-water tarn. Levers Water appears to have no aquatic macrophytes, nor does the highest tarn in Lakeland, Broad Crag Tarn, Scafell, that lies at 837m (2747 ft).

In tarns in which there is an accumulation of peaty material, derived from the surrounding land, various emergent, floating-leaved and marginal plants can become established. At lower altitudes, as at Harrop Tarn (290m : 952 ft) an attractive diversity of such species may be present. At Harrop Tarn they include Marsh Cinquefoil, <u>Potentilla palustris</u>; Yellow Water-lily, <u>Nuphar lutea</u>; Lesser Spearwort, <u>Ranunculus flammula</u>; Marsh Marigold, <u>Caltha palustris</u>; and Bogbean, <u>Menyanthes trifoliata</u> as well as various rushes, sedges and others.

Often present at the margins of such tarns and in and around small pools are Bog mosses, <u>Sphagnum</u>. These mosses merit separate treatment (page 147).

<u>Marshes and the seral succession of vegetation in lakes</u>.

Lakes are ephemeral. Gradually they silt up and are encroached upon by terrestrial vegetation. Some extinct lakes (page 42), now under pasture, show the end point of such succession, as modified by man. The boundaries between aquatic, marsh, and terrestrial vegetation, are often ill-defined. A sequence might read :-

Submerged vegetation ⟶ Floating-leaved aquatic plants ⟶ Emergent aquatic plants ⟶
⟶ Marsh vegetation ⟶ Terrestrial vegetation.

Such a series, besides describing a transition in space, represents the sequence of changes that take place through time. Unmolested, the sequence would proceed to a climax — forest. Such a succession constitutes a <u>sere</u> (or an example of <u>seral succession</u>). For obvious reasons this particular kind of succession is a <u>hydrosere</u>. Hydroseres are often best seen at the head of a lake where most of the incoming silt is deposited. Here a marsh develops.

There is a small but attractive and interesting marsh at the north-west corner of Grasmere. This is fringed on the lakeward side by <u>Carex rostrata</u> with some <u>Phragmites</u>, <u>Phalaris</u>, <u>Equisetum fluviatile</u>, and <u>Eleocharis palustris</u> — the Common Spikerush, actually a

144

sedge!   Offshore of this fringe is much <u>Littorella</u> and <u>Lobelia</u> with occasional water-lilies, both yellow and white, and <u>Nitella opaca</u> is plentiful in deeper water. Behind the fringe is an expanse of soft, quaking, waterlogged vegetation, negotiation of which requires waterproof boots.   This displays great floral diversity, over 50 species of higher plants being represented.   These include such attractive species as Marsh Marigold, <u>Caltha palustris</u>, Meadow Sweet, <u>Filipendula ulmaria</u>, Marsh Bedstraw, <u>Galium palustre</u>, Marsh Cinquefoil, <u>Potentilla palustris</u>, Violets and Forgetmenots, Skullcap, <u>Scutellaria galericulata</u>, Bog Bean, <u>Menyanthes trifoliata</u> and the Yellow Iris, <u>Iris pseudacorus</u>.   Mosses are abundant and varied and there is much <u>Sphagnum</u> in places, which is helping to raise the level of the marsh as it grows from the accumulated basal parts that decay but slowly.   Already trees — Alder, <u>Alnus glutinosa</u>, a lover of wet places, Willows, <u>Salix</u> spp., and the Silver Birch, <u>Betula pendula</u>, have established themselves.   If visited, this small marsh should not be trampled.

A classical marsh is that called the North Fen at the head of Esthwaite Water. In its early days Esthwaite Water extended up its valley for more than a kilometre beyond its present limits.   Silt deposition by Black Beck and colonisation by marsh and terrestrial vegetation have robbed it of this region since its youth.   The small tarn, Priest Pot, just north of the lake remains as a remnant in a deeper hollow of its former northward extension.   Its persistence may have been helped by peat cutting in the past.   Much of the former extension is now grassland but, in immediate proximity to the lake is a splendid marsh.   At its lakeward margin is a broad zone of <u>Phragmites</u>, to which <u>Schoenoplectus lacustris</u> contributes an outer fringe except at the beck mouth where <u>Typha latifolia</u> is dominant.   Behind the <u>Phragmites</u> the marsh vegetation is diverse and differs from place to place according to conditions.   For example, where silt deposition is low, and the organic content of the soil high, the Purple Moor Grass <u>Molinia caerulea</u> is established.   In wet places there is <u>Sphagnum</u> moss, sometimes accompanied by <u>Molinia</u>, Sweet Gale, <u>Myrica gale</u>, and, in raised areas Cross-leaved Heath, <u>Erica tetralix</u>.   Elsewhere there are several species of <u>Carex</u> (sedges), <u>Phalaris</u>, <u>Filipendula ulmaria</u> and numerous other lovers of wet and marshy places.   These include such attractive species as the Royal Fern, <u>Osmunda regalis</u>, and the Globe Flower, <u>Trollius europaeus</u>, and a number of rarities such as the Great Spearwort, <u>Ranunculus lingua</u> and the sedge <u>Carex elongata</u>.   The moss flora is also varied and interesting. Trees have become established on the marsh which is now really an area of wet woodland. This has taken place since the middle of the 19th century. Alder, <u>Alnus glutinosa</u> and Sallow, <u>Salix cinerea</u> are plentiful and the Purple Willow, <u>S. purpurea</u>, Crack Willow, <u>S. fragilis</u> and Downy Birch, <u>Betula pubescens</u> occur, as do occasional Hawthorns, <u>Crataegus monogyna</u> and Bird Cherries, <u>Prunus padus</u>. A few seedlings of the Sessile Oak, <u>Quercus petraea</u> became established in 1963 and were associated with saplings of Ash, <u>Fraxinus excelsior</u>, Holly, <u>Ilex aquifolium</u> and Hazel, <u>Corylus avellana</u>.

The speed of encroachment by the marsh in the distant past can be calculated very roughly, but more precise information exists for the period since 1848 when the first accurate map was made. Subsequent maps and aerial photographs enable the advance to be followed. Between 1848 and 1967 southward movement has been 47m (154 ft) at the mouth of the stream and 28m (92 ft) in the middle region of the marsh. Progress has thus not been uniform over the whole margin. Nor has it been consistent over time. Sometimes the advance was rapid — about 3m per year : at others much slower — about 20 cm per year. The reasons for this are not clear.

Esthwaite North Fen is a National Nature Reserve. Trampling would damage it. In the early 1980s the level of Esthwaite was irresponsibly lowered by excavating an outlet channel. The long-term effects on the North Fen remain to be seen.

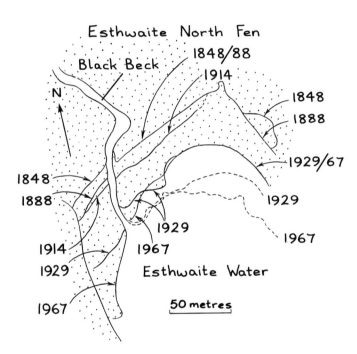

The advance of Esthwaite North Fen into the lake. Dashed lines indicate the outer edge of the reed swamp.

Bog mosses : <u>Sphagnum</u>

Among the mosses the Bog mosses, <u>Sphagnum</u>, of which there are many species, are of particular ecological importance. As a group, members of the genus <u>Sphagnum</u> are easy to recognise, but the identification of individual species is often difficult. These are the soft spongy mosses so frequently encountered in acidic peaty situations where they occupy both aquatic and terrestrial habitats. Some grow completely submerged in water, others form soggy masses in wet places and sometimes cover large expanses of ground, others occur in less wet, though never really dry, places, while others build-up hummocks.

Their anatomy is such that the non-aquatic species are able to retain large quantities of water. They have an erect stem that bears clusters of side branches at more or less regular intervals, each branch being densely covered with leaves. These leaves have a very characteristic and easily recognised anatomy. Each consists of a single layer of cells. Narrow lining cells containing chlorophyll form a network whose meshes are occupied by empty hyaline cells. These, whose walls are pierced here and there with holes, support the living cells. A similar arrangement of cells covers the surface of the stem. The empty cells act as a water storage and conduction system. This is an important attribute as <u>Sphagnum</u> mosses have no roots for absorbing soil moisture and no means of conducting water internally. This absorbing power has made dried <u>Sphagnum</u> useful as a surgical dressing. Their water-holding capacity also means that even 'terrestrial' forms in effect provide habitats for certain aquatic animals.

Most species flourish best, or even only, in acidic conditions. Here, as in many parts of the Lake District, nutrients are scarce. <u>Sphagnum</u> mosses have the ability to exchange hydrogen ions for mineral cations thus enabling them the more readily to obtain nutrients. This attribute

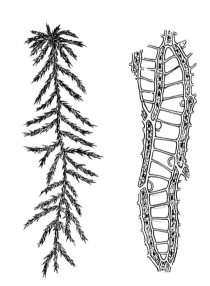

<u>Sphagnum cuspidatum</u> and details of a hyaline leaf cell surrounded by lining cells.

147

also helps to maintain the acidity of their enviroment.

Sphagnum is typical of wet places, but individual species have their own preferences. The very common Sphagnum cuspidatum often lives completely submerged in boggy pools where it forms pale green feathery masses, though it also occurs at the margins of pools and in wet hollows. S. auriculatum is another species that occurs commonly in pools, hollows, springs and seepages. Streamsides and wet flushes provide habitats for S. subsecundum, while S. recurvum and S. tenellum occur in wet places between pools and near the bases of hummocks. S. compactum is another species of wet hollows and pool margins, where it is occasionally submerged, but also forms low hummocks. S. imbricatum and the generally rarer S. fuscum produce hummocks up to a metre high on wet blanket mires (a rare habitat in the hilly Lake District) while S. papillosum is widespread in peatlands where it sometimes forms both a living carpet and hummocks and is often the principal peat-former. S. palustre, which can be found at lake margins, also forms carpets and tussocks in wet woodland. S. contortum is one of the few species able to tolerate a high base status (but still lives in peaty places). This is a species of fens and swamps, often associated with Phragmites and Carex.

The Lake District, especially the upland parts, provides many habitats for Bog mosses. All the above-mentioned species, and several others, are found there, sometimes in abundance. The submerged forests of pool-frequenting species are inhabited by certain mites and crustaceans and by a range of such insects and their larvae (among which beetles are conspicuous) as can tolerate the acidity of such habitats, while wet expanses of these mosses effectively extend aquatic habitats over large areas for certain small, truly aquatic animals. Some of these have become specialised for living among Sphagnum.

Drainage schemes are inimical to Sphagnum (and to wetland habitats in general) nor can most species tolerate nutrient enrichment, as when fertilizers find their way into their habitat. Nationally many species have declined markedly in recent years. The wilder parts of the Lake District are important refuges for these plants.

Aquatic Fungi

Fungi are plants that lack green (photosynthetic) pigments. This means that they can't manufacture their own food in the presence of light as can green plants. They have therefore either to be saprophytic — that is live on dead or decaying organic matter — or parasitic and live at the expense of some other plant or animal. Except in the most primitive forms, the body of a fungus consists of branching filaments that make up a <u>mycelium</u>, each filament being called a <u>hypha</u> (plural hyphae). The conspicuous fruiting bodies of terrestrial fungi, such as mushrooms and toadstools, are made up by the aggregation of masses of hyphae, but the mycelium of these fungi generally consists of an amorphous mass or tangle of filaments (hyphae) that wander through the soil or dead wood. Aquatic fungi do not produce such large, elaborate fruiting bodies, and most of them are minute. Nevertheless they are important elements of the freshwater biota and are plentiful almost everywhere. Some play a significant role in the breakdown of organic matter — such as dead leaves and wood — others are parasitic on a variety of freshwater organisms.

Dead insects, fishes and other organisms quickly acquire a 'fur coat' of fungal hyphae if they lie in water. These belong to <u>Saprolegnia</u> and its allies, commonly referred to as water moulds. Under such conditions <u>Saprolegnia</u> acts as a saprophyte, utilizing the decaying material on which it sits. It can, however, grow on living fishes, where it appears to be a parasite. To decide whether this is so is not always easy. It may only be growing on damaged and 'decaying' tissue and thus really be a saprophyte.

<u>Saprolegnia ferax</u>. Above — part of a hypha. Below — a swollen region (a sporangium) in which zoospores develop.

<u>Saprolegnia</u> consists basically of simple tubular hyphae. From time to time the terminal part of a hypha swells somewhat to form a sporangium — a receptacle for spores, here called zoospores. Each zoospore has two flagella, the beating of which enables it to swim. Each settles and from it another spore, again with two flagella, emerges, swims for a time, and then settles down. If it settles on material on which it can grow — on a suitable substrate — it gives rise to a new hypha.

Different materials attract different saprophytes. Dead leaves are colonised by Clavariopsis aquatica, species of Pythium, Phytophthera, and others, while dead wood is attractive to a different assemblage, including Heliscus. Chitin, the material from which the skeleton of insects and crustaceans is made, which is plentiful in freshwater, is attacked by Actinoplanes, which also attacks dead leaves, and by certain tiny, simple fungi such as Asterophlyctis sarcoptoides, that belong to a group called the chytrids. Most chytrids, however, are parasites of algae. These are very simple fungi with a unicellular body that never forms a true mycelium. Zygorhizidium affluens, a parasite of the diatom Asterionella (page 125) is a typical example. In its early stage it is a simple spherical object that sits on its host. From it a fine thread issues, penetrates the algal cell and forms a rhizoidal (root-like) system within it. The body of the fungus enlarges and becomes a sporangium (a receptacle for spores). Within it several zoospores are formed. Each is a minute object with a single flagellum by means of which, after the sporangium has burst, it swims freely. Its job is to find a new host. If successful it settles, loses its flagellum, and becomes the precursor of the next generation.

A related group of simple fungi comprises the so-called biflagellate phycomycetes. The life cycle is similar to that of the chytrids. As their name suggests their zoospores each have two flagella. A zoospore settles on a host and then penetrates the cell. As a consequence it grows into a sporangium inside the cell. The sporangium is often sac-like or tubular in shape. It does not develop rhizoids. As in chytrids it matures at the expense of its host, and zoospores are formed within it. These have to escape, which poses problems. Often an exit tube is formed

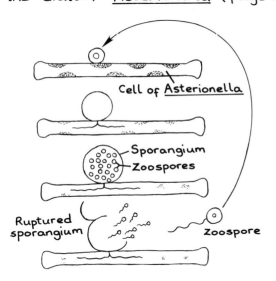

Cell of Asterionella

Sporangium
Zoospores

Ruptured sporangium

Zoospore

The life cycle of Zygorhizidium affluens
Apart from a brief free-swimming stage the entire cycle is enacted on (and in) a single cell of the diatom Asterionella.

and the entire contents of the sporangium migrate through it into a temporary vesicle within which final maturation of the zoospores takes place. This bursts and the zoospores are liberated.

Sometimes thick-walled, non-flagellate resting spores are formed. These can lie dormant and enable the fungus to survive adverse conditions or periods when the host species is not available.

Both chytrids and biflagellate phycomycetes are parasitized by other fungi. Parasites of parasites of this sort are called hyper-parasites. In the case of chytrids, they simply sit on the sporangium and send rhizoids into it. _Zygorhizidium affluens_ for example is parasitized by another chytrid, _Rozella parva_.

Some parasitic fungi occur regularly each year at particular seasons — just as terrestrial plants have their cycles —but some of the fungi are present for only a couple of weeks each year. Others are about for longer. Numbers fluctuate from year to year. Some of them are responsible for epidemics among their algal hosts, whose populations may in some cases be to a large extent controlled by them.

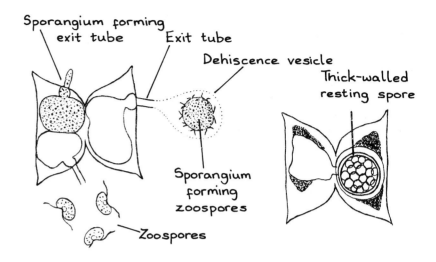

A biflagellate fungus that lives parasitically within a desmid. The formation and escape of motile zoospores and the presence of a thick-walled resting spore are shown.

Together with the organisms long called Blue Green Algae (page 128), that are not really algae, bacteria make up a group of primitive ('simple') organisms known technically as the prokaryotes.   These organisms do not have their genes (the instructors of their activities) enclosed in a true nucleus as are the genes of all 'higher' living things, even those that are single-celled.   Bacteria have no 'organelles' such as are found in eukaryotes — a name that embraces all other organisms, from Amoeba to man.

In size bacterial cells range from about $0.3\,\mu m$ to $100\,\mu m$ ($1\,\mu m$, or micron, is $\frac{1}{1000}$ mm). The majority of those found in water are in the range $0.5\,\mu m$ to $2\,\mu m$.

Bacteria have a very long history.   Incredible as it may seem, some bacteria, very similar to those of today, were fossilized in chert, a flint-like substance, 3,000 million years ago.   This is well over 2,000 million years before the earliest simple jellyfishes and 'worms' appeared in the fossil record, so they have been around for an immense period of time.

Although freshwater bacteria display a wide range of shapes, they do not possess the intricate structures of higher organisms.   Most take the form of straight or curved rods, or are spherical.   The latter are referred to as cocci.   Their interest is not so much in their structure as in what they can do.   They cannot perform the innumerable activities of animals but can do many clever chemical tricks. They can also live in what other organisms regard as very inhospitable places, such as hot springs or very salty water.

Invisible to the naked eye, individual bacteria sometimes congregate in such enormous numbers as to be noticeable. Rust-coloured masses of iron-bacteria such as Leptothrix whose walls are encrusted with

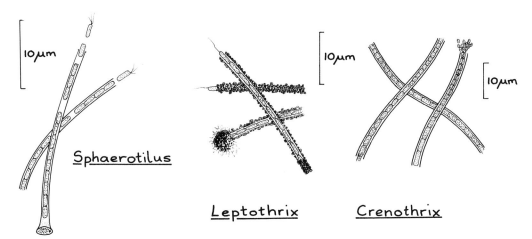

Sphaerotilus

Leptothrix   Crenothrix

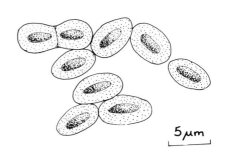

5μm

<u>Ochrobium</u>

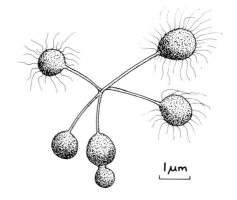

1μm

<u>Planctomyces</u>

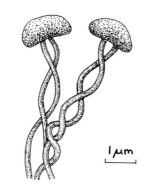

1μm

<u>Gallionella</u>

iron compounds are sometimes very conspicuous and some of the sulphur-bacteria such as <u>Chromatium</u> that contains bacteriochlorophyll and carotenoid pigments can occur in suspension in such numbers as to impart a reddish colour to the water.   Colonies of <u>Lamprocystis</u> are purple.   The so-called sewage fungus, <u>Sphaerotilus natans</u>, which is actually a bacterium, attaches itself by holdfasts and forms enormous masses of filaments several inches long that grow as an unpleasant furry carpet over stones in polluted rivers and streams.   Not common in most of the clean, unpolluted streams of the Lake District, <u>Sphaerotilus</u> nevertheless occurs at sources of pollution.   It has been a nuisance at such sites in the River Kent and occurs, for example, below the trickling filters that discharge into certain streams.   The stream near the Ferry Nab car park (Bowness) receives foul storm water at times, and the growth of sewage fungus here is a suitable accompaniment to the stench that sometimes prevails.

Bacteria have many roles.   Some are responsible for unpleasant or fatal diseases.   In lakes, where some of them, such as <u>Ochrobium</u> and <u>Planctomyces</u>, occur in suspension, while many others live on the surface of, and within, bottom deposits, they sometimes serve as food for other organisms and are involved in the cycling of matter.   They help to decompose dead plants and animals and animal faeces.   In so doing they release

153

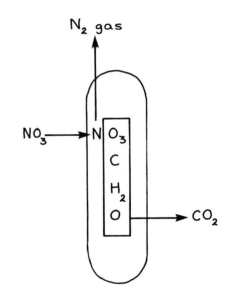

nutrients, such as nitrates and phosphates, that are needed by plants.   As they decompose dead material, many bacteria respire in the same manner as other organisms, using free oxygen.   This is the process that is largely responsible for using up the oxygen in the depths of eutrophic lakes like Esthwaite in summer (page 73).   Such oxygen-using bacteria are said to be aerobic.   Others do not require free oxygen.   These are said to be anaerobic.   In oxygenless regions of lakes, aerobes may survive by forming spores or cysts and lying dormant until oxygenated conditions return at the overturn (page 74). Others simply enter a 'shut-down' state in which they slow down their metabolism, sometimes decreasing in size, and await the return of better times.

In spite of their name, anaerobic bacteria need oxygen but don't rely on its presence in the free state.   Indeed free oxygen actually kills some such bacteria.   They get it from molecules of such substances as carbon dioxide (CO_2), and from nitrates (NO_3) and sulphates (SO_4) in which it is combined with other elements.   When a source of nitrates is 'attacked' by some bacteria the oxygen it contains is as it were prised out and nitrogen escapes as a gas.   This process is called denitrification. The nitrate is used instead of free oxygen to generate energy.   This is called anaerobic respiration.   What happens is that the bacterium transfers hydrogen from a food source (such as a carbohydrate) to the O part of the NO_3.   This releases the N as nitrogen gas (N_2).   We do much the same when we respire except that we transfer the H from the carbohydrate to oxygen.   Other bacteria also use nitrates but produce ammonia (NH_3). Some bacteria, such as <u>Microspira desulfuricans</u> and others, convert sulphates to hydrogen sulphide (H_2S), a poisonous substance that smells of rotten eggs, whose presence can often be detected by stirring a foul muddy pool. It similarly accumulates in oxygenless lake muds.   The

The utilisation of nitrate (NO_3) by a bacterium during anaerobic respiration. Its respiratory needs are met and nitrogen escapes as a gas.

process is reversible as some bacteria can oxidize (give oxygen to) hydrogen sulphide, removing the sulphur (S) which they store as droplets inside their bodies. This sulphur can then be oxidized to sulphate which returns to circulation in the water.

Some bacteria that obtain their oxygen from carbon dioxide produce methane (CH_4). Methane, or marsh gas, is a flammable gas which, when it ignites spontaneously, becomes the Will o' the wisp in swamps. It sometimes accumulates under ice. A hole made in the ice allows it to rush out and it can be ignited to give a jet of flame. This is the gas, produced by bacteria millions of years ago, that we now burn as natural gas. The bacteria that produce it are called methanogens and have such names as Methanosarcina methanica, which is abundant in natural waters, Methanobacterium and Methanococcus. All these are anaerobes that can flourish only in the absence of oxygen.

As is already apparent, different bacteria do different jobs. One, Clostridium cellulolyticus, as its name suggests, is important in the breakdown of cellulose, the main constituent of plant cell walls. Others break down chitin, the material of which insect and crustacean skeletons are composed. Some chitin fragments, however, are almost immune to such attack and it is these that accumulate in lake sediments contributing both to these and to our understanding of their history (page 34). Others can deposit iron, manganese, calcium carbonate or elemental sulphur.

Iron bacteria are often noticeable. These include filamentous forms that have a thick gelatinous sheath in which iron compounds may be deposited, energy being obtained by oxidizing ferrous salts and precipitating ferric hydroxide. In certain streams, bogs and waterlogged situations these produce rust-coloured flocs that are sometimes sufficiently conspicuous to add colour to the landscape. One iron bacterium, Leptothrix is at times a nuisance to the water industry. Individual cells are sometimes released from the normally anchored filaments in such numbers as to make reservoirs rusty red and to clog filters. Another, Gallionella is often responsible for clogging iron pipes.

Bacteria occur in enormous numbers in lakes. They are more numerous in nutrient-rich, eutrophic, lakes such as Esthwaite Water than in nutrient-poor oligotrophic lakes such as Wastwater and Ennerdale. When a lake is used as a receptacle for sewage effluent, as is Windermere, bacterial numbers are increased both by providing the material they require and by direct discharge. This means that the water has to be carefully treated if it is to be used for drinking as some of the bacteria that find their way into it are the kind that cause intestinal upsets or worse.

The Windermere sewage plant passes between 600,000 and 700,000 faecal streptococci and between 400,000 and 4 million Escherichia coli into the lake with each litre of effluent. E. coli is a non-pathogenic coliform bacterium that frequents the human intestine (though it can live elsewhere). It is widely used as a measure of faecal contamination. In many countries drinking water is deemed satisfactory if it contains less than 20 E. coli per litre: unsatisfactory if it contains more than 1000. Bacterial densities near the sewage outlets into lakes are rapidly diluted but it is wise to select sites remote from such discharges even for bathing.

A notable attribute of bacteria is their ability to multiply rapidly when conditions are favourable. They can divide and re-divide several times a day. To estimate their numbers is difficult. Different methods of estimation can give answers that differ a thousand-fold! From a million to 10 million bacteria in a ml. (c.c.) of water is probably not unusual in moderately rich lakes. Even allowing for a large margin of error these are big numbers and give some idea of the abundance of bacteria in natural waters.

Not only are bacteria numerous in lakes but they belong to many species. One of the problems facing those who study these organisms is the difficulty of identifying and categorising them. So little is known about freshwater bacteria that perhaps as many as 95% of the species living in a lake such as Windermere cannot be identified with certainty. Considering their importance in the economy of nature and the need to know just which species are responsible for particular processes, this is clearly an unsatisfactory state of affairs. Some of the species that cannot yet be identified, and whose roles remain to be elucidated, may prove to have abilities that can be exploited for man's benefit. Some may prove useful as agents of fermentation or as producers of esoteric but useful chemicals. This is the world of biotechnology.

Single-celled animals are called protozoans.   They have a nucleus (a pellet of material that controls the activities of the cell), which distinguishes them from bacteria — also single-celled — that have not.   That these tiny animals consist of a single cell doesn't mean they are 'simple' — a term difficult to define in biology.   Not only do they have to perform many different functions with their single cell (page 116) but, as a group, they display enormous diversity in structure and ways of life.   Although single cells are restricted in what they can do, their potentialities are enormous.   They have organelles (literally 'little organs') that enable them to crawl, swim or anchor themselves, catch food, secrete a protective shell, or even build a case from extraneous materials among which they live, and they earn their livings in many different ways in a wide range of habitats.

Protozoans are abundant in freshwater.   Their diversity is great and only a small selection of those known to occur in the Lake District is mentioned here, the aim being to give some idea of the great range of form and lifestyles that they display.   The number of species

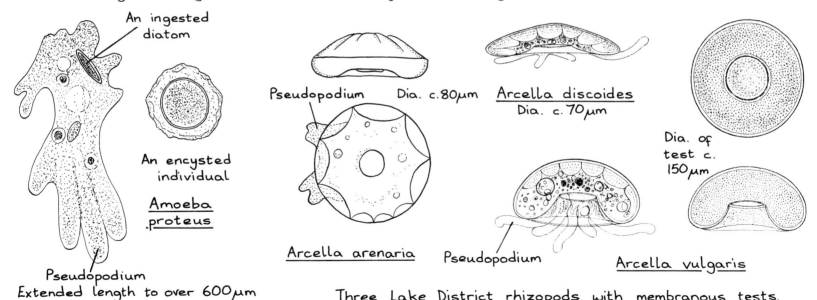

An ingested diatom

Pseudopodium

An encysted individual

Amoeba proteus

Pseudopodium
Extended length to over 600μm

Dia. c.80μm

Arcella arenaria

Arcella discoides
Dia. c. 70μm

Pseudopodium

Arcella vulgaris

Dia. of test c. 150μm

Three Lake District rhizopods with membranous tests.

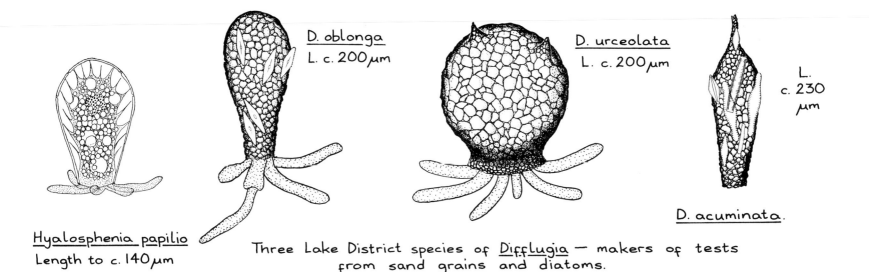

D. oblonga
L. c. 200 μm

D. urceolata
L. c. 200 μm

L. c. 230 μm

D. acuminata.

Hyalosphenia papilio
Length to c. 140 μm

Three Lake District species of Difflugia — makers of tests from sand grains and diatoms.

present in the area (of the several hundred reported in Britain) is unknown but is certainly large.   Although incompletely explored, Esthwaite Water alone has yielded more than 140 species.

    Amoeba, of which at least five species occur in the Lake District, so familiar from textbooks, is a naked cell that crawls by pushing out arms — pseudopodia (literally 'little false feet') — that are followed by the rest of the cell.   This deceptively simple but actually complex process involves changes in the nature of the cell contents — the cytoplasm — between fluid and gel phases.   The fluid flows, is converted to a gel that contracts, and drags the cell forward.   Minute food particles are engulfed by encirclement.   Amoeba reveals in a readily observable way the influx of water by osmosis (page 110) that faces all fresh-water animals.   Water that enters accumulates in minute reservoirs that gradually grow and eventually collapse, expelling their contents forcibly from the cell.   These are the so-called contractile vacuoles.   No such osmotic uptake of water takes place in sea water so marine amoebas have no contractile vacuoles — a neat demonstration of a physio-

158

-logical difference between life in fresh and in salt water.

Encystment — contraction of the cell and the secretion of a protective wall around it — takes place at times of adversity. Cysts are resistant to cold and drought. Some amoebas have become parasitic. One that lives in the gut of man causes amoebic dysentry — a serious disease. A freshwater species, Pansporella perplexa is a parasite in the gut of Daphnia, a 'water flea'.

Amoeba is but one genus of that group of protozoans known as rhizopods (literally 'root footed' organisms) that employ pseudopodia. Not all of these protrude such long mobile pseudopodia. Pelomyxa for example has a more definite, almost slug-like, form than Amoeba and puts out only short pseudopodia. P. palustris, which usually has several nuclei, and whose body usually contains mineral grains, frequents bottom detritus and sometimes lives in foul situations. An asset in such habitats is its ability to tolerate periods of complete oxygen lack.

Many of the relatives of Amoeba secrete a protective gelatinous or membranous shell or test, while others build beautifully symmetrical, usually urn- or flask-shaped tests from minute particles of sand or other materials embedded in an organic matrix. Examples of the former include several species of Arcella. These look like an amoeba with a lid on. Hyalosphenia papilio provides another example. This species, which lives among vegetation, is transparent and has a yellowish test. It characteristically contains oil droplets. Rhizopods that build tests from sand grains and diatoms include several species of Difflugia. Of these D. oblonga is common and widespread. The more spectacular D. urceolata is perhaps one of the rarer species but has been found in Easdale Tarn.

All these have lobose pseudopodia like Amoeba. Other rhizopods have long, almost thread-like, filose pseudopodia. One such is Paulinella chromatophora, a species that has been found at Tarn Howes but which will probably be found elsewhere if sought. This species has acquired symbiotic algae, one or

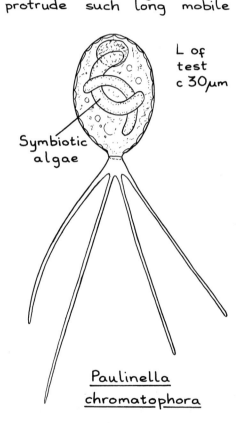

L of test c 30μm

Symbiotic algae

Paulinella chromatophora

two cells of which are always present within the protozoan. Symbiosis, literally 'living together', is an association of two organisms for mutual benefit. Here, use of the products of the algae by Paulinella eliminates the need to capture food. In return the algae benefit from the carbon dioxide produced by the respiration of the protozoan.

Testaceous rhizopods are exceedingly abundant in freshwater in a wide variety of habitats. Almost any bottom sample from a lake or tarn produces examples, sometimes in large numbers. A diversity of species also abounds in Sphagnum bogs in upland areas of the Lake District. The leaves of Sphagnum are adapted to retain a film of water (page 147) that, although thin, is adequate for the needs of many protozoans. Indeed this habitat has been exploited by a distinctive assemblage of these animals, some of whose members are seldom found elsewhere. Testate rhizopods dominate this fauna. Their little world is not uniform. Conditions differ considerably from the surface of a Sphagnum patch to the zone occupied by the lower parts of the moss stems only a few inches away. For example it is often cooler, wetter, darker and less well oxygenated near the base of the stems than near the surface. The protozoan – moss situation is analagous to that of birds in a forest. Some species of the latter live on the ground, others forage on the trunks of trees, others on low branches, and yet others on higher branches or in the uppermost canopy. A similar situation prevails among the testaceous rhizopods of a Sphagnum patch. Here too they feed on different foods — algal cells, other tiny animals, including each other, and bacteria. More than 60 species of testaceous rhizopods are known from Sphagnum in Britain. The Lake District fauna is as yet inadequately known.

Another group of rhizopods is known as the Helioza or Sun animalcules. These are spherical and have stiff radiating spines — axopods. Some axopods support streaming protoplasm and are the equivalent of the pseudopodia of amoebas. Heliozoans are motionless or drift with currents, or in a few cases are anchored by a slender stalk. Prey that touches them appears to be stunned. Perhaps they secrete a toxin. It is then enveloped by cytoplasm as in Amoeba.

Among the heliozoans that occur in the Lake District is Acanthocystis chaetophora of which there are two forms. In Windermere one occurs in the plankton in early summer: the other is to be found among vegetation near the shore. Another example is Actinosphaerium eichorni, a species that has several nuclei.

160

Other protozoans are armed with one or more whiplash-like organelles called flagella (singular, flagellum) by the beating of which they drive themselves through the water. This has led to such forms being referred to as flagellates. Some are very simple in shape, others highly complex. Some species collect food particles drawn in by the flagellum, others entangle prey with it. Others, looking very similar, have green chloroplasts and can flourish without ingesting food, provided they have access to light and a supply of inorganic salts. These in fact behave like plants. They are said to be holophytic. One species, <u>Euglena gracilis</u>, is usually green, but permanently colourless forms without any chloroplasts can be produced experimentally by various techniques. In one sense these have been changed from plants to animals.

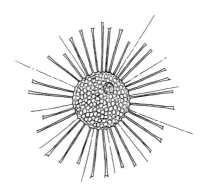

<u>Acanthocystis chaetophora.</u>

The inshore <u>simplex</u> form.

<u>Actinosphaerium eichorni.</u>

Note the ingested diatoms.

Some species form colonies. Many of these are claimed as plants by botanists and some are illustrated as algae (page 124). Tiny flagellates of simple body form are abundant in the plankton of many Lake District lakes.

Dinoflagellates comprise one well-defined group of flagellates, here treated as animals. These have two flagella, both in grooves, one trailing behind, the other girdling the body transverse to the long axis. In some the body is encased by many plates. Greenish pigment is usually present, so they can behave like plants, but small organisms are often ingested by amoeboid-like action at one point. <u>Ceratium hirudinella</u> is a common dinoflagellate in the plankton of the richer Lake District lakes. At its peak around August, numbers in the epilimnion of Esthwaite Water may reach half a million per litre, and in concentrated patches up to 3 million per litre have been recorded. The active stage disappears from the plankton in winter, this season being spent as a resting cyst.

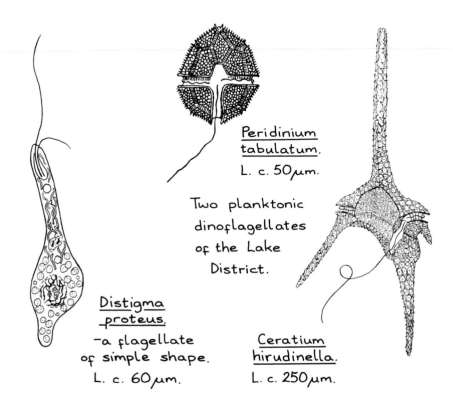

Peridinium tabulatum.

L. c. 50 μm.

Two planktonic dinoflagellates of the Lake District.

Distigma proteus.

— a flagellate of simple shape.

L. c. 60 μm.

Ceratium hirudinella.

L. c. 250 μm.

Some flagellates are parasitic. These swim, not in water but in the blood or other body fluids of their host. They include trypanosomes and their allies that are the agents of sleeping sickness, kala azar and tropical boils in man. Related trypanosomes live in the blood of freshwater fishes.

As the name suggests, ciliated protozoans, or ciliates, are provided with cilia — smaller versions of flagella. Sometimes these, which may be extremely numerous, cover the entire body; in other species they are arranged in well-defined tracts. They serve for locomotion and food collection. In some species certain cilia fuse to form more robust structures or membrane-like plates that, by undulating, can propel food particles down a groove, or gullet, to the 'mouth'. Tufts of cilia may fuse to give large stiff bristles called cirri that are movable in all directions and, in some species, are used like legs for crawling. Euplotes provides an example. Other, smaller, stiff bristles derived from cilia that are sometimes present are apparently sensory — serving as detectors of external stimuli.

Ciliates are diverse in form and adapted to many different ways of life. Some, such as species of Coleps, which secretes a protective 'shell' around itself, and Didinium hunt and ingest large prey — sometimes organisms bigger than themselves. Many others drive minute particles into a cilia-lined gullet.

Some of these ciliates flourish best where there is much putrefaction and where oxygen concentrations thus tend to be low. This enables them to live near the boundary between

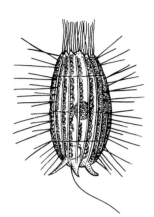

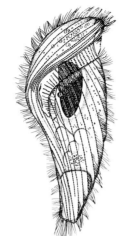

Metopus striatus.

Metopus contortus.

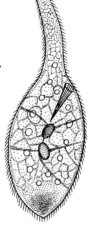

Holophyra simplex.

Trachelius ovum.

Coleps hirtus.

—a carnivorous species with a wide mouth at one end.

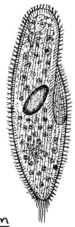

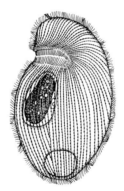

A few of the many ciliated protozoans of Esthwaite Water.

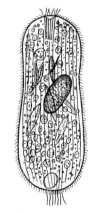

Paramecium caudatum.

Plagiopyla nasuta.

Prorodon teres. Note the ingested diatoms.

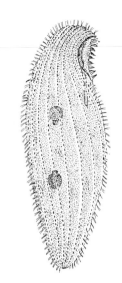

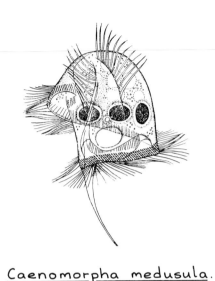

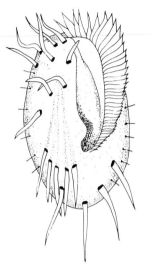

Two ciliates with stiff fused cilia or cirri.
<u>Euplotes daidaleos</u> harbours symbiotic algae — <u>Chlorella</u>.

<u>Caenomorpha medusula</u>.

<u>Loxodes striatus</u>.

<u>Euplotes daidaleos</u>.

the oxygenated and deoxygenated water of a lake like Esthwaite Water in summer, where several species flourish at this time.   Some of these, such as <u>Frontonia leucas</u>, which eats dinoflagellates, <u>Holophyra simplex</u> and species of <u>Coleps</u>, can survive for several days without oxygen. Indeed both oxygen and light are toxic to species of <u>Loxodes</u> at quite low levels.   Members of this genus have other remarkable attributes.   They exhibit geotaxis (that is they respond to gravity) in connection with which they have a minute organelle that looks rather like the statocyst (balancing organ) of certain multicellular animals.   They can also respire nitrate in the manner described for certain bacteria (page 154).   No other eukaryote is yet known to perform this feat.

Like the rhizopod <u>Paulinella</u>, several ciliates have established a symbiotic relationship with algae.   The symbionts of ciliates are always species of <u>Chlorella</u>.   Several such ciliates live in Priest Pot, a rich eutrophic water body just north of Esthwaite Water.   These include <u>Euplotes daidaleos</u> and <u>Frontonia vernalis</u>.   (<u>F. vernalis</u> is related to <u>F. leucas</u> that has no

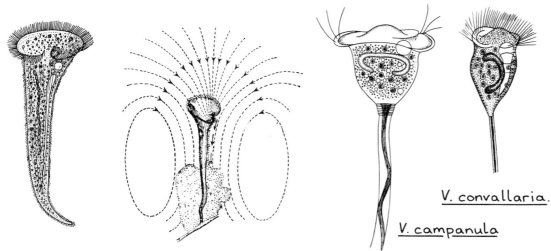

Stentor
polymorphus.

The feeding currents of
an attached Stentor.

V. convallaria.

V. campanula

Two species of Vorticella.

Vorticella similis.

—a gregarious species fixed
to the alga Anabaena. Note
the three contracted zooids.

symbionts).   Both these are primarily bottom dwellers — where Euplotes can crawl on its cirri.
In summer, however, Priest Pot stratifies and the hypolimnion becomes devoid of oxygen.
Euplotes and Frontonia are then forced to leave the bottom and swim upwards in search of
oxygen.   This they encounter in the vicinity of the thermocline and go no further.   This is
indeed a suitable place to live.   Bacteria and particulate matter accumulate here and
provide a source of food and there is sufficient light for the symbiotic Chlorella, which can
function at low light intensities, to photosynthesise.   This reduces the dependency of the
protozoans on particulate food, making life easier for them.   When Priest Pot overturns in
autumn, and oxygen is carried down to the bottom, Euplotes and Frontonia return to the
sediments.

      Some species are trumpet-shaped.   Among such, species of Stentor are very common.
These are often attached to some object at the narrow end, but frequently break free and
swim.   An attached Stentor reveals very nicely the use of cilia as a means of setting up

165

Trichodina pediculus.
A ciliate that glides over
the surface of hydras.

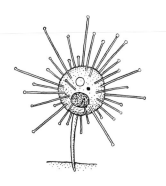

Podophyra.
A suctorian.

feeding currents.   Just as the beating of cilia can drive a protozoan through the water, it can drive water past a stationary individual or divert it down a convenient groove or tube — in the case of Stentor into the cavity of the trumpet.   Currents carry particles that are collected as food.   The drifting particles also reveal the course of the currents.   When swimming freely Stentor also often feeds on other, smaller, ciliates.

Other ciliates are stalked, sedentary, and bell-like.   Of these, species of Vorticella have a contractile stalk; species of Epistylis, which are colonial, a non-contractile stalk with many branches each terminating in an individual cell.   If disturbed, a Vorticella contracts its stalk, withdrawing the vital ciliated body, sometimes called a zooid, from the source of irritation, and thus to comparative safety.   When the disturbance ceases, the stalk relaxes and the zooid again extends.   V. similis is gregarious and planktonic, attaching itself to the alga Anabaena, and sometimes to copepods.

Other ciliates have become flattened and live on the surface of various animals, including fishes over which they skim like tiny hovercraft.   Trichodina pediculus is a common commensal on the surface of hydras (page 171).

Probably derived from ciliates are the suctorians.   These lack cilia but have long tentacles.   They are sessile, often sitting on other animals.   Prey, usually other protozoans or rotifers (page 179), adheres to the tentacles.   It is paralysed by a toxin and sucked in by a canal in a tentacle by an as yet mysterious process.   There is no mouth.   Suctorians encyst when food is scarce.

Suctorians are little known in the Lake District.   Podophyra fixa is one of the few species recorded.

Worthy of brief mention are the parasitic protozoans that make up the Sporozoa.   These are parasites of many animals, including man.   Those great scourges the malarial parasites are sporozoans.   These are transmitted by freshwater animals — mosquitoes — though this is no longer the case in Britain. Many freshwater organisms found in the Lake District are infected by sporozoans, though little is known about these infections, their causative agents, or their effects.

Protozoans often reproduce simply by dividing — binary fission. Such asexual reproduction facilitates the rapid build-up of populations under favourable conditions. Other forms of asexual reproduction, such as budding, are practised by certain species. Sexual reproduction is also widespread. Sometimes two cells simply unite. In other cases multiple internal fission gives rise to several tiny swarmers that are released and fuse in pairs, there being many variants of this method. Sometimes a tiny swarmer, essentially a male gamete (a 'sperm'), fuses with a larger, often immobile, cell that behaves in a manner analagous to the female gamete ('egg cell') of multi-cellular animals. In some ciliates two individuals come together, exchange nuclear material, and separate. As in their structure, ways of life, and behaviour, the reproductive habits of freshwater protozoans are very diverse.

The organisms discussed in this section are usually incon-spicuous to the casual observer. One protozoan, however, is very noticeable and can be easily recognised with the naked eye. This is the ciliate _Ophrydium_ which is related to such stalked forms as _Vorticella_ and _Epistylis_. This organism forms spherical, ovoid, or flattened gelatinous colonies that are sometimes several centimetres in diameter. As the cells of _Ophrydium_ contain symbiotic green algae (zoo-chlorellae) colonies have a greenish hue. Attached to plants, or sometimes to stones, they form conspicuous, green, jelly-like objects, whose identity is a mystery even to many naturalists. They are particularly striking when many colonies occur together. _Ophrydium_ can be found in several places in the Lake District where it shows a preference for the richer sites. For example it occurs in Grasmere, Esthwaite Water and Blelham Tarn and is sometimes abundant in some of the lower-lying tarns. Examination, even with the naked eye, reveals that the living cells are confined to the surface of the otherwise greyish mass of jelly.

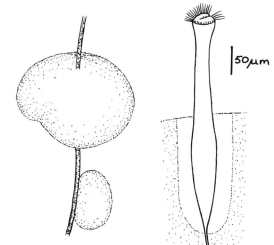

50μm

Colonies of _Ophrydium_ on a plant stem and an individual zooid.

167

Sponges occur especially in the sea, but the family Spongillidae inhabits freshwater. (Another family inhabits Lake Baikal in Siberia.)   Although as many as eight species allegedly occur in the British Isles, some of the records are dubious and some refer to species known only from Ireland.   Only two species are known from the Lake District — and from most other areas in Britain.

Sponges are made up of many cells so might reasonably be expected to be included in the Metazoa — the group that includes all other multicellular animals. However, their component cells are to a large degree independent of each other; often they do not touch, and no nervous system co-ordinates their activities. They are also relatively unspecial--ised, some of them being able to change from one type to another when the need arises.   For these and other technical reasons sponges are placed in a subkingdom of their own, the Parazoa, distinct both from the one-celled Protozoa and the multicellular Metazoa.

Both our freshwater sponges are encrusting organisms. Euspongilla lacustris is sometimes called the Pond Sponge and

Ephydatia
fluviatilis

Euspongilla lacustris

Spicules of
Euspongilla lacustris.
Ephydatia has only
the large
smooth type

Encrusting growths of freshwater sponges. Finger-like prolongations are particularly characteristic of Euspongilla lacustris.

Ephydatia fluviatilis the River Sponge, but these names, both common and scientific, are misleading as the so-called River Sponge often occurs in lakes and the Pond Sponge is by no means averse to slow flow.   The River Sponge tends to form flat growths on stones, plant stems, old twigs and similar objects whereas E. lacustris often produces finger-like outgrowths.   Shape, however,

168

is a poor guide to identity.   E. lacustris often forms clumps about the size of a man's fist, and tree-like growths a foot high sometimes develop.

   Both species are yellowish in colour but often assume a greenish tint due to the growth within them of cells of the alga <u>Chlorella</u>.   They are rough to the touch because they are supported by a mass of tiny <u>spicules</u> made of silica that are secreted by certain of their component cells.   The spicules form a kind of skeleton, though they have no definite arrangement.   (Those of some marine sponges are very elaborate and make up a definite skeleton.)   The spicules of <u>Euspongilla lacustris</u> are of two kinds: large elongate and smooth, and smaller, rough and irregular.   Those of <u>Ephydatia fluviatilis</u> are all of the larger, smooth type.

   The component cells, of which there are several kinds, are so arranged that within the sponge body there are numerous inter-connected chambers.   These communicate with the exterior via numerous very small holes through which water is drawn in by the beating of the flagella of certain cells (collar cells or choanocytes) that line the underlying chambers.   From this water, which also serves for respiration, minute food particles are extracted before it

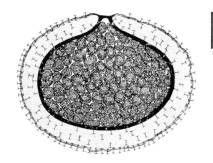

100μm

A gemmule of <u>Ephydatia fluviatilis</u> seen in section. The wall is reinforced by a special kind of spicule.

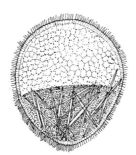

100μm

Free swimming larva of <u>Euspongilla lacustris</u> seen in optical section.

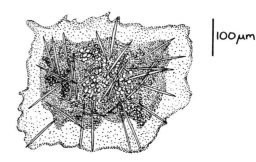

100μm

Young sponge 24 hours after the larva has settled and attached itself to a surface.

exits via larger holes called oscula (sing. osculum). Large volumes of water are thus filtered each day.

Growth is by multiplication of the cells, the sponge gradually creeping over the object to which it is attached.

Towards the end of summer numerous (sometimes thousands) of pin-head sized, dark brown spherical objects with tough walls are produced inside the sponge. These are gemmules, each of which encloses a number of amoeboid cells. The sponge disintegrates in winter but, like plant seeds, the gemmules survive, and from them new sponges are derived in spring. In the south of England Ephydatia sometimes survives the winter without producing gemmules.

Eggs and sperms are also found in sponges. Sperms are liberated and drawn into another sponge where they fertilize the eggs. These give rise to tiny ciliated larvae, seldom seen, though certainly numerous, that swim by means of cilia for two or three days before settling down and growing into new sponges.

Although never specifically studied in the Lake District, sponges are widespread and common in some, probably many, places. Jetties are worth examining for growths of Euspongilla. It is possible that the diligent searcher may be rewarded by the discovery of species not yet reported from the area.

Coelenterates — Hydras

The only Lake District representatives of the Coelenterata (the group that includes sea anemones, corals, and jelly-fishes) are species of <u>Hydra</u>. So familiar as text-book animals, these primitive (lowly) creatures are in fact but little known, even by many naturalists. Composed of two layers of cells they represent a grade of construction termed diploblastic. Higher animals have three layers and are said to be triploblastic.   Hydras, which are in fact specialised coelenterates, have a soft, tubular trunk or column that can be extended or contracted, that is anchored at the base, and terminates in a circlet of re-tractable tentacles, 5 to 13 in number.   Such an animal is frequently termed a polyp.   At the top of the column, surrounded by the tentacles, is the mouth — in essence a simple hole — that leads directly into the cavity of the trunk, itself continuous with the cavity of the hollow tentacles. When extended, the trunk of some hydras may exceed 1 in. (c. 25mm) in length : other species are much smaller.

Hydras feed by catching small animals, such as 'water fleas' (page 236) with their tentacles that are armed with stinging cells called nematocysts.   These are discharged when bumped into by prospective prey.   Discharge involves the 'sting', previously 'inside out' like the pushed-in finger of a glove, being everted.   It penetrates the body of the prey and injects poison into it.   Nematocysts are not under nervous control but act independently. Chemical stimulation by prospective prey increases their sensitivity.   They are therefore easily triggered by prey: less so by being touched by other objects.   As well as stinging nematocysts there are others that discharge coiled filaments which help to hold the prey.   The stinging nematocysts stun the prey which is then enveloped by the tentacles that push it into the mouth.   It is digested in the central cavity.   There is no anus — an indication of the primitive organisation of these animals — so undigested

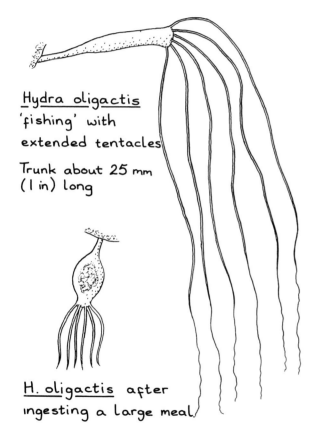

<u>Hydra oligactis</u>
'fishing' with

extended tentacles

Trunk about 25 mm
(1 in) long

<u>H. oligactis</u> after
ingesting a large meal.

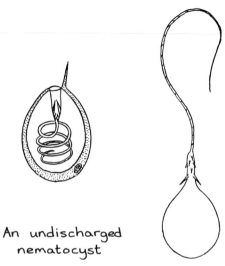

An undischarged
nematocyst

A discharged
nematocyst

waste has to be driven out via the mouth by a sudden contraction of the trunk.

Generally sessile (more or less permanently anchored) hydras can move when necessary either by looping — like a looper cater- pillar — or, much more rarely, somersaulting, and they some- times drift as they hang suspended from the surface film of still water.

Hydra was the first animal in which striking powers of re- generation were observed. If cut in two, each piece will re- generate a complete animal. This remarkable fact, now taken for granted because of its familiarity, caused much justifiable scientific excitement when discovered in the early part of the 18th century.

Reproduction is often by budding. Daughter polyps develop from the trunk of the parent and eventually separate (bud off). Sexual reproduction also occurs. In some species, such as the Brown Hydra, Hydra oligactis, the sexes are separate; in others, such as the Green Hydra, H. viridissima, all individuals are hermaphrodites (male and female in the same animal). Eggs develop as swellings on the trunk and are fertilized by sperms produced in smaller swellings, the testes. Each egg becomes invested with a usually thick coat (thin in H. oligactis) and the cells within it multiply so it is now better termed an embryotheca. This, which is cast off by its producer, is resistant to adverse conditions and remains dormant for some time. It can also act as a dispersal agent, enabling the hydra to move from one water body to another.

Of the Lake District hydras, the Brown Hydra, H. oligactis (sometimes called Pelmatohydra oligactis) is probably the most widespread. Typically it occurs under stones on exposed shores of productive lakes but it also frequents aquatic plants. Perhaps surprisingly to many, it is also frequent in rapid streams provided these are productive and at the same time stony. For example it is to be found in large numbers in Cunsey Beck that takes the overflow from the productive Esthwaite Water and is presumably rich in food. The trunk of a Brown Hydra can exceed 25mm (1 in.) in length and when expanded in still water, the 4 to 6 tentacles can extend to a length many times that of the trunk — sometimes to as much as 8 in. (more than 20cm).

The most attractive hydra is the Green Hydra, <u>H. viridissima</u> (sometimes called <u>Chlorohydra viridissima</u>). Up to about 20mm (¾ in.) in length and with 5 to 13 tentacles that it holds erect, its bright green colour is due to the presence within the cells of both trunk and tentacles of unicellular algae (page 117). These, sometimes called zoochlorellae, have a symbiotic (mutualistic) relationship with hydras. The algae are like the free-living <u>Chlorella</u> and can indeed live independently if removed from the hydra. As well as protection, they obtain carbon dioxide and nitrogenous and phosphorus wastes from the hydra, to which they provide oxygen and synthesized food. In the Lake District the Green Hydra frequents shallow pools, tarns and small streams, but is not apparently found in any of the larger lakes.

<u>Hydra circumcincta</u> is a greyish or brownish species never more than about 7mm (just over ¼ in.) in length and has from 5 to 8 short tentacles. While scarcely known in Britain outside the Lake District, it is often abundant in unproductive high altitude tarns, and is the only hydra that has colonised such water bodies. Here it is often plentiful under clean stones near the shore, usually achieving maximum densities above and below the tarn outlet.

The Lake District has the distinction of being the first, and as yet the only, place in which another species, <u>Hydra graysoni</u>, has been found. It is as yet known only from a stream, Smooth Beck, that drains Hodson's Tarn on Claife Heights and flows into Esthwaite Water. About the size of the Green Hydra, this brownish species has from 4 to 8, usually 6 or 7, tentacles that when fully extended are almost as long as the column.

<u>Hydra viridissima</u> bearing a daughter polyp

<u>H. oligactis</u> bearing an embryotheca, and details of the latter

173

Notwithstanding their carnivorous nature and the presence of stinging cells, hydras serve as host to a variety of other animals and are attacked by others. Some protozoans such as the ciliates <u>Kerona pediculus</u> and <u>Trichodina polyporum</u> glide over the body surface, the former apparently utilising secretions of the host, the latter browsing on bacteria on its surface. Others, such as the amoeba <u>Hydramoeba hydrozoena</u>, known from Cunsey Beck, its first recorded English locality, and from the outflow of Hodson's Tarn, parasitize hydras. A rotifer (page 179) <u>Pleurotrocha petromyzon</u> is probably commensal (lives harmlessly) with hydras but flatworms of the genus <u>Microstomum</u> (page 191) kill and eat them — and use the stinging cells for their own protection! Remarkable too is the 'Water flea' (page 236) <u>Anchistropus emarginatus</u>, known from several Lake District localities that, instead of being eaten by hydras, as are its relatives, has acquired a protective suit of armour against the stinging cells and devices for gripping the soft body of its host from which it rips pieces and consumes them.

Among the most attractive freshwater invertebrates are the bryozoans or 'moss animalcules', so called from their superficial resemblance to a clump of moss. They are also sometimes referred to as polyzoans. To the casual observer they appear very un-animal-like, and indeed the early naturalists had some difficulty in deciding their nature.

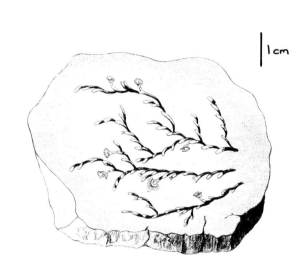

Plumatella repens attached
to a stone

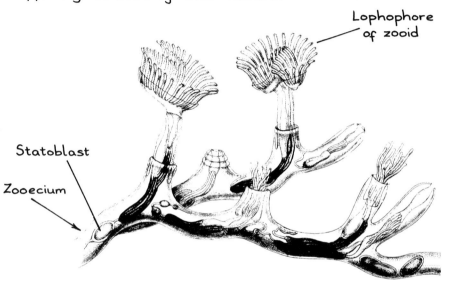

Part of a colony of Plumatella repens with
two zooids expanded

Bryozoans are colonial animals. Each member of the colony is called a zooid and is in continuity with other individuals via a tubular connection. The whole is protected by a tough, membranous, or sometimes gelatinous, sheath, the zooecium. Each zooid is a soft-bodied, sac-like object crowned by an array of tentacles. These arise from a ridge that is horseshoe-shaped or, less commonly, oval in one group (the Phylactolaemata) and circular in another (the Gymnolaemata) and is called the lophophore. Each tentacle is abundantly provided with cilia

175

and, by the beating of these tiny whiplash-like structures, currents are set up that drive particles into the mouth. In the group with a horseshoe-shaped lophophore this is situated at its open end. The tentacle-bearing region can be rapidly retracted within the protective zooecium by powerful muscles. It is extended more slowly by contracting circular

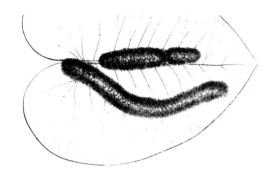

Colonies of <u>Cristatella mucedo</u> on the underside of a water-lily leaf The upper colony has almost divided into two.

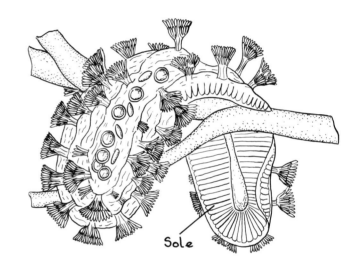

Sole

A colony of <u>Cristatella mucedo</u>
Normally the sole is pressed against a surface

muscles that build up internal pressure and, as it were, squeeze it out.

In most species, colonies are attached permanently to stones and similar objects and grow by budding at their margins. An exception is <u>Cristatella mucedo</u> that forms sausage-shaped colonies that sometimes exceed 5 cm (c. 2 in) length. These adhere to leaves and other objects by a 'sole' on which, by an incompletely understood process they glide slowly. Speeds of up to about an inch (2·5 cm) an hour can be achieved. Colonies divide from time to time.

Each zooid is hermaphrodite and produces both eggs and sperms. Fertilized eggs develop within the body and what is essentially a juvenile emerges though it is initially contained in a ciliated coat that enables it to swim briefly before settling down.

In the Phylactolaemata, especially at the end of summer, groups of cells accumulate within the tissues of the colony and become enclosed in tough chitinous envelopes whose shape resembles two saucers stuck

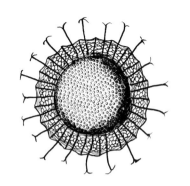  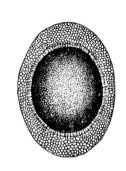

A statoblast of <u>Cristatella mucedo</u> seen from two aspects

A statoblast of <u>Plumatella repens</u>

together at the edges. These are called <u>statoblasts</u>. Each species makes statoblasts of a characteristic form. Those of <u>Cristatella mucedo</u> are fringed by distinctive hooks. When a colony dies, usually in autumn, the statoblasts are either released or remain within the zooecium. They are resistant to freezing and drying and tide the organism over winter. They sometimes serve also for dispersal, for example by becoming attached to the feet of water birds. Some statoblasts sink: others float. They are often washed up on the shores of lakes and ponds, those of <u>Cristatella</u> being common and easily recognised objects in such situations. They hatch in spring and give rise to new colonies by budding.

The Gymnolaematata have no statoblasts but produce overwintering bodies called hibernacula covered with a simple pellicle.

Seven of the nine British species of Bryozoa occur in the Lake District. <u>Cristatella mucedo</u> is common in the area, at least in low-lying lakes and tarns and occasionally occurs in rivers. At least three species of <u>Plumatella</u> occur in the area, of which <u>P. repens</u> is perhaps the commonest though <u>P. fruticosa</u> has been found in several lakes and tarns and in the R. Rothay.

177

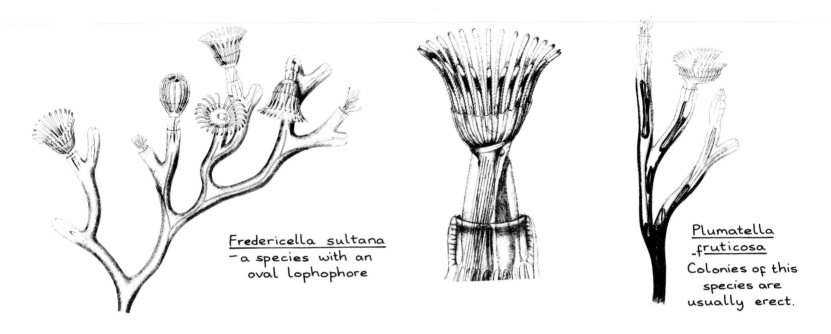

Fredericella sultana
– a species with an
oval lophophore

Plumatella
-fruticosa
Colonies of this
species are
usually erect.

P. fungosa , which sometimes forms huge colonies — several metres in extent — occurs in Esthwaite Water, Grasmere, and perhaps elsewhere.   Hyalinella punctata , a rare species in Britain, has been found in Elterwater.

The only truly freshwater gymnolaematan in Britain is Paludicella articulata , a relatively inconspicuous species, whose headquarters appear to be in the Lake District.   Here it is common and widespread and extends into upland waters.

Rotifers or Wheel animalcules (The Rotifera)

Rotifers or Wheel animalcules are extremely abundant in freshwater, much more so than in the sea.   Many of the 500 or so British species occur in the Lake District.   However, their minute size necessitates the use of a microscope for their study.   Indeed it caused the early micro-scopists to confuse them with protozoans, but they are multicellular.   Early investigators also

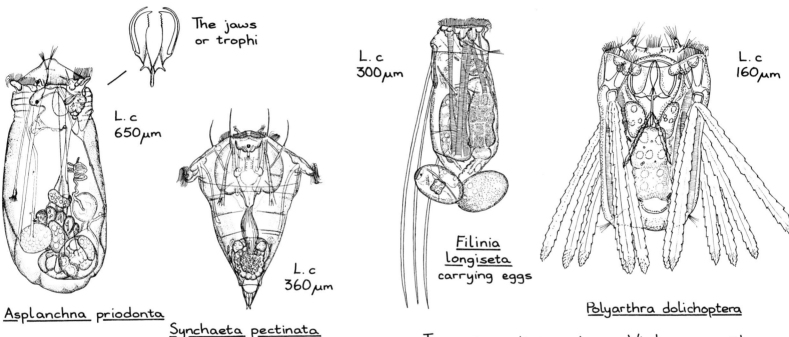

The jaws or trophi

L.c 650μm

L.c 360μm

L.c 300μm

L.c 160μm

Asplanchna priodonta

Synchaeta pectinata

Filinia longiseta carrying eggs

Polyarthra dolichoptera

Two common carnivorous rotifers of open water in the Lake District.   Asplanchna feeds on other rotifers and sometimes on small crustaceans.

Two open water species of Windermere with movable spines.   Polyarthra has blade-like 'skipping spines'.   When flipped these cause the animal to skip.

179

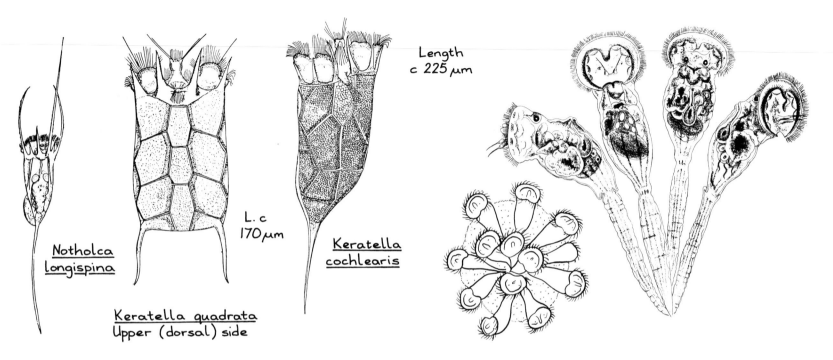

Notholca
longispina

Keratella quadrata
Upper (dorsal) side

L. c
170 μm

Keratella
cochlearis

Length
c 225 μm

Three common loricate rotifers of the
open waters of Windermere and other
English lakes.

A colony of Conochilus unicornis
and some individuals of Conochilus
more highly magnified.
A common colonial planktonic rotifer in
Windermere.

thought that some of the rotifers they discovered bore wheels on their heads — hence the name,
from the Latin rota — a wheel and fero — to bear.   In fact the 'wheels' are circlets of cilia
by means of which some species propel themselves and which many use to collect food particles.
Body form is extremely diverse and is related to equally diverse habits.   Many have an

elaborate arrangement of cilia at the 'head' end. Highly characteristic is the gizzard or <u>mastax</u> within which are jaws or <u>trophi</u> that deal with the food.

Many species occur in the open waters of the English Lakes as components of the plankton. Some of these are naked, others bear a protective case or <u>lorica</u>. Planktonic species often have long spines that counteract sinking. Naked species sometimes have movable spines, like those of <u>Filinia</u> that can be swung forward. Loricate species have fixed spines. The sexes are separate and many planktonic species carry their eggs. Shed freely they would sink, which would be disadvantageous.

Very common in certain

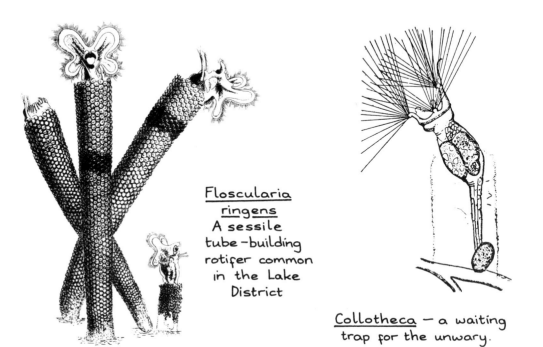

<u>Floscularia</u>
<u>ringens</u>
A sessile
tube-building
rotifer common
in the Lake
District

<u>Collotheca</u> — a waiting
trap for the unwary.

lakes is <u>Conochilus</u> which forms radial colonies that revolve gracefully as they swim. The young of this viviparous species adhere to the mother by a foot inside a delicate globule of jelly. When the colony becomes large it breaks into smaller ones. The similarity of such colonies to those of the protozoan <u>Vorticella</u> (page 165) is an interesting example of convergence. Similar approaches to similar lifestyles by unrelated organisms have given rise to animals that resemble each other in various ways — though in their basic structure they are fundamentally different.

Planktonic rotifers often reproduce by parthenogenesis (no males being involved) during favour-

-able periods.   This enables large populations to be built up quickly as every individual is capable of producing offspring.   As unfavourable conditions arrive males appear.   These, which are sometimes much smaller than females, fertilize the eggs then produced.   These become resting eggs which remain dormant during unfavourable periods, often throughout the winter. They can withstand adverse conditions and can remain viable for several years if necessary. Usually they hatch when favourable conditions return.   Different species favour different seasons but most achieve their maximum abundance sometime between spring and autumn.

Rotifers abound in other habitats and have many different habits   Many swim or creep among vegetation collecting particulate food as do many of the open-water species.   Some have become sedentary and some build protective tubes.   One sedentary species, very common in certain places in the Lake District, is Floscularia ringens.   Using a gelatinous ring as a base, that can be seen in the illustration of the juvenile, it builds up a tube of faecal pellets.   These it places in position one by one with the precision of a skilled bricklayer.   In Floscularia the corona, as the ciliated 'head' complex is called, is drawn out into four rather elongate lobes.   In species of Collotheca the corona is extended into up to seven lobes that surround the mouth.   These are fringed by tufts of long setae.   When minute organisms wander into this trap the lobes close and the prey is captured.

Some rotifers have adopted commensal habits (living in association with other animals without doing harm), others have become parasitic.   Pleurotrocha daphnicola attaches itself to the carapace of the 'water flea', Daphnia (page 239) by means of secretions exuded from large pedal glands. It also cements its eggs one by one to this crustacean.   Species of Testudinella attach themselves to the Water Louse, Asellus (page 228) in the vicinity of the abdominal appendages which, by beating, draw in currents.   These, intended for the respiration of their producer, also bring in a stream of minute particles that are utilised by Testudinella.   Currents set up by colonies of bryozoans (page 175) are similarly exploited by rotifers.   Among the parasitic forms Ascomorpha volvocicola is noteworthy. It lives inside colonies of Volvox (page 118) and feeds on the daughter colonies.

It is among vegetation and on the surfaces of other submerged objects, however, that littoral rotifers occur in greatest profusion.   To such tiny creatures a weed bed is like a forest and here many species earn their living by browsing and foraging in the many different situations that such habitats afford.   In such places a single dip of a suitable net provides material for hours of study and enjoyment.

Bdelloid rotifers live in many peculiar habitats.   These tiny creatures sometimes attach them

182

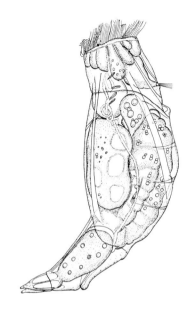

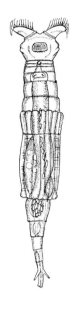

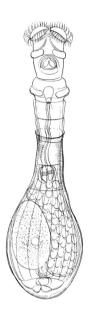

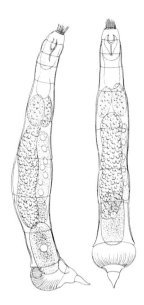

__Pleurotrocha daphnicola__
— that sits on __Daphnia__.

__Philodina roseola__
The 'bird—bath rotifer.'

__Callidina angusticollis__
—that lives among terrest-
-rial mosses and among
__Fontinalis__ on lake shores.

__Albertina intrusor__
A bdelloid rotifer that
lives in the gut of the
oligochaete worm __Stylaria__.

-selves by use of a foot, and often move around by a looping action like a looper caterpillar.
Bdelloids are remarkable organisms that reproduce entirely by parthenogenesis, males being unknown.
They often live in small volumes of water — __Philodina roseola__ is common in bird baths! — or in damp moss.
A few, such as __Albertina intrusor__ that lives in the gut of a freshwater oligochaete worm, are parasitic. If
the habitat dries out bdelloids become dry and apparently lifeless. In this condition they can remain
dormant for many years and can tolerate temperatures above the boiling point of water and down to
below −200°c. If moistened after such treatment they rapidly revive.

Gastrotrichs, sometimes called 'hairy backs', live both in freshwater and in the sea.   They are minute, unsegmented animals, whose freshwater representatives are seldom more than half a millimetre in length and often much smaller.   Their shape is simple — elongate with some elaboration at the head end, and character-istically with two 'tails' at the rear.   The body is protected by a delicate cuticle that often bears long spines or scales.   Flattened below, they glide over surfaces by use of myriads of tiny whiplash-like cilia, of

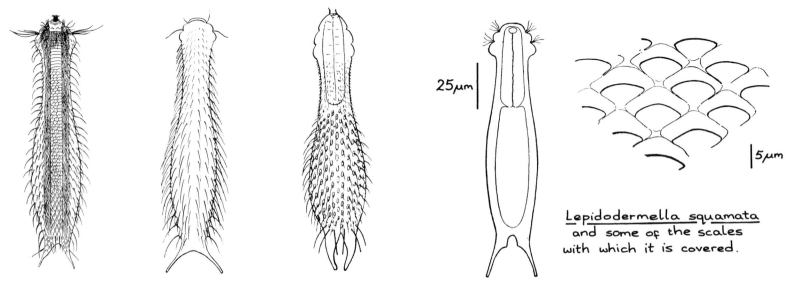

25μm

5μm

Lepidodermella squamata
and some of the scales
with which it is covered.

<u>Chaetonotus maximus</u> (left) seen from below, and
   two other species of the genus, from above.

which there are two longitudinal bands in most freshwater species.   Occasionally they swim clear of the bottom.   Their relationship to other animals is obscure.   Although they sometimes abound, especially in standing waters of almost all kinds, and often occur in thousands, indeed hundreds of thousands, per square metre of bottom, they are but little studied in Britain, and have been almost entirely ignored in the Lake District.   At present just over twenty species have been recorded in Britain.   About 150 are known from Europe.

As they glide over the bottom, or over plant surfaces, they whisk minute organisms and detritus into the mouth with cilia.   Some species have tufts of long setae in the head region that produce vortices which bring minute particles to the animal.   These are then driven into the mouth by other setae located near the front of the head.

Freshwater gastrotrichs were long thought to be parthenogenetic — males being unknown.   In fact sperms were seen in the mid 19th century but the reports were forgotten. Sperms have recently been rediscovered, first in <u>Lepidodermella squamata</u>, later in several other species, and it seems that some gastrotrichs at least sometimes function as hermaphrodites. Both quick-hatching and resting eggs are produced.   Sometimes these may well be fertilized, but often fertile eggs of both kinds are produced by individuals in which no sperms are present.

In <u>L. squamata</u> both kinds of eggs are covered with blunt-tipped spines.   They are deposited on suitable objects, several often being laid near to each other.   Rapidly-developing eggs generally develop and hatch within about 48 hours, but take longer in cold water and may hatch even more quickly at high temperatures.   A small version of the adult emerges. Only about 5 eggs at the most seem to be produced in the course of a lifetime of potentially about 20 days or a little more.   The lifespan in nature is doubtless often less than this.   The rapidly developing eggs cannot stand freezing or drying but the resting eggs can, and may survive for periods of several years of such adverse conditions

Gastrotrichs often occur among organic detritus and some of them are able to tolerate low oxygen levels.   Individuals living in deep, oxygen-poor water often have small magenta-coloured bodies in the gut wall whereas those in well oxygenated water do not.   In marine species such bodies contain sulphur and it is suspected that they are concerned with the detoxification of hydrogen sulphide (H_2S) by precipitating elemental sulphur.

This is a group that would be rewarding to the amateur investigator.

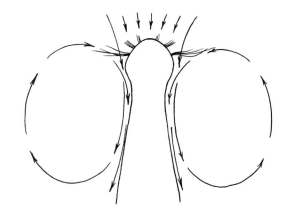

The feeding currents of <u>Chaetonotus</u>

The free-living flatworms known as Planarians, of which there are several groups, are related to the parasitic flukes and tape-worms.   Largest in size are the Tricladida.   These are flattened creatures that glide smoothly over surfaces by means of tiny waves, invisible to the naked eye, that travel backwards along the under side of the body.   These are aided by the beating of tiny whip-lash-like filaments (cilia) that can propel small, but not large, individuals unaided.   Like caterpillar tractors they lay down their own 'road' in the form of a carpet of mucus ('slime') on which they glide.   Most species have simple eyes; often two, sometimes a row of many tiny eyes along the margin of the head.

Dugesia with its pharynx protruded.

Dugesia polychroa showing the typical posture of a triclad flatworm as it glides over a stone.

Triclad flatworms are very lowly creatures on the evolutionary scale.   They have no body cavity other than that of the gut, so their organs, unlike those of 'higher' animals that lie in a cavity (the coelome) are packed in spongy tissue.   Lack of complexity has its advantages.   A decapitated flatworm can grow a new head — and the head another trunk.   They can, however, learn very simple things, and it has been claimed that if a worm that has learned something, such as how to locate certain food, is killed, ground up, and fed to its brothers, the eaters acquire some of this knowledge!

These are carnivorous creatures that feed on worms, snails, crustaceans and other small organ-

	Dendrocoelum lacteum	Dugesia polychroa	Planaria torua	Bdellocephala punctata	Polycelis nigra	Polycelis tenuis
Wastwater					X	
Ennerdale Water						
Buttermere					X	X
Crummockwater					X	X
Ullswater	X				X	X
Coniston Water	X	X		X	X	X
Derwentwater					X	X
Bassenthwaite Lake	X	X			X	X
Windermere	X	X	X	X	X	X
Esthwaite Water	X	X		X	X	X

The distribution of triclad flatworms in some of the major lakes. Note how the 'poor' (oligotrophic) lakes have few species, the 'richer' (eutrophic) lakes more species.

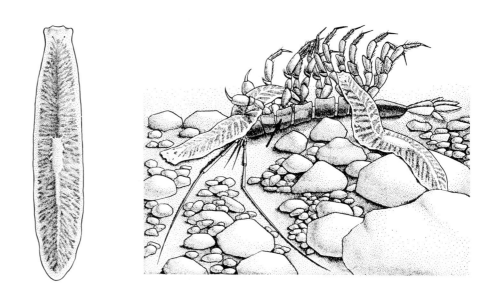

<u>Dendrocoelum lacteum</u>. Length about 25 mm. Of the individuals feeding on a Water Louse, <u>Asellus</u>, that on the left has inserted its proboscis (arrowed) into the prey.

isms, usually on injured individuals. When prey is seized, mucus is secreted to help to hold it. Carrion is also eaten. Each has a tubular pharynx that it can protrude and insert into the body of the prey and through which it sucks up food into its blind gut which has three arms — hence the name Tricladida. Any waste has to be ejected through the pharynx.

187

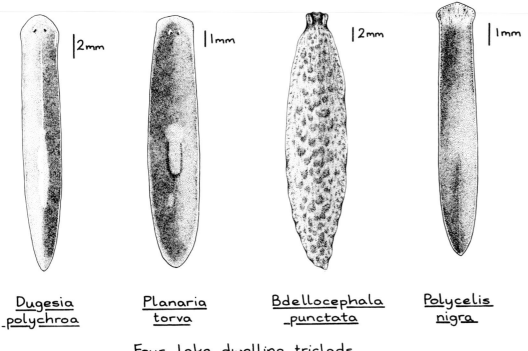

Not only do triclads grow, like other animals, but when food is scarce they can shrink — to grow again when food again becomes available. Some species, (e.g. species of <u>Polycelis</u>) live for several years, others (e.g. <u>Dendrocoelum lacteum</u>) usually attain maturity, reproduce, and die within a year.

Although in contrast with Continental Europe, Britain has an impoverished triclad fauna, in the British context the group is well represented in the Lake District, 9 of the 10 native species having been recorded. (An introduced N. American species has been seen in an aquarium!) Six of these have been found in lakes, the other 3 in running water or seepages.

The distribution among the major lakes has been worked out and shows very nicely how

Dugesia
_polychroa

Planaria
torva

Bdellocephala
_punctata

Polycelis
nigra

Four lake dwelling triclads

the barren oligotrophic lakes have few species (only one has been found in Wastwater and as yet none in Ennerdale), while the richer, eutrophic lakes often harbour several species.

Of the lake-dwelling species, the inch long (25mm), and occasionally larger, white <u>Dendrocoelum lacteum</u> occurs in several of the more productive lakes and tarns. It feeds often on the 'Water louse', <u>Asellus</u> (page 228) two individuals being shown doing so in the illustration.

The somewhat smaller <u>Dugesia polychroa</u> also favours the richer lakes and tarns where it feeds largely on snails. It is brown or grey above, paler below.

188

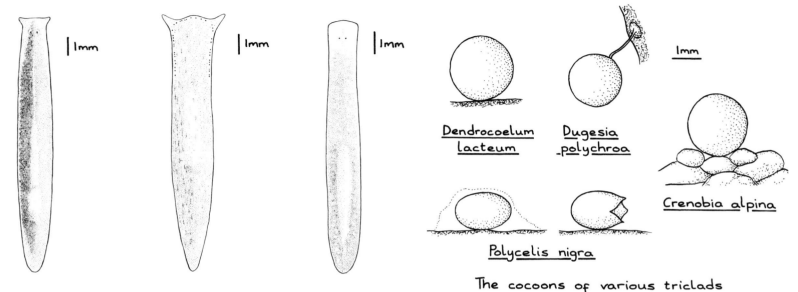

Crenobia
alpina

Polycelis
felina

Phagocatta
vitta

Two 'glacial relict' triclads and a frequenter
of seepages and ground water.

Dendrocoelum
lacteum

Dugesia
polychroa

Crenobia alpina

Polycelis nigra

The cocoons of various triclads

Planaria torva, which is rare, is possibly an
introduced species in Britain.   Two individuals
have been found in Windermere.
Achieving a length of 35 mm (1·5 in.)
Bdellocephala punctata is our largest triclad.
It is uncommon but occurs in several of the richer Lake District lakes, usually under stones.   In
colour it is brown with dark spots.   It eats a range of foods — snails, Asellus, Gammarus (page
227) and other prey.
Only about 12 mm (0·5 in.) long, Polycelis nigra is usually black in colour ('nigra' means black) but
occasionally brown.   It has many tiny eye-spots (Polycelis means many spots).   It is a very
common species and is often abundant in a variety of habitats.   It eats a wide range of foods.
The browner, mottled, P. tenuis is very similar.

189

Of the three predominantly running water species, two, <u>Crenobia alpina</u> and <u>Polycelis felina</u> have particularly interesting distributions, both geographical and ecological. The usually greyish <u>C. alpina</u> is common in Alpine and northern regions of Europe and is also found in scattered localities in between, usually in hilly districts where there are cold springs. (The name <u>Crenobia</u> means 'spring-dweller', and <u>alpina</u> is self-explanatory.) To these and the streams fed by them it is largely confined. It seldom occurs at temperatures above 15°c, though it can tolerate higher temperatures for short periods. Species restricted to cold water in this way are called <u>cold-water stenotherms.</u> Its distribution reflects the effects of the recent Ice Ages (Pleistocene glaciations). As the ice retreated, <u>C. alpina</u> followed it northwards, and also into the Alpine region, but was able to survive in much of central and lowland Europe only where it found refuges in cold springs. Here it persists as a <u>relict</u> species. It reproduces sexually only at temperatures between about 6° and 12°c; by fission at higher temperatures.

<u>Polycelis felina</u> is brownish in colour often with a reddish tinge. The name <u>felina</u> refers to its supposedly cat-like head region. It too is a cold-water species but favours slightly higher temperatures (c. 13°–17°c) than <u>C. alpina</u> and therefore tends to occur downstream of it. It probably arrived in Europe towards the end of the Ice Ages and has not colonised Fennoscandia. Both it and <u>C. alpina</u> are common in the Lake District where they reproduce sexually during the winter. Most other species breed in spring or summer.

The white <u>Phagocatta vitta</u> is mostly a northern species in Britain. It penetrates ground-waters as well as living at the surface. It seems to be widespread in suitable habitats in the Lake District but a detailed survey is needed. It is the only British species other than the ice age relicts to breed in winter.

Triclads are hermaphrodite, that is each individual is simultaneously both male and female. Reproduction can be either asexual — an individual divides transversely into two — or sexual when two individuals unite and a mutual exchange of sperm takes place. Some species employ both methods; in others only sexual reproduction is practised.

Fertilized individuals produce eggs that are enclosed in a tough, leathery cocoon, brown or red in colour, that gradually becomes almost black. This is usually attached to some firm object, in some cases directly, in others via a stalk. <u>Crenobia alpina</u> is unusual in that its cocoons are not attached. From a cocoon tiny replicas of the adult eventually emerge. The number of eggs, and therefore young, per cocoon differs according to species. Most species produce from about 2 to 10 per cocoon but in <u>Dugesia polychroa</u> the number is usually only from 1 to 4,

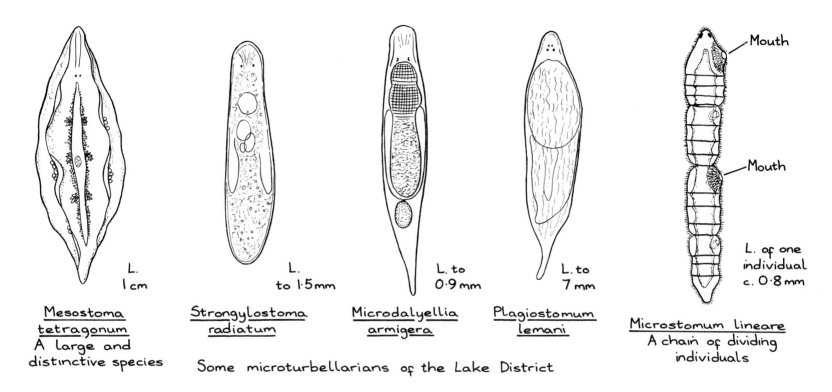

Mouth

Mouth

L. 1 cm

L. to 1·5 mm

L. to 0·9 mm

L. to 7 mm

L. of one individual c. 0·8 mm

Mesostoma
tetragonum
A large and
distinctive species

Strongylostoma
radiatum

Microdalyellia
armigera

Plagiostomum
lemani

Microstomum lineare
A chain of dividing
individuals

Some microturbellarians of the Lake District

and species of Polycelis are more prolific.   P. nigra produces up to about 12 young per cocoon,
P. tenuis up to about 14, and P. felina as many as 30.   Several cocoons may be produced
during the breeding season.
     Related to the triclads are the so-called Microturbellaria whose classification has been
treated in several ways.   Those found in Britain belong to the Rhabdocoela and Allocoela.
These resemble triclads but are often much smaller, sometimes less than a millimetre long,
though some exceed a centimetre, and have a simple gut.   They usually propel themselves through
the water by means of cilia.   Their study has been neglected in Britain and almost nothing is

191

known of their distribution and ecology in the Lake District, in which region they would make an excellent group for study by an amateur naturalist.

The shapes of microturbellarians are more diverse than those of triclads. Likewise, while all triclads are carnivorous, microturbellarians consume a wider range of foods. Some eat fine detritus, algae, including diatoms, and bacteria. Others are carnivorous. The food of the latter includes small oligochaete worms (page 202) and tiny nematodes (page 196), while several species apparently feed extensively on bdelloid rotifers (page 182).

The illustrations give some idea of what these animals look like. Only about 20 of the 50 or more species that occur in Britain have so far been found in the Lake District. Of these, three, all found in tarns, have as yet been found nowhere else in the country. These are <u>Gieyztoria expedita</u>, <u>Castrada stagnorum</u> and <u>Olisthanella truncula</u>. Of the species known in the area most have been reported from only one or a few places but may in fact be common.

<u>Microstomum</u> is interesting in several respects. An elongate organism, it multiplies by division, constricting half way along its length. Before it has divided, however, each potential daughter individual may begin to divide. Each of their daughters, and each of <u>their</u> daughters may do likewise so that a chain of what will ultimately be 16 new individuals may be formed. More remarkable <u>Microstomum lineare</u> feeds on hydras. It ingests their stinging cells (nematocysts) (page 171) without causing them to discharge. These then migrate to the surface of the turbellarian and can be employed in its defence! <u>M. lineare</u> is a common animal. In the Lake District it has been found in Derwentwater and in tarns and is probably widespread.

Of the other species illustrated, the first three have been positively recorded in the Lake District. Uncertainty remains about whether <u>Plagiostomum lemani</u> occurs in the area.

Flukes (Trematoda) and Tapeworms (Cestoda)

Trematodes (flukes) and cestodes (tapeworms) are two important parasitic groups that, like the free-living flatworms, are components of a large group, the Platyhelminthes. They often have aquatic larval stages, and some spend their entire life in freshwater. Although several of these 'worms' are of great importance as parasites of man, his domestic animals, and of wild animals exploited by him, including fishes, they are seldom seen by those not given to probing inside animals or examining the gills of fishes where some flukes live. When such 'worms' have larval stages, these are often microscopic and seldom encountered by the casual observer of freshwater animals. Information on them is to be sought in specialised textbooks, but a brief introduction is meritted here.

Flukes (Trematoda)

Members of one group of flukes — the monogenetic trematodes — are parasites mainly of cold-blooded vertebrates. Most are external parasites but some penetrate the gut or bladder of the host. <u>Gyrodactylus elegans</u>, a parasite of various freshwater fishes provides an example. This 1mm long fluke attaches itself to the skin, and especially to the gills, of its host by an array of hooks at its rear end. This enables it to press its mouth against the host's skin and browse on it. <u>G. elegans</u> is viviparous. A young fluke develops inside the parent. When it is released not only is it almost as big as its mother but it too may already have a daughter fluke developing inside it. Such fecundity is one of the hallmarks of many parasites.

The Liver Fluke of sheep, <u>Fasciola hepatica</u>, provides an example of a digenetic trematode. It is the cause of liver rot in sheep, a disease that formerly caused the death of about a million sheep each year in the United Kingdom, and of far more following wet periods. While still a serious disease it is now more carefully controlled. Such control only became possible after its remarkable life cycle was worked out.

The adult fluke is flattened, oval in shape and up to about 50mm (2 in.) in length. It lives in the liver of its host. It is an hermaphrodite. Eggs are shed in large numbers with the droppings of the host. If these land in water — even in wet grassland — they hatch. From each a ciliated

<u>Gyrodactylus elegans</u> — with a young individual (stippled) developing inside its parent.

193

larva, the <u>miracidium</u>, emerges.
This swims freely but only for 24
hours or so.   To survive longer it
must find a freshwater snail of a
particular species — only <u>Limnaea
truncatula</u> will do — into which it
bores.   Inside the snail it becomes
transformed into a <u>sporocyst</u>, a sac-
like larva that grows at the expense
of its host.   The sporocyst also has
the ability to multiply !   Within it
many cylindrical larvae, each called
a <u>redia</u>, develop.   These grow and
eventually rupture the sporocyst and
are therefore liberated — but they are
still inside the digestive gland of the
snail.   Each redia larva also
multiplies !   Within it daughter redia
are formed, and germ cells also
give rise to a succession of larvae
of yet another kind.   These, the
<u>cercariae</u> (singular <u>cercaria</u>), escape
from the redia via a birth pore,
force their way through the tissues
of the snail, and escape into the
surrounding water.   A cercaria,
which is just visible to the naked eye,
resembles a miniature tadpole and
swims freely.   After a few hours,
however, it wriggles up a blade of
grass and thus out of the water.
Here it stops, sheds its tail, and

194

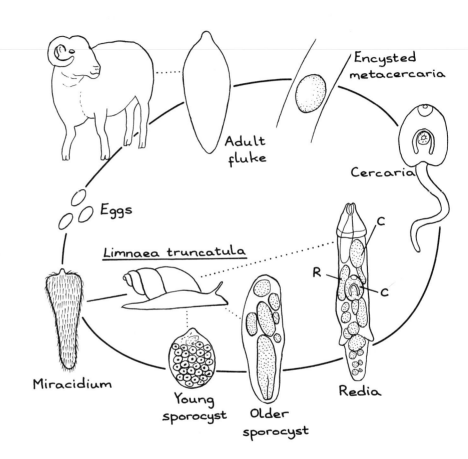

The life cycle of the Liver Fluke; <u>Fasciola hepatica.</u>
Within the older sporocyst developing redia larvae can
be seen.   Within the redia a daughter redia (R) and
two developing cercariae (C) are present.

secretes a hard cyst over itself.   It is now called a <u>metacercaria</u>.   All that now remains is for the cyst to be eaten by a sheep as it crops the grass.   Not until the cyst reaches the intestine of the sheep is it digested, releasing the metacercaria within.   This, usually by boring through the gut wall and migrating thence, eventually reaches its goal, the liver of the sheep, where it grows to adulthood thus completing a life history of almost unbelievable complexity.

The distribution of liver rot is governed by that of <u>Limnaea truncatula</u>.   In the Lake District this snail lives in many wet places, near streams, and occasionally in tarns.   It seldom enters lakes but has been found in Bassenthwaite Lake and Derwentwater.

Other flukes have equally remarkable life cycles often involving freshwater hosts.   They include the blood flukes (schistosomes) of man that cause bilharzia (schistosomiasis), a serious and debilitating disease of millions in the tropics (but not in Britain).   The intermediate hosts are again freshwater snails.

Tapeworms (<u>Cestoda</u>)

Tapeworms too, often have complex life cycles, sometimes involving freshwater stages, and sometimes enacted entirely in freshwater.   Two examples must suffice.   In Windermere a small percentage of individuals of the small planktonic crustacean <u>Cyclops abyssorum</u> contain the larva of a tapeworm of the genus <u>Diphyllobothrium</u>.   Such larvae are acquired by ingesting a free-living tapeworm larva — a <u>coracidium</u> — that has emerged from an egg shed by an adult tapeworm. In the <u>Cyclops</u> it has changed into a <u>procercoid</u> larva.   If the <u>Cyclops</u> is eaten by a fish (and sometimes infected crustaceans become red in colour which attracts fishes) the procercoid will be digested out and will develop into a <u>plerocercoid</u> larva in the fish.   To complete the life cycle this larva must wait until the fish is eaten by another fish or, depending on which species it is, by a bird.   Life is a chancy affair for such creatures, but for those that reach the definitive host the rewards are great.   Safe within the body of the host the 'worm' is protected and surrounded by limitless food.   All it is called upon to do is to produce eggs.

<u>Schistocephalus gasterostei</u>

Sticklebacks serve as intermediate hosts to <u>Schisto-</u>
<u>-cephalus gasterostei</u> whose large plerocercoids mature if eaten by an appropriate bird.

Although nematodes, commonly called threadworms or roundworms (the scientific name comes from the Greek word for a thread) are common and widespread in freshwater, and indeed are sometimes the most abundant multicellular animals in the bottom fauna, they are poorly studied.   To the non-expert they all look very much alike and seem to differ mainly in size.   Indeed considering the enormous range of their habits and of the habitats they frequent, nematodes are remarkably uniform in structure.   They almost always have what is said to be a filiform shape and are often white or off-white in colour, but some are transparent.   Their cuticle is tough and elastic.   Besides living in freshwater, where there are many species, nematodes are abundant in the soil where, as they often live in the film of water around soil particles, they are perhaps to be regarded as aquatic.   Many are parasites, some of plants, others of animals, some being responsible for serious diseases of man.   Some tropical species of the latter, such as the metre-long Guinea Worm, <u>Dracunculus</u>, and the causative organisms of onchocerciasis (river blindness) and elephantiasis, use fresh-water animals — cyclopoid copepods (page 223), simulium flies (page 312) and mosquitoes (page 300) respectively as intermediate hosts.

The freshwater nematodes of the Lake District are very poorly known. Many are small — <u>Rhabdolaimus aquaticus</u> is only a millimetre long.   Not only do they occur as members of the bottom fauna of lakes and tarns but they are found in moss in streams, and indeed in almost all freshwater habitats. Some, such as species of <u>Rhabditis</u> feed on bacteria, others on algae, protozoans and other minute organisms : others are

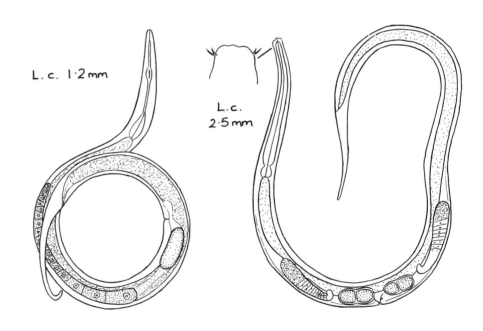

L.c. 1·2mm

L.c. 2·5mm

<u>Tylenchus davainei</u>   <u>Tobrilus gracilis</u>

carnivores.   Some are tolerant of extreme conditions.   The so-called Vinegar Eel, <u>Anguillula aceti</u> that lives in acidic situations, including vinegar, is a nematode that has claims to be called a freshwater species. Some can be frozen in ice and revive when the ice melts.   Some, such as <u>Dorylaimus stagnalis</u> (length to about 8mm) seem to occur in many parts of the world.   Distinguishing features are seldom obvious to the uninitiated, but <u>Tylenchus davainei</u>, which lives among moss in fast-flowing streams has a hooked 'tail' that it appears to use as an anchor.   <u>Tobrilus gracilis</u> has tiny hooks at the head end.

Development of the free-living forms is from eggs, that sometimes hatch within the parent, via stages that generally look very similar to the adult.   The illustration of <u>T. davainei</u> shows an egg almost ready for laying.

In view of our ignorance of most freshwater nematodes it is ironical that the tiny <u>Caenorhabditis elegans</u>, (length about 1·3mm, diameter about 80μm) which has some claims to be regarded as a freshwater species, is in some ways one of the best understood of all animals.   This nematode is the first multicellular organism for which the origin of every cell of the body is known.   Complete cell lineages from the fertilized egg to the mature adult have been followed.

<u>C. elegans</u> inhabits the interstices between damp soil particles or rotting vegetation.   It lives in a film of water whose thickness is critical.   If the film is too thin, or dries out, the animal becomes desiccated and dies : if it is thicker than the diameter of the worm locomotion becomes very difficult.   This is because in a film of the correct thickness, the worm is held against solid surfaces by surface tension.   Locomotion is achieved by flexing the body, which propagates a wave along it.   Dorso-ventral and not lateral flexures are employed, which means that the animal has to lie on its side.   If the wave runs from front to back it drives the worm forward : if it is reversed, backward.   The head region is capable of additional flexure in all directions.   Hydrostatic pressure within the body cavity is high — which gives rigidity and acts as a so-called hydrostatic skeleton.

Most individuals of <u>C. elegans</u> are self-fertilizing hermaphrodites and each produces about 300 eggs.   Generation time is about 3−4 days.   There are four larval stages, that look very similar to the adult.   If food is scarce stage 2 can moult into a resting stage which can withstand desiccation and other extreme conditions for long periods.   When good conditions return the resting stage is activated, moults, and continues its development.   About one individual in a thousand is a male.   These are capable of mating with hermaphrodites.

<u>C. elegans</u> is now an important experimental animal.   Probably widespread, those cultured in laboratories derive from ancestors isolated from mushroom compost obtained near Bristol !   Taken as a whole, however, nematodes comprise perhaps the most outstanding example of a group of freshwater animals that is abundant, probably very important, but inadequately studied.

Hair Worms are so called because of a fanciful resemblance to horse hairs — which gives some indication of their form. They are sometimes called Gordian worms (one genus is called <u>Gordius</u>) because several individuals sometimes become entangled and bring to mind the Gordian knot said to have been cut by Alexander the Great.

Adult hair-worms are long, often very long, slender creatures. British species often range from 13 to 18 cm (5 to 7 inches) in length, and continental specimens of one of them, <u>Gordius villoti</u>, as long as 91cm (about 3ft) have been recorded! They are brown to black in colour and the body is protected by a tough cuticle. The sexes are separate, males being re-cognisable by their forked 'tail'. The gut is degenerate and adults never feed though in some cases a trace of a mouth is present at the head end, suggesting that the ancestors of the group fed.

Many kinds of standing water are frequented, including such small sites as cattle troughs. They sometimes turn up in domestic water supplies, when they tend to cause much un-necessary alarm.

Fertilization is internal, the male, which tends to be more active than the female, coiling itself around the latter. Eggs, produced in vast numbers

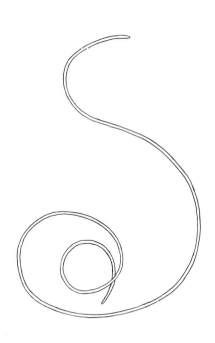

Adult <u>Gordius</u>
Length c. 15 cm (6 in)

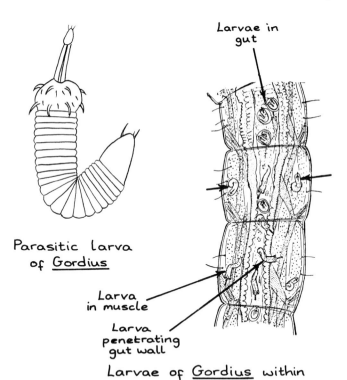

Parasitic larva
of <u>Gordius</u>

Larvae in gut

Larva in muscle

Larva penetrating gut wall

Larvae of <u>Gordius</u> within a chironomid larva

—sometimes several million—are laid in strings, usually between April and August.   These are attached to aquatic plants and are embedded in gelatinous material that swells after laying.   The adults then die.   Minute larvae eventually emerge.   These are destined for a parasitic way of life and have to find their way into an insect host.   Stylets that appear suitable for boring a way in are present, but their use for this purpose appears not to have been proved.   In some cases larvae apparently encyst on vegetation within about 24 hours of hatching and are ingested by the host.   Many different kinds of insects serve as hosts.   Larvae of chironomid midges (page 305) are often victimised and sometimes an individual larva contains many parasites.   These have usually been ingested. They find their way through the gut wall — for which the stylets will be useful — and settle among the muscles.   Even terrestrial insects, which must encounter hair-worm larvae near the water's edge, are utilised.   It was believed in the past that larvae are sometimes passed from one host to another if the first host is eaten, but this is now doubted.

Larvae appear generally to overwinter in the host where they gradually change to the adult form.   At no time do they possess a gut.   Food material is absorbed through the surface.   In spite of their great length, more than one adult sometimes matures in a single host, from which they emerge in spring. If the host happens to be a terrestrial insect it is essential for survival of the hair-worm that it dies near water.

At least two of the four British species have been found in the Lake District.   These are Gordius villoti and Parachordodes violaceus.   Another species, P. wolterstorffii is known elsewhere in northern England and may also be present.   All species look very much alike and are best separated by the pattern of the cuticle, which requires microscopical examination.

Hair-worms have been but little studied in Britain and much remains to be learned of their habits and distribution.

The Acanthocephala are parasitic 'worms', cylindrical in form, with a characteristically retractile proboscis armed with recurved hooks by means of which anchorage is achieved.   It is the proboscis that gives them both their common and their scientific names — which mean the same thing.   They are usually less than 1 inch (25 mm) long, and often much smaller, though one South American species attains a length of up to 65 cm.   They are common parasites of vertebrates, mostly fishes, birds and mammals, and are among the most dangerous of all parasitic 'worms'.   Their hooks damage tissues, cause nodules to form, and lay tissues open to other infections

Several species of acanthocephalans occur in freshwater fishes in Britain.   Others parasitize birds.   Of the latter Polymorphus minutus, a parasite of many aquatic birds, can afflict domestic ducks, that are sometimes killed by it.   Up to 1000 individuals have been found anchored to the gut wall of a single duck.

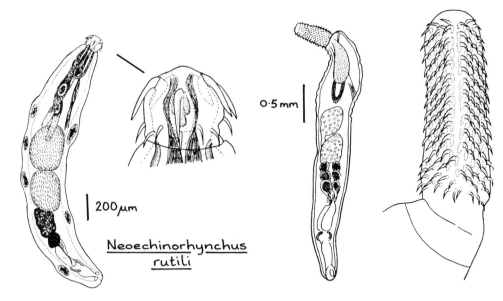

0.5mm

200μm

Neoechinorhynchus
rutili

Pseudoechinorhynchus clavula

The sexes are separate.   Life cycles include an intermediate host, often an aquatic animal.   'Eggs' — actually a well-developed stage, the acanthor, enclosed on a tough shell — are shed with the faeces of the host and ingested by the intermediate host. In aquatic species this is usually a larval insect or a crustacean.   Thus species of Gammarus (page 227) serve as the intermediate host of Pseudoechinorhynchus clavula, a parasite of fishes, and of Polymorphus minutus. In the gut of the intermediate host the shell splits, the contained larva emerges, penetrates the gut wall, through which it eventually passes, and enters the haemocoele (a fluid-containing space present in arthropods). Here it gradually develops into a cystacanth.   One or

a few cystacanths may be present.   Gammarus infected
with Polymorphus minutus can often be found in the Lake
District.   If eaten by an individual of the final (definitive)
host, development continues to maturity.

Of the fish-frequenting species Pseudoechinorhynchus
clavula is common and widespread in the intestine of many
host species, as is Neoechinorhynchus rutili, whose intermediate host is the larva of the Alder Fly, Sialis (page 312).

10 μm

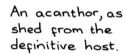

An acanthor, as
shed from the
definitive host.

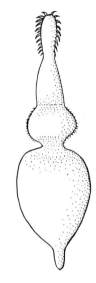

A cystacanth from
Gammarus, the
intermediate host.

Early stages of Polymorphus mintus
the adult of which parasitizes
aquatic birds.

The familiar earthworms have various aquatic relatives.   These segmented worms (annelids) show many advances over the flatworms.   The body, which is divided into compartments (segments), is covered by a thin protective cuticle.   As well as the gut, which runs through it from end to end, beginning at the mouth and terminating at the anus, the body has an additional cavity filled with fluid.   Under pressure this can serve as a hydrostatic 'skeleton'.   Flatworms are always soft.   The body also has muscles that enable it to be stretched out and contracted, providing a means of locomotion.   Annelids also have a blood system, and a more elaborate nervous system than flatworms.

Earthworms and their allies belong to the Oligochaeta (meaning "few chaetae"), a reference to the bristles or <u>chaetae</u> that project from the body wall.   These chaeta are what make an earth-worm feel rough to the touch.   They enable it to grip the soil as it moves.   Polychaetes (with many chaetae) abound in the sea. Both belong to the Chaetopoda (literally, 'bristle footed').   Some aquatic oligochaetes are very much like earthworms and indeed one normally terrestrial species <u>Allolobophora chlorotica</u> is common in Windermere.   <u>A. chlorotica</u>, which achieves a length of 6cm (over 2 in.) is a common inhabitant of soil in gardens and meadows. It also frequents piles of leaves, lives under stones and elsewhere, but is not usually aquatic.   Strangely, in Windermere it lives on sandy and stony shores among Shoreweed, <u>Littorella</u>, and reeds, <u>Phragmites</u>, and can be found 20m from the shore where it lives permanently submerged.   To use oxygen dissolved in water is not very different from what an earthworm, with its damp cuticle, does, so the change of habitat is perhaps less remarkable than it seems at first sight.

Another earthworm-like worm of Windermere, though belonging to a different family, is the 10cm (almost 4 in.) long <u>Sparganophilus tamesis</u>.   This is a rare worm, known otherwise only from the R. Thames (hence its name), but in Windermere it occurs under moderate sized stones in the littoral zone, where several individuals

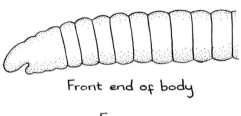

Front end of body

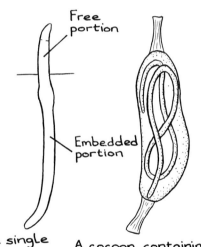

Free portion

Embedded portion

A single chaeta

A cocoon containing a young worm

<u>Sparganophilus tamesis</u>

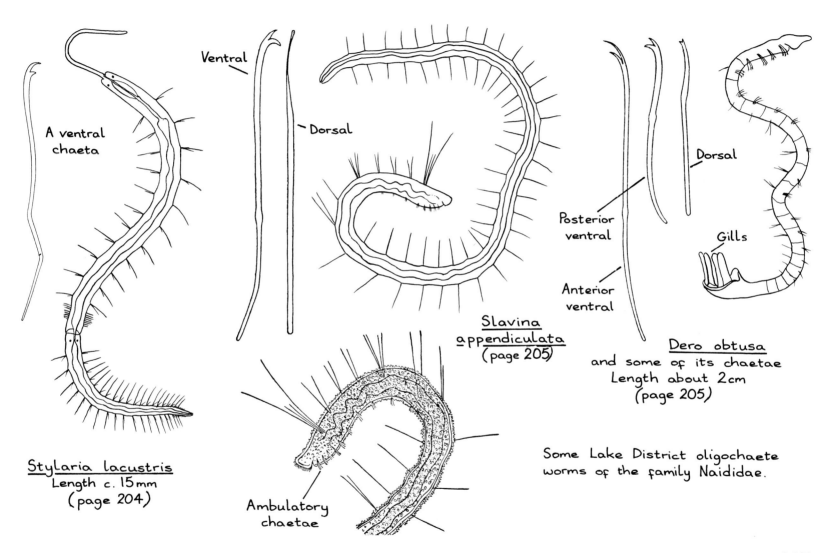

A ventral chaeta

Ventral

Dorsal

Stylaria lacustris
Length c. 15mm
(page 204)

Ambulatory
chaetae

Slavina
appendiculata
(page 205)

Posterior
ventral

Anterior
ventral

Dorsal

Gills

Dero obtusa
and some of its chaetae
Length about 2cm
(page 205)

Some Lake District oligochaete
worms of the family Naididae.

203

can sometimes be found together, in the sand among the roots of <u>Littorella</u>, and particularly in the firm, black, evil-smelling mud among the roots of <u>Phragmites</u>. <u>Sparganophilus</u> has two chaetae on each side in the lower (ventral) part of each segment, and two in the upper (dorsal) part. These are stout and grant purchase when crawling.

These worms are hermaphrodite, having both male and female reproductive systems. When they mate they lie side by side and the male part of each fertilizes the female part of the other. A cocoon is secreted by a region in the middle section of the body (the clitellum) which

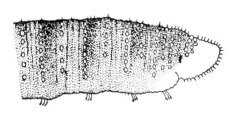

The head end of <u>Ophidonais serpentina</u>. Length c.3mm Note the ambulatory chaetae. A common worm in Windermere, especially among plants, and penetrating to at least 20m.

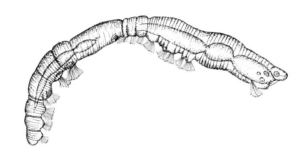

<u>Chaetogaster limnaei</u> — a tiny worm that crawls on the body of certain snails.

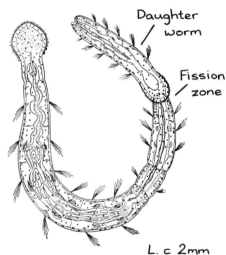

Daughter worm

Fission zone

L. c 2mm

<u>Aeolosoma hemprichi</u>

receives the egg or eggs and out of which the worms slips. The eggs develop within the protecting cocoon and small worms, miniature replicas of the parents, eventually emerge. Cocoons of some species contain several eggs : those of <u>Sparganophilus tamesis</u> only a single egg.

Many aquatic oligochaetes, of which there are several families, are small, slender, delicate, and often rather transparent worms. Such are <u>Stylaria</u>, readily recognised by its long tentacle, <u>Dero</u> which has four posterior gills, and <u>Slavina</u>. Representatives of all these genera are common in Windermere, Esthwaite Water and elsewhere in the Lake District. They have mostly short chaetae

204

with cleft tips ventrally, on which they crawl, and long slender bristle-like chaetae dorsally. These worms are often adept at crawling by the use of their ventral chaetae. This is particularly well seen in the case of <u>Chaetogaster</u>, which lacks dorsal chaetae. One species, <u>C. limnaei</u>, has taken to living on snails such as <u>Limnaea peregra</u> (page 216) and the limpet <u>Ancylus</u> (page 213) over whose body it crawls nimbly and under whose shell it takes refuge. It is common in the Lake District and several individuals can often be seen on a single snail often lifting and waving around their 'heads'. The food evidently consists of mucus and debris and they appear not to inconvenience their host.

<u>Dero</u> is a mud dweller that constructs a tube of this material. Its posterior gills are organs of respiration. These can be expanded and contracted and through them red blood circulates. <u>Dero obtusa</u> is common in Windermere and Esthwaite Water among aquatic plants where the bottom is muddy. It shares this habitat with <u>Stylaria lacustris</u> and <u>Slavina appendiculata</u>. The latter worm is generally covered with debris.

Among the most attractive of worms are species of <u>Aeolosoma</u> that belong to the family Aeolosomatidae. These are

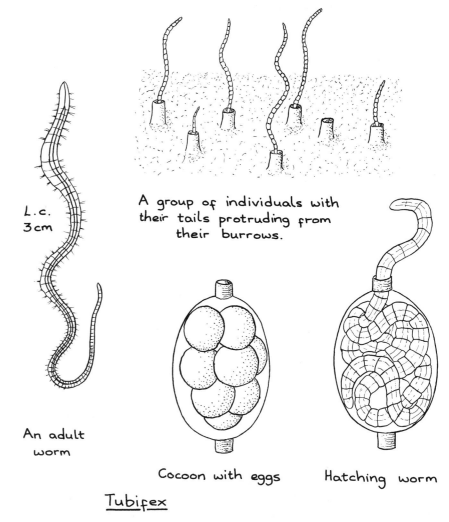

L.c. 3cm

An adult worm

A group of individuals with their tails protruding from their burrows.

Cocoon with eggs

Hatching worm

<u>Tubifex</u>

205

only 1-2mm long and beautifully transparent.   Coloured spots — yellow, pink or green — are present in the skin.   The under surface of the head is covered with cilia that whisk food particles into the mouth.   Like several worms of the family Naididae, including <u>Ophidonais</u>, <u>Stylaria</u> and <u>Chaeto</u>-<u>gaster</u> , they can multiply asexually by budding.   It is not known how many of the half dozen British species of <u>Aeolosoma</u> occur in the Lake District, but as individuals are not infrequently encountered, search may reveal several.

Oligochaete worms, especially of the family Tubificidae, make up an important element of the deep-water (profundal) bottom fauna (benthos) of lakes.   Thirteen species, not all tubificids, have been found in the profundal region of 17 explored English Lakes, but no lake seems to have more than 7 species.   Numbers are generally low in barren oligotrophic lakes (average 98 worms per square metre of bottom in Wastwater for example), much higher in rich eutrophic lakes (9519 per sq.m. in Esthwaite Water).   One species, <u>Stylodrilus heringianus</u> has been found only in oligotrophic lakes, another, <u>Potamothrix hammoniensis</u>, only in the richer lakes.   The commonest species is <u>Tubifex tubifex</u> , which occurs in most lakes.   It achieves densities of almost 8000 per sq.m. in Esthwaite.

<u>Tubifex</u> , 3cm or more in length, inhabits mud in which it makes a tubular burrow out of which it extends its rear end which it waves about to collect oxygen.   It is very good at this.   Its blood is red because it contains haemoglobin, the same pigment as we use.   This enables it to obtain oxygen from water that is only 1·5% saturated.   It can also survive for long periods without any oxygen at all.   This is very necessary as the deep water of eutrophic lakes becomes completely deoxygenated in summer.   The period of deoxygenation generally lasts about 12 weeks in Esthwaite. <u>Tubifex</u> can survive even longer periods than this without oxygen.   This ability is shared by other worms such as <u>Limnodrilus hoffmeisteri</u>, which is also common in Esthwaite.

<u>Tubifex tubifex</u> , which produces cocoons containing several eggs, is a long-lived creature. In Lake District lakes it probably takes 3 years or more to reach maturity.   <u>Limnodrilus</u> <u>hoffmeisteri</u> probably doesn't breed until it is 5 years old and 'average sized' individuals seem to be about 9 years old.   If a series of cold years is experienced development is slowed down and it may be that some of these worms in Lake District lakes are 20 years old — or even older.

Leeches are annelids and share various attributes with oligochaetes, such as a generally 'worm-like' segmented body covered by thin cuticle, an hermaphroditic reproductive system (male and female in the same individual) and a similar device for producing cocoons. They differ in the lack of chaetae (except in a group not represented in our fauna) and by the possession of suckers at each end of the body. There are 33 segments — some claim 34! of which several go to make up the suckers. Each segment is sub-divided into more superficial rings, or annuli (sing. annulus), 3 or 5 in number. There are from 2 to 10 eyes — small pigment spots. Of the 16 British species 12 occur in the Lake District.

Leeches are predominantly freshwater animals. All are predators, though by no means all are blood-suckers. Most are active creatures that walk in a manner superficially like that of the familiar looper caterpillars, but with the important difference that while the cater-pillar doesn't stretch its body, a leech does. A leech can also contract into a hump when necessary. Some species also swim very well by undulating the body in a dorso-ventral manner like a traditional 'sea-serpent' and not from side to side as do fishes and snakes.

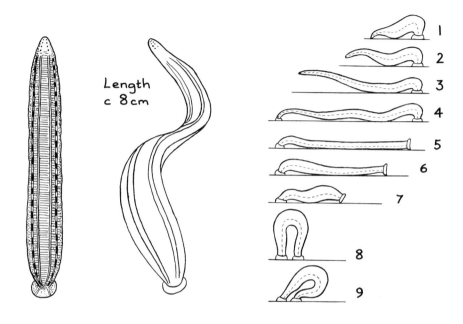

Length c 8cm

The Medicinal Leech
Hirudo medicinalis

How a Medicinal
Leech 'walks'

Best known by name, though not in fact, is the Medicinal Leech, Hirudo medicinalis which is now rare in Britain though it was once sufficiently common in the Lake District to merit collecting for medicinal use as recorded in Wordsworth's poem describing an old leech gatherer. It still survives in at least one small tarn in the south of the district, and in a few scattered local-

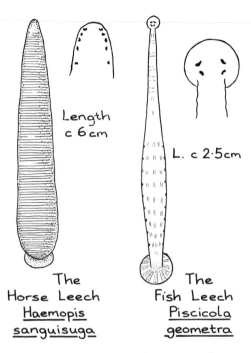

Length c 6 cm

The
Horse Leech
Haemopis
sanguisuga

L. c 2·5cm

The
Fish Leech
Piscicola
geometra

-ities elsewhere in Britain.   It was formerly much used in blood-letting.   The native stock was supplemented by imports from the continent, literally millions being brought in.   These were often kept in handsome leech jars of which examples can still sometimes be seen in pharmacists' shops.   This is our only leech capable of piercing human skin.   Its jaws enable it to feed on mammals—such as cattle seized when they come to drink—but it can also take the blood of amphibians.   It can ingest up to five times its own weight of blood at one meal. Blood is highly nutritious and Hirudo digests it slowly so one meal suffices for many months.   As it can also live for many weeks with an empty gut, a good meal can keep it going for almost a year, and two such meals a year is ample.   It probably takes at least two years to grow to sexual maturity, perhaps three or four years in some individuals.   At mating sperms are exchanged as in earthworms.   A simple cocoon is deposited in damp places near the water's edge.   Each contains 3 to 30 eggs and several may be deposited in one breeding season.

In life the Medicinal Leech is distinguished from the related Horse Leech, Haemopis sanguisuga by it larger size and by red stripes that run the length of its body.   The Horse Leech is grey-green in colour, yellowish beneath.   In spite of its name ('sang-uisuga' means 'blood sucker') it cannot suck blood but ingests whole worms and similar-sized prey — including young of its own species.   It also eats carrion.   It often takes refuge under stones. Common and widespread in Britain it occurs in several places in the Lake District, including at least three lakes — Windermere, Esthwaite Water and Coniston Water.   It is not, however, confined to lakes but occurs also in rivers.   Its breeding habits are similar to those of the Medicinal Leech.

The Fish Leech Piscicola geometra ('piscicola' means 'fish-loving', 'geometra' literally 'earth measuring' a reference to its looping gait) is a parasite of various fishes but is often encountered away from its host.   It 'angles' for a passing fish by attaching itself to a suitable object by its posterior sucker and stretching out its body so that the anterior sucker can 'hook' a victim, the posterior anchor being simultaneously released.   It usually pierces its host's skin in a soft place such as the

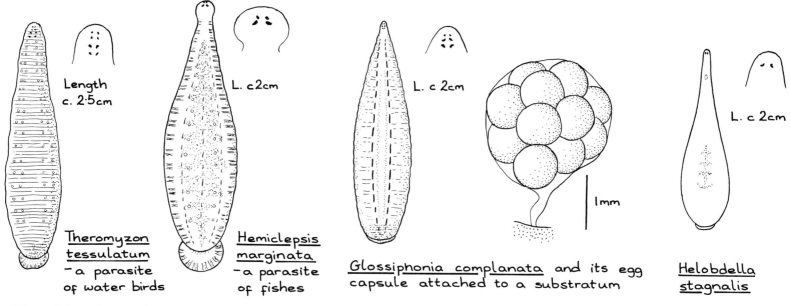

Length c. 2·5cm

Theromyzon tessulatum — a parasite of water birds

L. c 2cm

Hemiclepsis marginata — a parasite of fishes

L. c 2cm

Glossiphonia complanata and its egg capsule attached to a substratum

1mm

L. c 2cm

Helobdella stagnalis

Two blood–sucking leeches   Two leeches that feed on invertebrates.

gills or near the base of a fin and sucks its blood.   When satiated it falls off.   Mating takes place when living free and involves the transfer of a spermatophore — a packet in which sperms are wrapped.   Cocoons are deposited under water.   Each cocoon contains only one egg but from 50 to 90 cocoons can be laid at a rate of up to 3 per day during the reproductive period, which is in spring and early summer.

Piscicola is near the northern limits of its range in the Lake District, from the northern part of which there are no positive records, though it is known from a few places in southern Scotland. It is common and widespread further south in England and Wales.

Like Piscicola, Theromyzon tessulatum lacks jaws and uses an eversible proboscis to penetrate its victim's tissues.   It is a parasite of water birds and usually enters their nostrils and inserts its

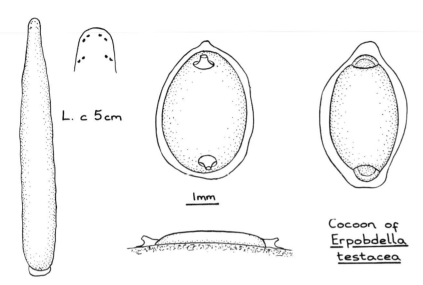

L. c 5cm

1mm

Cocoon of
Erpobdella
testacea

Erpobdella octoculata and its cocoon

proboscis into the tissues to which it there gains access.   It has been known to kill young ducks and geese and can be a pest of domestic ducks. After feeding it leaves the host and frequents a wide range of water bodies.   Mating involves the transfer of a spermatophore as in Piscicola. Cocoons are deposited on some suitable object, 3 to 5 at a time, each containing 50 to 150 eggs. Like several other leeches Theromyzon shows parental care.   The eggs are brooded by the parent and hatch within about 3 weeks.   The young then attach themselves to the parent which sometimes carries as many as 400.   They some-times remain attached for as long as 5 months. After this exertion the adult dies!

As it is readily dispersed by its host, Theromyzon is widely distributed in Britain, including the Lake District.

The light brown, rather flattened, Hemiclepsis marginata is a parasite of fishes, various species of which are attacked.   Of these the commonest Lake District species are Pike or Perch.   Soft places, such as the base of a fin are generally attacked but little time is spent on the host.   Eggs are carried on the under side of the parent and the resulting young, from a dozen to about 150, remain attached there for some time.   Breeding takes place in summer.   Hemiclepsis transmits trypanosomes — protozoan blood parasites of the kind that cause sleeping sickness in man — from one fish to another.

Two species of Glossiphonia, G. heteroclita and G. complanata, especially the latter, are common in the Lake District.   Both suck the body fluids of snails and occasionally other invertebrates.   Both carry their young on their ventral surface.   In G. heteroclita the eggs are carried there also.   In G. complanata they are put in soft, transparent cocoons that are attached to some convenient object, up to 7 cocoons being deposited to-gether.   The parent covers them for 5 or 6 days until they hatch and a few days later the young attach themselves to the parent's under surface where they are carried for 2 to 3 weeks.

Another Lake District leech, Batracobdella paludosa also feeds on snails.

	Piscicola geometra	Theromyzon tessulatum	Hemiclepsis marginata	Glossiphonia heteroclita	Glossiphonia complanata	Helobdella stagnalis	Batracobdella paludosa	Haemopis sanguisuga	Erpobdella octoculata
Wastwater									X
Ennerdale Water					X	X			X
Buttermere				X	X	X			X
Crummockwater		X			X	X			X
Ullswater				X	X	X			
Coniston Water					X	X		X	X
Derwentwater					X	X			X
Bassenthwaite Lake				X	X	X			X
Windermere	X	X		X	X	X	X	X	X
Esthwaite Water	X	X	X	X	X	X		X	X

The distribution of leeches in some of the major lakes.

Leeches reflect the poverty or richness of Lake District lakes. The most barren, oligotrophic lake — Wastwater — supports only one species: the richest, most eutrophic, lake — Esthwaite — supports 8.

The very common whitish, Helobdella stagnalis feeds on a wide range of invertebrates, especially chironomid larvae. The breeding habits of Helobdella are basically the same as those of Glossiphonia complanata. It also feeds parasitically on the Medicinal Leech! At a Lake District site about 15% of almost 1300 Medical Leeches caught over a four year period (and released alive) bore H. stagnalis. Parasitized leeches seldom carried more than three individuals of Helobdella, but as many as 13 were twice found on a single Medicinal Leech.

Two species of Erpobdella occur in the Lake District. E. octoculata — the name means 8 eyes — is extremely common; E. testacea much less so. Both ingest a wide range of insects, such as chironomid larvae, which they swallow whole, as well as worms and small crustaceans. Both put their eggs inside cocoons that are stuck to stones, plants or other convenient objects that are first coated with a sticky secretion emanating anteriorly. An ovoid, initially colourless, cocoon is secreted by the clitellum in the mid region of the body. From 3 to 11 eggs are laid in it and the body is withdrawn leaving the eggs behind. The exit holes are then sealed and the cocoon is flattened into a gently domed structure which hardens and becomes dark brown. Several cocoons are laid by one individual. Young emerge after about 3 to 7 weeks according to temperature.

A rarer leech of the Lake District is Trocheta bykowskii. It too swallows whole worms and insects, and it also ventures out of the water and eats slugs.

Molluscs

Molluscs ('mollis' means 'soft') are soft-bodied, unsegmented animals that are abundantly represented in the sea and on land as well as in freshwater.   Of enormous diversity, the group includes slugs, snails, oysters, cuttlefishes, squids and various others.   The freshwater molluscs of the Lake District belong to two distinct classes — the snails (Gastropoda) and the mussels (Bivalvia or Lamellibranchia).

Snails inhabit a single shell of their own making.   Geometrically a snail shell is, at its simplest, a cone.   Two limpets ('limpet' is a term of no precise scientific standing) found in Lake District lakes have shells of very simple shape.   The shell of Ancylus fluviatilis, sometimes called the River Limpet, though it occurs also in lakes, is rather like the conventional pixie's cap: that of the Lake Limpet, Ancylastrum lacustris is more flattened.   Most snails however, have longer conical shells that are spirally coiled, sometimes in one plane like a watchspring, sometimes in a corkscrew-like manner. Shells of the latter type are therefore conical in shape; the cone being made up from an elongate, spiralling cone!   Of the common Lake District snails, Planorbis albus provides an example of the first kind, Limnaea peregra of the second.

Snail shells are of complex three-layered construction.   A thick layer of calcium carbonate (lime)

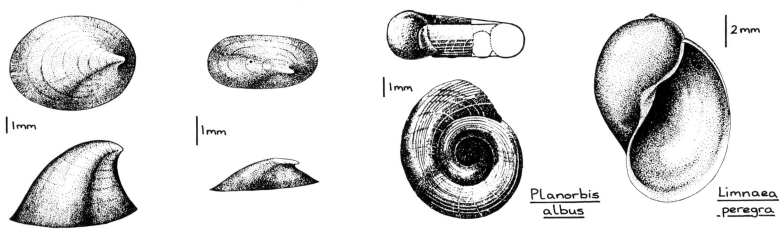

|1mm

|1mm

|1mm

|2mm

Planorbis
albus

Limnaea
peregra

Ancylus fluviatilis

Ancylastrum lacustris

The simple conical shells of two freshwater limpets

Snail shells spirally coiled in one plane (left)
and in a helical manner (right).

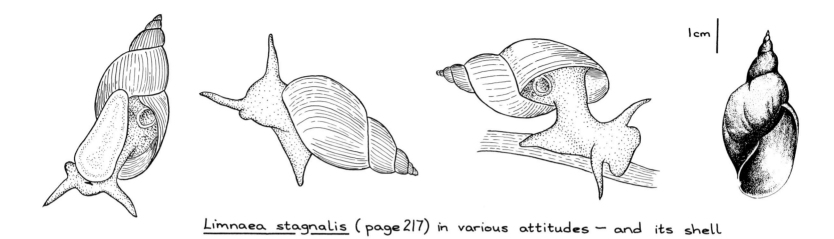

1cm

Limnaea stagnalis (page 217) in various attitudes — and its shell

Reflexed mantle

Physa fontinalis (page 217)

2mm

1mm

Ancylus fluviatilis (page 217)

Some pulmonate snails of the Lake District.

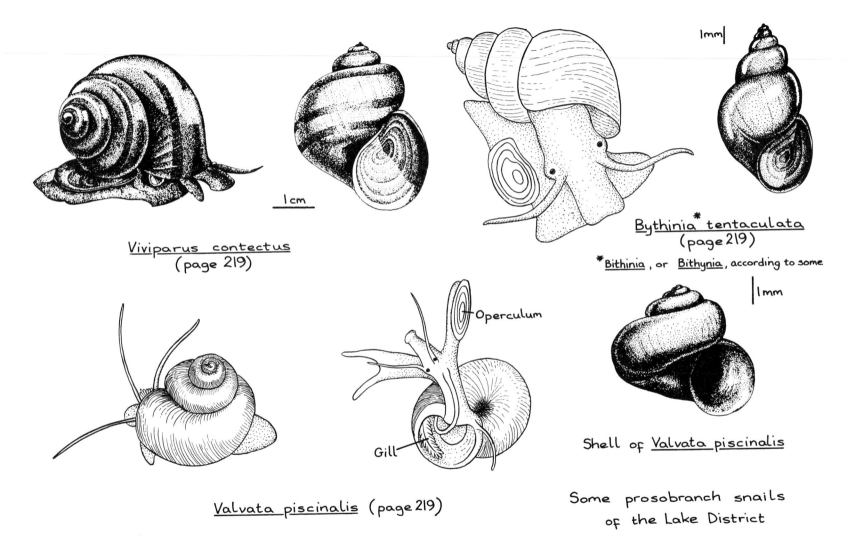

1cm

Viviparus contectus
(page 219)

1mm

Bythinia* tentaculata
(page 219)

*Bithinia, or Bithynia, according to some

1mm

Operculum

Gill

Shell of Valvata piscinalis

Valvata piscinalis (page 219)

Some prosobranch snails
of the Lake District

in the form of calcite or aragonite is sandwiched between a thin, horny outer layer called the perio-stracum that is made of conchiolin — an organic, protective material — and an inner nacreous layer ('mother of pearl'), also mostly of calcium carbonate. The periostracum is a proteinaceous material, resistant, for example, to acids, and helps those few snails that penetrate acid waters to do so without having their shells dissolved.

The shell is lined by a layer of living tissue. This, called the <u>mantle</u>, is what secretes the shell. There is also a space between the mantle and the dorsal (upper) part of the body — the mantle cavity.

The shell is a protective device, always embracing a mass of tissue, the visceral hump, which contains many of the vital organs. Within it the rest of the body can be withdrawn when necessary. In some snails, following such retreat, the shell aperture can be sealed by a lid — the <u>operculum</u> — carried towards the rear of the body, which fits neatly into the aperture. The division of the Lake District snails into operculate (lid-bearing) and non-operculate types conveniently separates them into two groups, the prosobranchs, with an operculum, and the pulmonates, without. Prosobranchs breathe by means of a gill: pulmonates by use of a lung — or at least this is the basic division. Nature, however, is almost infinitely subtle and some pulmonates, which invaded freshwater from the land, where a lung and not a gill is required, have developed a secondary gill — quite different from the true gill (or ctenidium) of the prosobranchs, which came from the sea. It is the mantle cavity, whose walls are richly supplied with blood vessels, that serves as a lung in pulmonates.

Both prosobranchs and pulmonates have a conspicuous foot on which they glide by means of waves of

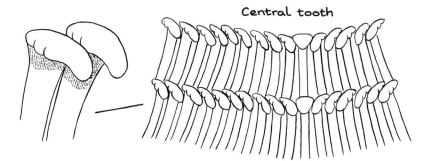

Central tooth

A row of radula teeth of <u>Limnaea stagnalis</u>

Part of two rows of radula teeth of <u>Ancylus fluviatilis</u>

Central tooth

Radula teeth of
Physa fontinalis

Radula teeth of
Bythinia tentaculata

Wastwater	— 2
Ennerdale Water	— 2
Buttermere	— 3
Crummockwater	— 4
Ullswater	— 7
Coniston Water	— 7
Derwentwater	— 7
Bassenthwaite Lake	— 8
Grasmere	— 9
Windermere	— 11
Esthwaite Water	— 9

The number of species
of snails in some of
the major Lakes.

muscular contractions.   The head is all of a piece with the foot and bears eyes, tentacles and the mouth.
  Within the aperture of the mouth are simple, horny jaws for biting, and a file-like structure, the radula, with many rows of horny teeth that are used to rasp food from surfaces much as the metalworker's file rasps material from a lump of metal.   The teeth, which differ from species to species according to the kind of food collected, also often differ in different parts of a row.   There may be several dozen teeth in a row and more than 500 rows in the entire radula.   As teeth wear out they are replaced.
  All Lake District pulmonates are essentially grazers which scrape algae from rocks or plant surfaces, sweep up detritus or, in some cases bite and rasp pieces from the leaves of higher plants.   Limnaea stagnalis, however, is not averse to feeding also on decaying, or even fresh, animal matter and is perhaps best regarded as an omnivore.   Some prosobranchs collect food particles by trapping them in mucus of which streams pass into a groove that leads to the mouth.   Bythinia tentaculata, that occurs on the fringes of the district, collects some of its food by this means, the rest of it by rasping with the radula.
  Because the shell requires large amounts of calcium carbonate (lime), freshwater snails tend to be best represented in calcareous (lime-rich) 'hard' waters. Lake District waters are mostly poor in lime — they are 'soft' — and many of them have impoverished snail faunas.   Indeed the barren oligotrophic Wastwater and Ennerdale each have only two species of snail.   Not unexpectedly these are the most tolerant species, Limnaea peregra, sometimes called the wandering snail ('peregra' comes from a word meaning to wander) and the limpet Ancylus fluviatilis.
  Limnaea peregra is a versatile snail.   Because it is a pulmonate, and pulmonates

breathe atmospheric air through a lung, and because it has no secondary gill, it might be expected to be confined to shallow water where it can from time to time return to the surface to replenish its oxygen supply.   Individuals living close inshore do just that.   In others, living further out, the lung contains a bubble of gas which appears to act as a physical gill (see bugs, page 269).   Others, living in deeper water, have the lung filled with water, and respiration is entirely aquatic.   This is perhaps less strange than it seems.   Even our lungs have to be moist to allow gases to diffuse through them in solution. Deep water is generally cool.   Cutaneous respiration ('breathing through the skin') is aided here because cold water can hold more oxygen than can warm water.   Indeed, in cold water, individuals living inshore can manage to respire by this means

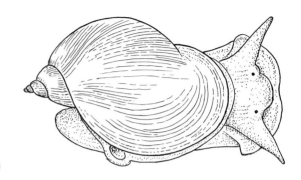

Limnaea peregra

without constantly having to refill the air chamber.   Such are the complexities of pulmonate respiration.
    Ancylus fluviatilis (pages 212 and 213) has virtually lost its lung but has a secondary external gill. It also lives in well aerated situations and probably obtains some oxygen by cutaneous respiration.   It frequents rocky, wave-washed shores where conditions are similar in many respects to those in the rivers and streams in which it also lives.
    As the calcium content increases and shorelines become more diverse so do the snail faunas.   Submerged vegetation and sheltered areas of rich plant growth provide suitable conditions for species that shun exposed shores.   There are also a few species that inhabit tarns or smaller bodies of water, but are not found in the lakes.
    Lake District pulmonates also include Ancylastrum lacustris, (page 212) which is related to Ancylus fluviatilis but has very different preferences.   It abhors the rocks beloved of the latter and is not found in barren rocky lakes.   Its preference is for the richer lakes, Grasmere, Windermere and Esthwaite Water, where it creeps on the stems of the reed Phragmites or of Water Lilies.   Like Ancylus it has a secondary gill.
    Physa fontinalis (page 213) also prefers the richer lakes where it frequents weed beds.   It also lives in rivers.   It has a thin, delicate shell over the outside of which lobes of the fleshy mantle (the sheet of tissue that secretes the shell) extend in an attractive manner.   These probably assist in respiration.
    Physa is independent of atmospheric air, though it has no secondary gill.   Limnaea stagnalis (page 213),

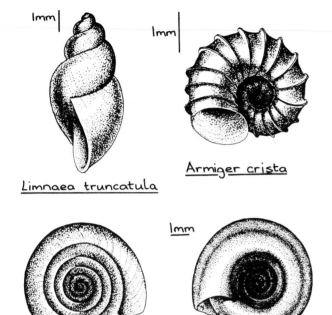

1mm

1mm

Limnaea truncatula

Armiger crista

1mm

Planorbis contortus seen from two sides

Shells of Lake District pulmonates.

the largest Lake District pulmonate, is not.   It has to fill its lung with air from time to time.   This snail has a mere toe-hold in the area, being well established in only one tarn, though it is found also in the Kendal Canal.

Limnaea truncatula is an example of a semi-aquatic snail.   As well as frequenting the margins of certain lakes and tarns it lives in damp and marshy places.   It is best known as the intermediate host of the liver fluke of sheep (page 193) and is therefore an important animal in the Lake District where sheep are so important.

Planorbis albus, present in several of the richer lakes, and in tarns, is a representative of a family whose members have a shell coiled like a clock-spring, and of which the district has several species.   The minute and beautiful Armiger crista, with its distinctive transversely-ribbed shell, is another planorbid.   It inhabits small, sometimes stagnant, water bodies.

In Windermere lives Myxas glutinosa, now a very rare snail in Britain, having been seen in only two places since 1950.   The other is in Wales.*   These sites are at the extreme north western limits of its former range.   It used to be thinly but widely distributed in south-eastern England from Yorkshire southwards, but seems to have vanished from all known sites in that region. It is still to be found in Ireland.   M. glutinosa has a shell that looks rather like that of Limnaea peregra but is extremely thin and delicate.   In life the mantle is greatly extended and, as in Physa, is folded back over the shell, which it covers except for a small oval space on the upper side of the last whorl.

All these pulmonate snails are hermaphrodites.   That is a single individual acts both as a male and as a female.   Physa is what is called a protandrous hermaphrodite — which merely means that it first functions as a male then, later in life, as a female.   The other pulmonates can fulfill both roles at the same time. As a consequence of the mechanical design of the reproductive organs, they do not, however, do so reciprocally at a single mating between two individuals.   A snail acting as a male during such a mating has to mate again

218   *M. glutinosa was not found during a recent search in Windermere but has recently been seen near Oxford.

in the role of a female before its eggs can be fertilised.

An interesting way in which such snails can behave simultaneously as male and female is to form a mating chain. This often happens in Ancylus. The shell of one limpet, acting as a female, is mounted by another which acts as a male. A third acts as a male towards the second and is treated as a female by a fourth and so on. The bottom limpet of the pile thus acts only as a female, the top one only as a male; all in between as both sexes simultaneously.

Individuals of at least some species of Limnaea can fertilise themselves if necessary, so a single snail can establish or pepetuate a population.

All these pulmonates lay their eggs in clusters, each cluster being embedded in a jelly — rather like frog spawn but firmer — and stuck to a stone or a plant. The shape and size of the cluster is characteristic of a particular species.

Prosobranchs are represented in the Lake District by only a few species. Viviparus contectus (page 214), the largest of those to be found there, is not a true native, the area being just beyond the northern limits of its range. Although generally regarded as a 'hard-water' species it has flourished for several decades in one tarn into which it was introduced. It has a greenish shell with brown bands.

Valvata piscinalis (page 214), which of all prosobranchs is the most tolerant of soft, calcium-poor water, is found in the richer lakes. By contrast Bythinia tentaculata (page 214), is a calciphile (literally calcium-loving) species and occurs only at the fringes of the area though it is abundant in the Kendal Canal. Both Valvata and Bythinia have a long snout which probes detritus from which food is collected by the radula. Valvata relies on this means of food collection alone : Bythinia supplements it by trapping particles in mucus.

Potamopyrgus jenkinsi , now well established in a few places — up to 10,000 individuals per square metre have been recorded at one

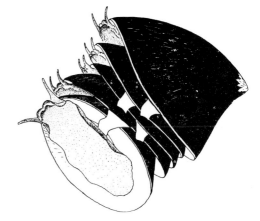

A mating chain of
Ancylus fluviatilis

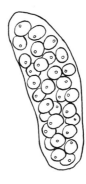

The type of egg
mass typical of
species of Limnaea.

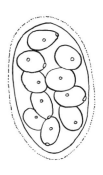

Eggs of
Physa
fontinalis

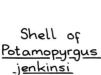

Shell of
Potamopyrgus
-jenkinsi

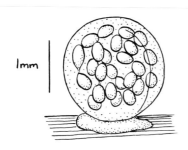

Egg capsule of
Valvata piscinalis

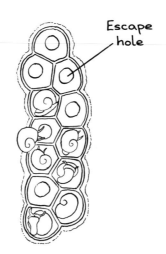

Escape
hole

Egg capsules of
Bythinia tentaculata
near hatching time

point in Windermere — was not known in Britain before 1889. It colonised much of England and Wales in the space of about 30 years. Its original home is uncertain.

The reproductive habits of these prosobranchs differ. Like the pulmonates, Valvata is hermaphrodite, but Bythinia is unisexual — some individuals are males, others females. Both species deposit their eggs in capsules. That of Valvata is spherical, only about 2mm in diameter, and contains several eggs. It is cemented to some suitable object. A line of weakness, or suture, runs along part of the capsule wall and it is here that it ruptures to allow the escape of the minute snails into which the eggs develop. The capsules of Bythinia are quite different. They are laid, usually under a leaf, in a place that is cleaned before they are deposited. Each contains a single egg, and they are laid in parallel rows, the capsules of each row alternating and interlocking with those of the adjoining row. Each capsule has a plug which yields to the young snail when the latter is ready to emerge.

Potamopyrgus employs different tactics. Apart from a single male found in 1958 (not in the Lake District) every individual is a female and reproduction is therefore by parthenogenesis (virgin birth). Furthermore Potamopyrgus is viviparous (brings forth its young alive). Some 35 to 40 young are brooded within the protection of the shell and released when they are fully developed. The ability of a single individual to found an entire population was probably an important element in the rapid spread of this species. As its name suggests Viviparus contectus is also viviparous. It is also unisexual.

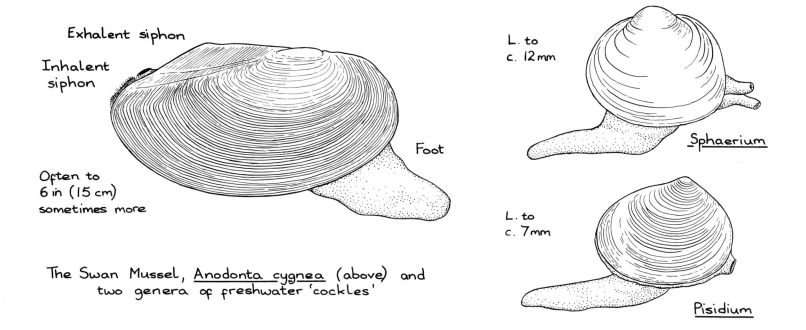

Exhalent siphon

Inhalent siphon

Foot

Often to 6 in (15 cm) sometimes more

The Swan Mussel, <u>Anodonta cygnea</u> (above) and two genera of freshwater 'cockles'

L. to c. 12mm

<u>Sphaerium</u>

L. to c. 7mm

<u>Pisidium</u>

   <u>Mussels</u>, or bivalves, have a bivalved shell, united at a dorsal (upper) hinge by a flexible ligament. The two halves can be drawn together by means of adductor muscles. Shell structure is the same as in snails. The nacreous layer is often thick. The living organism within is headless. Most voluminous is the enormous foot, but the mantle, which lines the shell halves, and large gills (ctenidia) at each side of the foot, are also conspicuous. To move, these mussels extend the foot forward by contracting transverse muscles and forcing blood to its tip, which swells and anchors the animal in sand or detritus. Contractions of longitudinal muscles now shorten the foot and drag the animal forward. Food consists of particulate matter sucked in by the action of cilia via a siphon — the inhalent siphon — made from the mantle. This is entangled in mucus and ingested. There is no radula — so important in snails. Waste

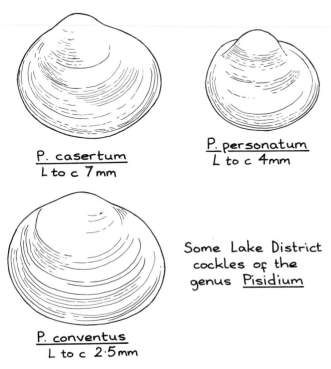

P. casertum
L to c 7mm

P. personatum
L to c 4mm

Some Lake District
cockles of the
genus **Pisidium**

P. conventus
L to c 2·5mm

material is ejected via another siphon — the exhalent siphon.

Most Lake District bivalves are small. These are the 'cockles' which belong to two genera <u>Sphaerium</u> and <u>Pisidium</u>, whose members generally frequent muddy or detritus-rich bottoms into which they burrow shallowly, and sometimes weed beds. While individual species are very similar in appearance the two genera are easy to separate. <u>Sphaerium</u>, up to about ½ inch (12 mm.) in length, has two siphons: <u>Pisidium</u> (up to about 7mm) only one — though this is actually two siphons that have fused. All these cockles are almost white in colour. Some of them are surprisingly active and, by use of mucus which facilitates attachment, can climb among vegetation by the mechanism used for progression among detritus.

Like the snails, cockles are best represented in the richer lakes. At least 9 species of <u>Pisidium</u> occur in Windermere. Two of these, <u>P. cinereum</u> and <u>P. personatum</u> have been found at depths of more than 40m, though they are not deep-water specialists. In fact they are both very tolerant species that occur in a wide range of habitats. Most other species, such as the very common <u>P. nitidum</u>, prefer shallow water with much organic matter but <u>P. Lilljeborgii</u>, a species with a glossy, strongly striated shell, frequents sandy bottoms.

One Lake District species, <u>P. conventus</u>, is characteristic of mountain lakes in Northern and Alpine regions. It has been found in Red Tarn (Hellvellyn) at an altitude of 2356 ft, and in the nearby Brown Cove Tarn, but also at a much lower altitude in a swamp near Grange-in-Borrowdale.

The large mussels, which can attain a length of about 9 in. (229 mm is the record in Britain) but are usually smaller, are not present in any of the lakes, but <u>Unio pictorum</u> has been found in the River Brathay which flows into Windermere. However, the Swan Mussel, <u>Anodonta cygnea</u>, occurs, especially in calcareous waters, on the fringes of the district. It is plentiful in parts of the Kendal Canal but has suffered much in those sections where power boats are active. These stir up the bottom and suffocate it. Swan Mussels have a normal life span of 10 to 15 years.

The Pearl Mussel, <u>Margaritifer margaritifer</u> (length to 134 mm — more than 5 in.) occurs in certain Lake District rivers and streams that are best left unspecified, for in order to search for pearls the mussel has to be killed. The Pearl Mussel is one of those curious molluscs that, although they require much calcium in order to construct their shell, prefer soft, calcium-poor waters. Clear, fast-flowing rivers with a gravelly or sandy bottom into which it is possible to burrow are preferred. Pearls are made of the same material (mother of pearl) as is used to line the shell. Concentric layers are deposited around intruding objects, such as sand grains, which are thus rendered less irritating. In one Lake District river, pearls were collected on a commercial, if small, scale in the 17th century.

Pearl Mussels live to a great age — up to about 100 years — and are among the longest lived of all invertebrate animals. Their reproductive life spans up to 75 years, during which they produce about 200 million eggs. Both males and females are to be found, as well as hermaphrodites, and sometimes females change to hermaphrodites and vice versa.

All other Lake District mussels are functionally ambisexual. There are no separate testes (male gonads) where sperms are produced, or ovaries which produce eggs. Instead both kinds of sex cells (gametes) are produced in different parts of the same gonad. Eggs pass into pouches in the gills. Here they are fertilised by sperms from another individual sucked in through the inhalent siphon. The cockles are viviparous. They retain the fertilised eggs and

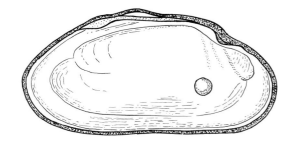

The inner face of a shell of the Pearl Mussel, <u>Margaritifer margaritifer</u>, and a pearl

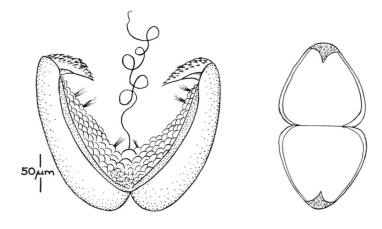

50 μm

The glochidium larva of <u>Anodonta</u> and its shell seen opened out brood them until they have developed into miniature replicas of the parents, when they are released. There is a possibility that some of the cockles reproduce partheno-genetically.

The Swan and Pearl Mussels release their young at a much earlier stage, and in vast numbers — over a million in some cases. The chance of survival of these tiny larvae, called glochidia, is slight. To survive a glochidium larva, which has a bivalved shell and a tentacle, has to find a fish — usually a cyprinid fish such as a Roach or Dace in Anodonta, a Trout or a Minnow in the case of Margaritifer. If found, the fish is used to sustain the mussel larva for a time. A fin is nipped by the shell spines and the glochidium soon becomes overgrown by host (fish) tissue which is liquified and absorbed by the larval mussel. After undergoing complex changes the larva drops from the fish as a tiny replica of its parent and embarks on an independent existence.

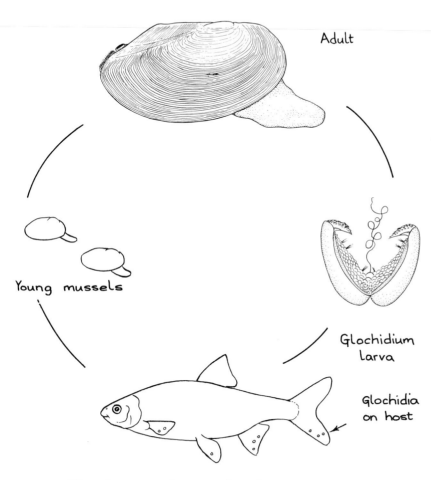

Adult

Young mussels

Glochidium larva

Glochidia on host

The life cycle of Anodonta

224

Crustaceans — animals with a 'crust', from the Latin 'crusta', a shell — are familiar as crabs, lobsters and prawns.   Such large forms are poorly represented in freshwater in Britain, but we have a rich fauna of smaller crustaceans, some of which are abundant.

Like insects, crustaceans belong to the Arthropoda — jointed limbed animals — and like them they have an exoskeleton made of chitin and develop by a series of moults at which they rid themselves of the old skeleton (cuticle).   Though this is not always appreciated, they also have an endoskeleton.   The body is divided into three regions — head, thorax and abdomen — each composed of several segments.   In many cases the head and thorax are closely associated to form a cephalothorax. Crustaceans often have compound eyes, with many facets or lenses, complex mouthparts, and frequently other elaborately constructed limbs.   Their life histories are very varied.

Our largest freshwater crustacean is the Crayfish, Austropotamobius pallipes.   Because we have only one species it is often referred to as the Crayfish though it is but one of the world's many freshwater crayfishes. Attaining about 5 in. (c.13 cm) in length, exceptionally as much as 7 in., the crayfish has its exoskeleton calcified for strength.   That is, lime (calcium carbonate) is incorporated in it.   The need for lime restricts it to waters containing sufficient of this material to be obtained without undue effort.

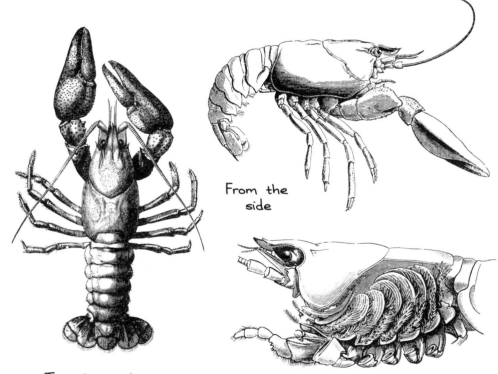

The Crayfish
Austropotamobius pallipes

From the side

With part of the carapace cut away to reveal the gills

Limestone districts are ideal : soft-water (lime-poor) areas such as the Lake District are not and, as acids dissolve lime, it is excluded from markedly acidic waters for this reason alone. The Crayfish nevertheless occurs in several streams in the south of the area, and not only in those on limestone. Here it lives, usually hidden beneath stones by day, foraging chiefly by night. An omnivore, it seizes food with its large pincers (chelipeds) and passes it to its mouthparts which tear and chew it. Further mastication takes place in a gizzard-like structure, the gastric mill, at the anterior end of the gut.

Elaborate gills, reminiscent of those of a fish, lie hidden beneath the <u>carapace</u> — the large shield that covers the front end of the body — which protects them.

A slowly ambling creature in the main, the Crayfish has an effective escape mechanism if its chelipeds fail to deter a molester. Rapid flaps of its tail from under the body propel it quickly backward.

After mating, the female lays eggs, usually about November, and these become attached to the appendages that lie beneath the abdomen — the swimmerets or pleopods. The deep orange eggs, up to about 200 in number, remain glued to the swimmerets throughout the winter and hatch only in late spring or early summer. Unlike those of a Lobster, which look very different from the adult, the young Crayfishes resemble the adult in general features. For some time they hang on to the swimmerets of their mother and are carried about by her. When the mother remains quiet they leave her and

A female carrying eggs

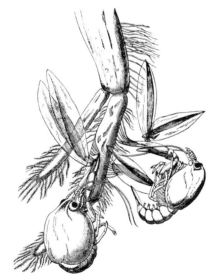

Newly hatched young clinging to a swimmeret of the mother

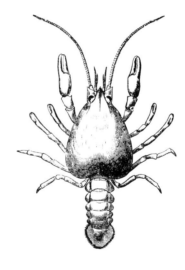

A newly hatched crayfish L.c. 4 mm

The Crayfish, <u>A. pallipes</u>

226

creep about nearby.   Any disturbance causes them to rush back and re-attach themselves, the female carrying them away if danger threatens.   After some days they forsake her and lead an independent existence.

A one year old Crayfish is generally about 2 in. (5cm) long, at 2 years almost 3 in., at 3 years about 3½ in., at 4 years 4 to 4½ in. and at 5 years about 5 in.   Some may live for 15 years, occasionally even more, but growth is slow in old individuals.

A frightful disease, the Crayfish plague, caused by a fungus, Aphanomyces astaci, now threatens our Crayfish population. This disease, a 100% killer, has been introduced on imported foreign species of crayfishes as a result of lax regulations relating to the importation of exotic animals.   It generally leads to the complete extermination of the crayfish population in streams to which it gains access.   It has already wreaked havoc in Scandinavia where crayfishes are extensively eaten as a delicacy and is doing so in Britain.   The transfer of crayfishes from one water body to another and, even more so, the introduction of alien species, should not be undertaken.

Other relatively large crustaceans are the amphipods — of which the British representatives are flattened from side to side — and the isopods that are flattened in the opposite plane. Gammarus pulex is a common amphipod in both lakes and streams in the Lake District.   Misleadingly called the Freshwater Shrimp — 'shrimp' is a name best reserved for the marine Crangon — Gammarus often hides under stones and scuds away briskly on its side when disturbed.   The three pairs of bristle-armed limbs beneath the abdomen are the equivalent of the swimmerets of the Crayfish.   They help the animal to swim, and when it is at rest they beat vigorously to draw a current of water over the gills that lie near the bases of the thoracic legs.   For the most part a vegetarian, Gammarus uses its chelate (pincer-like) gnathopods to hold food and to pass it to the mouthparts.   Males, which attain a length of about 16 or 17mm, are larger than females on whose backs they ride for some days

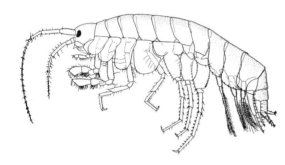

Gammarus pulex (male)
(Length c. 16 mm)

Crangonyx pseudogracilis
A North American invader now firmly established.   L. c. 9 mm

227

prior to mating.   This takes place after the female has moulted.   Fertilisation of the eggs occurs in a brood pouch or marsupium formed by overlapping plates that grow inwards from the second to fifth pairs of thoracic legs, and here the eggs are carried throughout development.   The young leave the marsupium within a few days of hatching.

A very similar species, G. lacustris, occurs in the adjacent Pennines but has yet to be seen in the Lake District.   In general its distribution is more northerly than that of G. pulex.

An alien amphipod, Crangonyx pseudogracilis, arrived in Britain, apparently in the 1930s, by means unknown and subsequently spread rapidly.   It was first noticed in Windermere in 1960.   A survey in 1961 showed it to be well established in the South Basin, but not in the north.   By 1962 it had spread some-what northwards, continued its progress in 1963, and by 1964 occurred around the entire North Basin. It is now established in several other lakes.   It is easily separable from Gammarus not only by its smaller size and more transparent nature, but by 'standing up' vertically as it walks and swims.   More tolerant of certain adverse conditions, such as low oxygen levels, than G. pulex, it may be a competitor of this species in standing water.

Isopods (the name means 'equal feet') include the familiar woodlice.   Of two very similar aquatic species that occur in the Lake District, Asellus aquaticus is the commoner.   It is often called a water-louse.   Very flattened in form, Asellus is a crawling, not a swimming, animal.   The limbs equivalent to the swimmerets of Gammarus are flattened plates that overlap each other rather like the leaves of a book. They serve as gills.   Extremely tolerant of a wide range of conditions, A. aquaticus occurs in both flowing and standing waters, and appears to be able to subsist on a wide range of foods, mostly of plant origin.   Decaying vegetation and the micro-organisms growing on it are much utilised.   Beautiful scrapers are involved in food collection.

Like amphipods, isopods carry their eggs and young in a brood pouch or marsupium formed by the overlapping outgrowths of anterior legs.   These are sufficiently transparent to enable the eggs, and later the young, to be seen through them.   The newly liberated young are miniature versions of the adults.   Breeding takes place mostly in spring.

Less common, and perhaps less tolerant than A. aquaticus, is A. meridianus.   Both are very similar in appearance and both sometimes occur together, as in Esthwaite.   Their ecological relationships are still incompletely understood.

One relatively large crustacean is found in one Lake District lake and, so far as is known, nowhere else in Britain, though it occurs in Ireland.   This is Mysis relicta which occurs in Ennerdale.   Mysids are related to amphipods and isopods (all belonging to a group called the Peracarida) and are mostly marine.

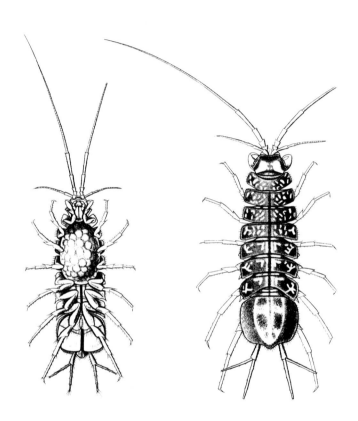

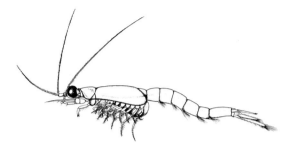

Mysis relicta (female)
L. c. 15 mm

Indeed some have supposed that Mysis relicta is of relatively recent marine origin, though, with good reason, this is disputed by others. Certainly the history of M. relicta in Ennerdale, which is shrouded in mystery, is related to events that took place during the retreat of the ice from the area at the close of the last glaciation (page 26). With a free-living copepod Limnocalanus macrurus (page 232) and a parasitic copepod Salmincola edwardsii (page 235) it makes up a trio of crustaceans that is found in Ennerdale and in no other English lake.

About 15mm long, M. relicta is an actively swimming species that appears to prefer the deep water of Ennerdale where it lives just above the bottom. It was first found by accident in 1941 in a sediment trap, and has otherwise been obtained only by dredging. It is at least in part a carnivore and eats other, smaller, crustaceans. It carries its eggs and young in a marsupium but details of breeding season — probably early spring — growth and longevity in

Asellus aquaticus — a female carrying eggs seen from below (left) and from above (right)
Length generally less than 2 cm

229

Ennerdale are unknown, and indeed it now appears to be scarce there, recent dredging having failed to locate it.

All the crustaceans so far mentioned belong to the group known technically as the Malacostraca. Most animals belonging to this group are relatively large but a few are minute. One such is the 1mm long <u>Antrobathy-nella stammeri</u>, a creature of extremely ancient antecedents. Bathynellids are related to some larger crustaceans, long known from Tasmania, that themselves show affinities with fossil forms that flourished in Carboniferous times, more than 250 million years ago. The first specimens of <u>Bathynella</u> were found in 1882 in a well in Czechoslovakia. More than thirty years elapsed before any other finds were made and these animals were long thought to be rare subterranean creatures. The first find in Britain was indeed made in a tunnel of a lime-stone quarry in 1927. More recently it has been realised that bathynellids occur particularly, and sometimes commonly, in the interstitial spaces between sand grains and gravel, that there are many species, and that they are almost world-wide in distribution. Their elongate, slender, flexible bodies are well adapted to moving in the essentially limitless labyrinth provided by such habitats

In Britain <u>Bathynella natans</u> lives in caves and wells. <u>A. stammeri</u> has been found in riverine sands and gravels in various places including a few in the Lake District. Here it feeds on detritus, with which such habitats are often richly provisioned. Eggs are shed. There is no parental care. Newly hatched young have only 10 trunk segments (13 in the adult) and 3 pairs of legs. Legs and segments are added progressively.

Most of the other freshwater crustaceans, of which there are almost 300 British species, are small to minute creatures, some less than half a millimetre in length, and seldom exceed 3 or 4 mm. Formerly referred to collectively as the Entomostraca — to distinguish them from the larger Malacostraca — they belong to several groups that are only remotely related to each other. Although small, these animals occur in vast numbers and have colonised many habitats. Many crawl on, or burrow in, bottom deposits, others live on the leaves of aquatic plants or among tangles of submerged mosses, some penetrate between sand grains, many can swim

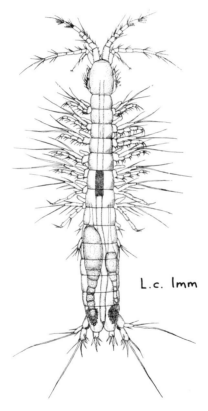

L.c. 1mm

<u>Antrobathynella stammeri</u>

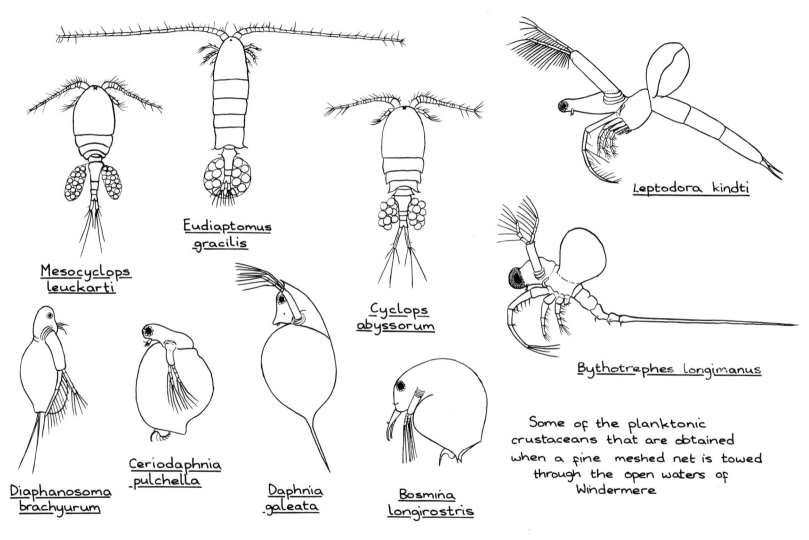

Mesocyclops
leuckarti

Eudiaptomus
gracilis

Cyclops
abyssorum

Leptodora kindti

Bythotrephes longimanus

Diaphanosoma
brachyurum

Ceriodaphnia
-pulchella

Daphnia
-galeata

Bosmina
longirostris

Some of the planktonic
crustaceans that are obtained
when a fine meshed net is towed
through the open waters of
Windermere

231

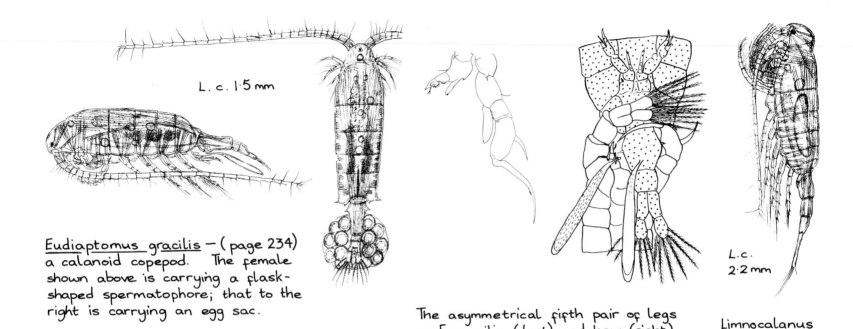

L.c. 1.5 mm

Eudiaptomus gracilis — (page 234)
a calanoid copepod. The female
shown above is carrying a flask-
shaped spermatophore; that to the
right is carrying an egg sac.

The asymmetrical fifth pair of legs
of E. gracilis (left) and how (right)
they are used to transfer a sperm-
-atophore to the female (spotted)

L.c.
2.2 mm

Limnocalanus
macrurus
(page 234)

freely and some are emancipated to varying degrees from the bottom.   Among the latter are some that,
having exploited their lightness and ability to swim, now occupy the open waters of lakes — a habitat
scarcely impinged upon by insects.   Here they sometimes occur in countless millions and make up an
important component of the plankton — the drifting community.   A fine-meshed net dragged through an
English lake at almost any time of the year will collect many thousands of these small crustaceans in a few
minutes.
      Although these animals are so small that they cannot be observed easily without a microscope, they are
sometimes of enormous mechanical complexity.   All that is done here is to give some idea of their diversity

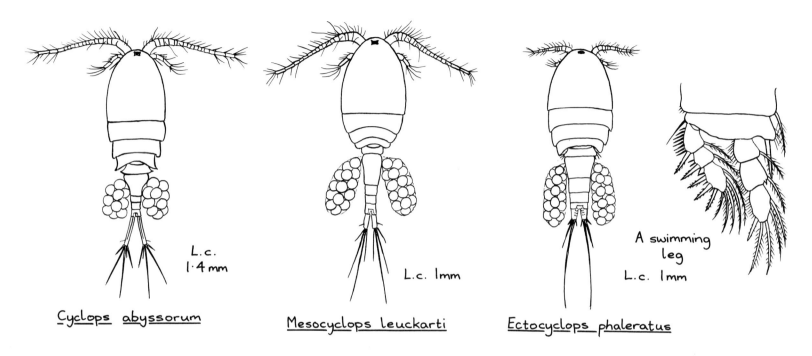

Cyclops abyssorum
L.c. 1·4 mm

Mesocyclops leuckarti
L.c. 1mm

Ectocyclops phaleratus
L.c. 1mm

A swimming leg

and ways of life.

Copepods have five pairs of legs, four of which are used as oars by many species. They lack eyes but have a single median eye spot. Sperms are transferred from male to female in a packet — a spermatophore. Eggs, in our species, are carried by the female in a sac or pair of sacs from which hatches a larva typical of many crustaceans called a nauplius. After 6 naupliar stages a moult transforms the larva into a copepodid that looks much more like the adult. Five such stages are passed through before adulthood is reached.

Copepods include species that frequent open water where many of them extract fine particles, often minute algae, as food, employing elegant filtering devices for this purpose. Others that are similarly planktonic seize other animals, including their filter-feeding relatives, with stoutly armed mouthparts and easily rend them. Many are weed-frequenters or true bottom dwellers. Some of the latter cannot

233

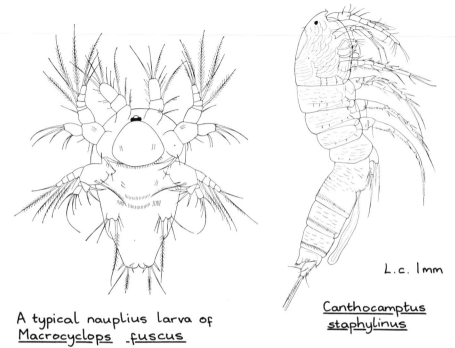

swim but crawl actively over a variety of substrata.

Examples of copepods found in the Lake District include <u>Eudiaptomus gracilis</u> — a calanoid. This is a common species in a variety of open-water situations. It balances itself by means of its long outstretched antennules (the first pair of limbs) and swims slowly by vibrating its antennae (the second pair). When necessary it swims powerfully by rowing with its first four pairs of thoracic legs. It sieves fine particles as food.

The fifth pair of legs in the female are small and symmetrical. In the male they are asymmetrical and the right leg is much larger than the left. The right antennule of the male is also hinged for grasping. When mating takes place, the male grasps the female with the right antennule and right fifth leg. It uses the small left fifth leg to grip a flask-shaped spermatophore that it plonks neatly onto the female.

A typical nauplius larva of
<u>Macrocyclops fuscus</u>

L.c. 1mm

<u>Canthocamptus staphylinus</u>

<u>Limnocalanus macrurus</u> is another calanoid. It is found in Ennerdale water and in no other lake in the British Isles. Its history, like that of <u>Mysis relicta</u> (page 228) is related to events that took place during the glaciation of the district (page 26).

Female calanoid copepods carry a single egg sac. Cyclopoids carry two; one at each side. <u>Cyclops abyssorum</u> is common in the plankton of many Lake District lakes. It is a carnivore that often siezes and devours <u>Eudiaptomus gracilis</u>.

<u>Mesocyclops leuckarti</u> occurs in the plankton of some of the 'richer' Lake District lakes. The last copepodid (pre-adult) stage 'sleeps' during winter on or just below the mud surface in deep water. As many as a million such sleeping (diapausing) individuals have been found on one square metre of bottom in Esthwaite Water.

By comparision with the slender planktonic cyclopoids, <u>Ectocyclops phaleratus</u> — a widespread but not very common species in the Lake District — is a squat bottom-frequenting form. Its swimming legs also reflect its way of life. Their segments are short. In the planktonic forms they are long and narrow.

Harpacticoid copepods are creeping, bottom-living forms whose females carry a single egg sac. Of the several Lake District species <u>Canthocamptus staphylinus</u> is the largest, and one of the commonest.

Some cyclopoid copepods are carnivores that kill and eat animals larger than themselves. Very young fishes are sometimes

1mm|

The 'Salmon Louse'
<u>Lepeophtheirus
salmonis</u>

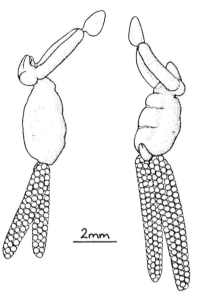

2mm

The Salmon 'Gill—maggot'
<u>Salmincola salmoneus</u>

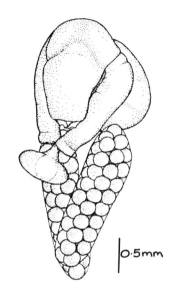

|0·5mm

<u>Salmincola edwardsii</u>
A parasite of the Char
of Ennerdale Water
(page 236)

attacked. If, after a meal, a copepod were to retain its hold on a still living victim it would be well placed for another meal later. By such a process parasitism may have originated among copepods. Some copepods that are parasitic, indeed still look like their <u>Cyclops</u>—like ancestors but have grasping antennae and specialised mouthparts. Others are now much modified in relation to parasitic habits.

Two parasitic copepods occur on the Salmon in the Lake District. Salmon newly returned from the sea carry the so-called 'Salmon Louse', <u>Lepeophtheirus salmonis</u>. These are large parasites; females are up to at least 18mm (¾ in) long and have even longer strings of eggs. They are good indicators of

235

a fresh-run fish as they cannot survive in freshwater for more than about 2 weeks.

On their gills Salmon often carry parasitic copepods that breed in freshwater but survive during the period that the host spends in the sea. These so-called 'gill maggots', <u>Salmincola salmoneus</u>, are firmly anchored to the gills by a plug-like structure, the bulla. Once settled they remain fixed throughout life. All gill maggots are females. Males are much smaller and die after fertilizing a female.

A related species, <u>Salmincola edwardsii</u> is a parasite of the fins of the Char in Ennerdale and in no other Lake District lake. It also occurs on the Char in a few Scottish lochs. Its history, like that of <u>Mysis relicta</u> (page 228) and <u>Limnocalanus macrurus</u> (page 235) is related to events that occurred during the glacial epoch.

Ostracods conceal and protect their legs and other appendages inside a structure not possessed by copepods — a carpace. In their case this takes the form of a bivalved 'shell' so that they look like miniature mussels. The similarity is enhanced by the fact that the carapace is impregnated with lime. Ostracods belong to a very ancient group whose fossils are important stratigraphic markers to oil geologists. That is, because rocks of different ages contain different kinds of ostracods, they serve as signposts or landmarks telling the geologist in which rocks he is drilling.

In freshwater, ostracods are less versatile than copepods. No species is planktonic in Britain. However they occupy a diversity of situations, mainly associated with the bottom to which some non-swimmers are confined. Others swim actively, and one regularly hangs beneath the surface film under which it slides effectively. Most are vegetarians. One British species (not recorded in the Lake District) carries its eggs in a brood pouch (as do some marine species) but the others lay them on firm substrata — an unusual habit for a crustacean. Some species have males and females: in others males are unknown and reproduction is entirely parthenogenetic. Male ostracods produce remarkable sperms — the longest in the animal kingdom and sometimes several times as long as the animal itself! Larval ostracods have a bi-valved carapace like adults but inside they show many similarities to the nauplius of copepods.

Ostracods occur in a variety of situations — crawling on or swimming over the bottoms of lakes and tarns, among vegetation, in springs, seepages and elsewhere. They are mostly intolerant of acidic water and, as they require calcium carbonate for incorporation in the carapace, they are very poorly represented in upland tarns and moorland habitats. Only about a third of the 90 or so British species have as yet been recorded in the Lake District, but Windermere, which offers a variety of habitats and has been tolerably well explored, has yielded 18 species. This is another group of animals about which the amateur investigator could learn much that is new.

Most diverse of all the groups of small crustaceans are the so-called cladocerans. The animals

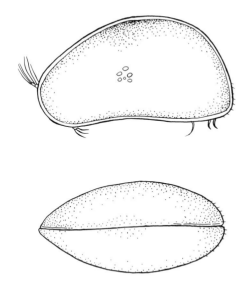

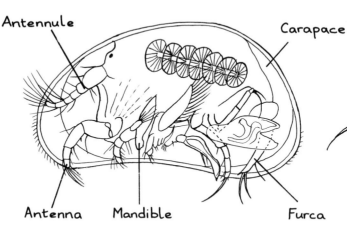

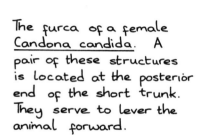

Antennule

Carapace

Antenna   Mandible   Furca

Candona candida — a common, bottom frequenting, non-swimming ostracod, seen from the side (top) and from above (bottom). Colour white. Length just over 1mm.

What a male Candona candida looks like when the left half (valve) of its carapace is removed. The appendages with which it crawls and collects its food are revealed. The curious whorled organ serves to discharge sperms.

The furca of a female Candona candida. A pair of these structures is located at the posterior end of the short trunk. They serve to lever the animal forward.

so named, however probably belong to four different groups.   Best known is Daphnia, often referred to as 'the water flea', a name sometimes also applied collectively to its relatives.   There are several species of Daphnia.   A Lake District representative is D. galeata, a beautifully transparent organism about 2mm long that is common in the plankton of several lakes.   Although drifted by currents it can swim well by means of oar-like antennae — the equivalent of the sensory antennae ('feelers') of insects.   It has a single compound eye with 22 lenses.   Of its 5 pairs of legs two are provided with elaborate filters that strain out from the water fine particles that serve as food.   These are passed forward to the mandibles and in-

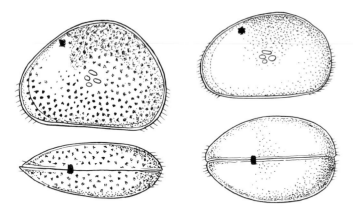

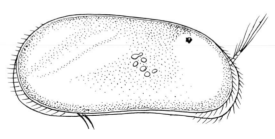

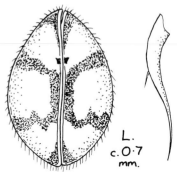

Cypria ophthalmica
L. to c. 0·6 mm

Cyclocypris ovum
L. to c. 0·5 mm

Two very common species. Both can swim

Herpetocypris reptans — A large greenish, crawling species. Common in lakes and smaller water bodies. L. c. 2·5 mm

L. c. 0·7 mm.

Cypridopsis vidua
A very common species with a reduced furca.

Lake District ostracods and some of their attributes

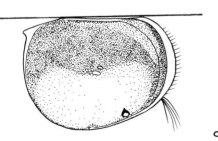

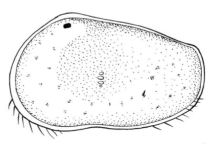

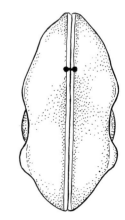

L. c. 1·1 mm

L. c. 0·9mm

Notodromas monacha — A swimming species that also glides under the surface film, from which it suspends itself upside down in quiet water. Almost black ventrally, and structurally modified for its specialised life style.

Cytherissa lacustris — A crawling species with a thick carapace and reduced furca. Dredged from 60m (195 ft) in Windermere, but also in shallow water.

238

-gested. The legs are protected by a delicate carapace that folds down each side of the body like a man's jacket folds forward. The space between the trunk and the carapace also provides a brood pouch for the eggs. Internal organs, including a rapidly-beating heart, are easily seen with the aid of a microscope.

Usually only females are found in the plankton. In Windermere males are exceedingly rare. Reproduction is therefore mainly by partheno-genesis. The eggs develop in the brood pouch and young that are miniature replicas of the adult are eventually released. At times of adversity, and in some species or populations in autumn, males appear. This is so in <u>D. hyalina</u> that replaces <u>D. galeata</u> in several oligotrophic lakes such as Ennerdale, Buttermere and Crum-mock Water. These fertilize the females which then produce clutches of just two eggs that are passed into the brood pouch whose walls — made from the carapace — are specially thickened. Such females look as if they were carrying a saddle and are said to be ephippial — from a Greek word meaning a saddle. When next they moult they cast off the ephippium, that encloses and protects the two eggs, and these eggs remain dormant over winter and hatch in the following spring. Many cladocerans produce such resting eggs. Often they can be dried or frozen yet retain their viability for several years. In fact they behave like plant seeds.

Planktonic species of <u>Daphnia</u> are very transparent. Pond species, which are rare in the Lake District proper but common in many places , are often pink in colour. This is because — like man — they have haemo-globin in their blood. This pigment assists in the take-up of oxygen from the water. Furthermore <u>Daphnia</u> can make haemoglobin on demand. If the habitat becomes depleted in oxygen more haemoglobin

Eye

A male

Heart

Antenna

Not much more than half as long as the female

Eggs in brood pouch

Filtering legs

Carapace

Gut

A female partheno-in the Length

with genetic eggs brood pouch c. 2mm.

A female with two fertilized eggs in its ephippium

<u>Daphnia galeata</u>

239

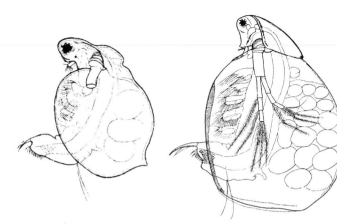

Ceriodaphnia
_pulchella
L. less than 1mm

Simocephalus vetulus
L. to c. 3mm

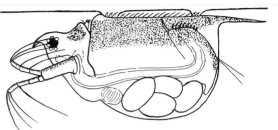

Scapholeberis mucronata
swimming inverted beneath the
surface film.   Note the black
pigmentation ventrally — as in
the ostracod Notodromas monacha
(page 238) that has similar habits
L. c. 1mm

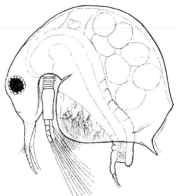

Bosmina longirostris
L. to c. 0·6 mm

is made and the animal becomes deep pink.   If the water then becomes well aerated, haemoglobin is lost and the animal becomes pale.   Planktonic species of Daphnia live in well aerated water and have no need to synthesise haemoglobin.   If they did they would in any case become conspicuous to predators.   In clear open water transparency is a form of camouflage.   Other cladocerans have haemoglobin; some bottom living species that live where low oxygen levels often occur are permanently red in colour.

A few relatives of Daphnia, such as species of Ceriodaphnia and the less closely related Bosmina (which belongs to a different family) are open-water animals that live independent of the bottom, though not all occur in the plankton.   All collect fine particles from suspension.   Simocephalus vetulus, a very common species, also collects suspended particles but spends most of its time attached to vegetation. Thereby the energy that Daphnia expends on swimming is saved and Simocephalus can afford to have a thicker, more protective carapace.   Scapholeberis mucronata swims inverted beneath the surface film to which its flat ventral carapace margins are adpressed — a remarkable parallelism to the state of affairs in the ostracod Notodromas monacha (page 238).

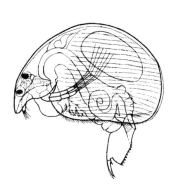
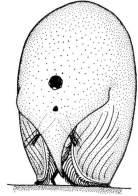
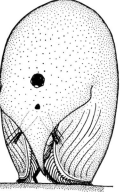
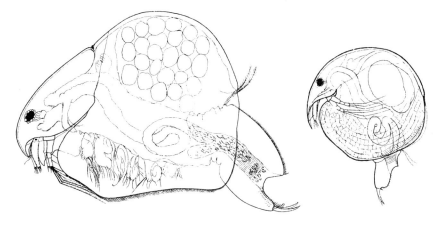

Alona guttata.
L.c.0·4mm

Peracantha truncata
Seen obliquely as it
crawls over a surface
L.c. 0·6 mm

Eurycercus lamellatus
A robust bottom dweller and
plant frequenter. L.to c. 4mm

Chydorus sphaericus
The commonest species
L. c. 0·5mm

Some common chydorid 'cladocerans'

Most members of the group to which <u>Daphnia</u> belongs — technically the Anomopoda — live on the bottom or among vegetation, often in pools as well as at lake margins. These have thicker carapaces than swimming, open-water species. All have five or six pairs of legs of complex structure that they use to collect and manipulate food, and often for other purposes as well. Most species feed on particulate detritus which they scrape into a chamber between the legs. Here it is either sieved or sifted and passed forward to the mandibles and ultimately to the mouth. The habits of these bottom-living species are very diverse though there are many with rather similar, though subtly different, ways of life.

<u>Alona guttata</u>, which likes rather muddy bottoms but is very tolerant, is one of several species of <u>Alona</u> that crawl over the bottom but can swim when necessary. <u>Peracantha truncata</u> is common among vegetation over which it crawls with great efficiency, sweeping up very fine particles as it does so. Having no need of its antennae when so engaged — though it can swim well when required — it tucks them inside its carapace where they cannot be seized and bitten off by a marauding cyclopoid copepod or other enemy.

241

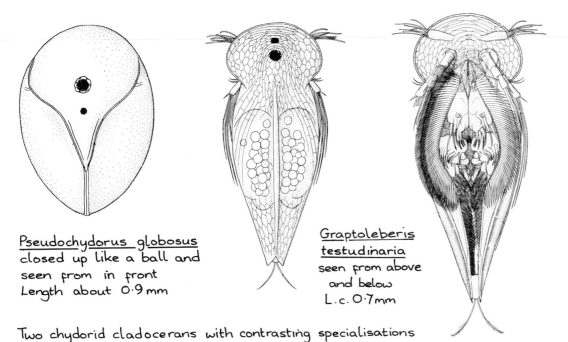

The giant *Eurycercus lamellatus* —sometimes as much as 4 mm in length —clambers about in vegetation whose surface it scrapes. Of all species the globular *Chydorus sphaericus* is the commonest.   It is extremely tolerant, occurs in a diversity of situations, and is often present in vast numbers.   A larger relative is *Pseudochydorus globosus* that can close its thick carapace completely so as to assume the form of a ball — to the frustration of would-be small predators.   Being much more numerous than fishes these are more important enemies. *Pseudochydorus* feeds, not on particles, but on the dead bodies of other small crustaceans.   It is a scavenger.

Pseudochydorus globosus
closed up like a ball and seen from in front
Length about 0·9 mm

Graptoleberis testudinaria
seen from above and below
L.c. 0·7mm

Two chydorid cladocerans with contrasting specialisations

Graptoleberis testudinaria is exceedingly specialised.   It glides on its carapace margins, used like the runners of a sledge, over plant surfaces to which it attaches itself by suction, scraping up food particles as it does so.

Acantholeberis curvirostris is a typical inhabitant of acidic peaty pools and is often associated with *Sphagnum* moss.   *Iliocryptus sordidus* (*Iliocryptus* means 'hidden in mud', *sordidus* means 'dirty') is a burrowing mud-frequenter that cannot swim.   It covers its carapace with particles of mud and is well hidden.   When it moults it retains its old carapaces so its coat of mud is not lost.   Its relative *Iliocryptus acutifrons* occurs in deep water in several of the English Lakes.   Elsewhere in Britain it is rare.

Somewhat different in structure are the ctenopods.   The name means 'comb footed'.   These have six pairs of legs, all very similar, that are used for filtering out particles.   *Diaphanosoma brachyurum*

242

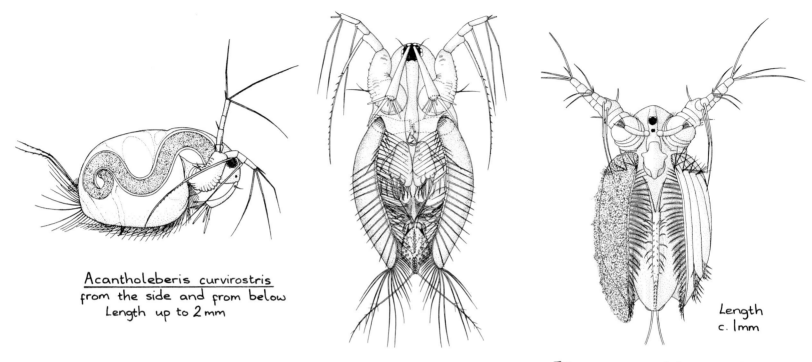

Acantholeberis curvirostris
from the side and from below
Length up to 2 mm

Two macrothricid cladocerans

Iliocryptus sordidus from below

Length
c. 1mm

is a member of the plankton.   Related to it is <u>Sida crystallina</u> which spends most of its time attached, usually to vegetation, by a sucker at the back of its head.

   <u>Holopedium gibberum</u> is another planktonic ctenopod and shows a remarkable specialisation for a drifting life.   It secretes around its body a thick coat of stiff transparent jelly that is slightly less dense than water, leaving a slit through which food particles can be drawn prior to filtration by the legs, and a space for the antennae.   The jelly layer perhaps serves also as a defence against small predators.

   <u>Holopedium</u> has a strong preference for oligotrophic lakes and for water of low calcium content, and is restricted to relatively few of the English lakes and tarns.   Ennerdale Water and Blea Water appear to

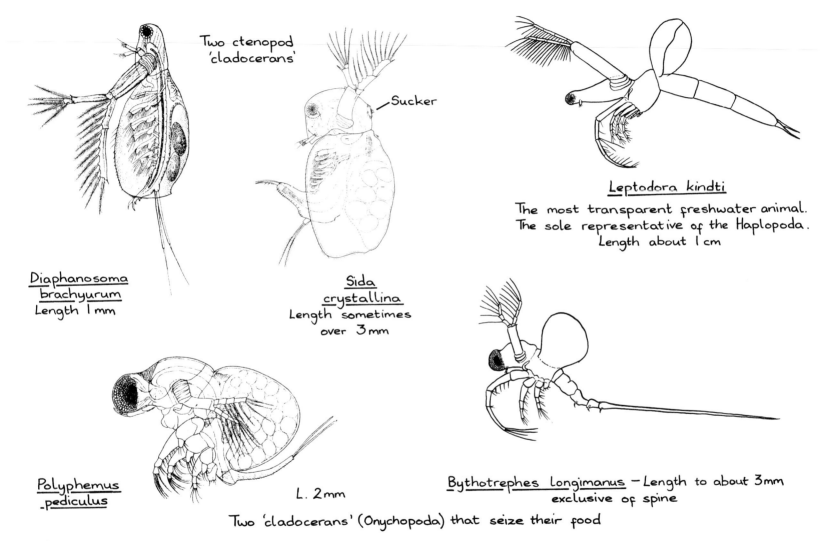

Two ctenopod
'cladocerans'

Sucker

Diaphanosoma
brachyurum
Length 1 mm

Sida
crystallina
Length sometimes
over 3mm

Leptodora kindti

The most transparent freshwater animal.
The sole representative of the Haplopoda.
Length about 1 cm

Polyphemus
pediculus

L. 2mm

Bythotrephes longimanus — Length to about 3mm
exclusive of spine

Two 'cladocerans' (Onychopoda) that seize their food

exemplify optimal conditions. It formerly occurred in Blelham Tarn and Grasmere. In the former it was present until 1956, since when it has not been seen. Its disappearance coincided with an increase in the amount of domestic sewage entering the tarn and increased use of fertilizers on nearby fields. It has also apparently disappeared from Grasmere which now receives effluent from a small sewage plant. Occasional individuals were formerly found in Windermere, having apparently been washed in from Grasmere or Blelham Tarn, but a permanent population seemed not able to establish itself.

Three very different animals, often called cladocerans but belonging to two probably distantly related groups, are Polyphemus pediculus, Bythotrephes longimanus and Leptodora kindti. All are predators that seize their prey with their legs. Polyphemus swims, often in swarms, in inshore regions, detecting its prey with its enormous single eye. Bytho-

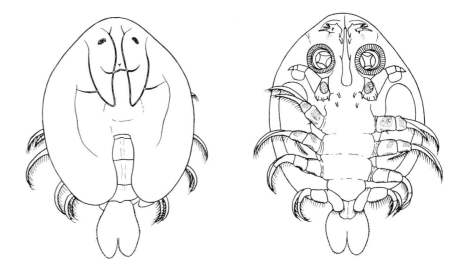

Argulus foliaceus (female) from above and from below
Length to about 1 cm

trephes is its planktonic equivalent. It occurs in many Lake District lakes. Leptodora is the most transparent freshwater animal. Almost invisible, it can often be detected by the disturbance it causes as it swims. It too is planktonic. All three produce parthenogenetic eggs in summer and carry them in a brood pouch until they hatch. Males appear in autumn and eggs fertilized by them are protected by a thick wall. They fall to the bottom and overwinter there to hatch in spring. Those of Polyphemus and Bythotrephes hatch as juveniles; those of Leptodora as nauplius larvae which later assume the adult form by a metamorphosis.

One other crustacean calls for mention. This is the so-called 'fish louse' Argulus foliaceus whose relationship to other groups of crustaceans is problematic. It belongs to a group called the Branchiura.

245

Argulus is a flattened creature that clamps itself to various fishes, often on their flanks. Flattening is an adaptation akin to that seen in certain torrential stream insects, to prevent it from being dislodged, but here it is the animal, carried by its host, and not the water, that moves, though the net effect is the same. Attachment is by two superb suckers that operate on the same principle as the rubber suckers used to attach things to window panes. They are in fact modified mouthparts. Argulus has a curious poison sting that irritates the host, perhaps stimulating the production of mucus that forms part of the food. Rasping mandibles also tear the skin and remove fragments. Argulus can 'walk' over the host lifting one sucker at a time. When necessary it can leave its host and swim efficiently with its four pairs of legs.

Males have elaborate claspers on their legs for grasping the females. Transferred sperm is stored in two flasks — the spermathecae. When the eggs are ripe the female leaves its host and deposits them on a stone or other suitable object. As each egg is laid a sperm from one of the spermathecae is injected into it. The female now has to find a new host, or perish. Eggs laid in summer may hatch within about 25 days; those laid late in the year overwinter. The emerging young look rather like the adult but are really modified nauplii. They have to find a host fish within about 48 hours if they are to survive. Several moults are required before adult structures are fully developed. What are eventually the suckers begin their development as hooks.

A. foliaceus is not a native of the Lake District. It was first seen in Esthwaite Water in 1971, having probably arrived on a fish brought as live bait by anglers. Since then it has become common on various fishes in that lake, in Windermere, and in Blelham Tarn. It provides a salutory example of the damage that can be done when fishes are transferred from one water body to another.

The related A. coregoni has also recently been found in the Lake District for the first time. Large numbers were found in 1987 on Bream that had been introduced into Rather Heath Tarn, near Kendal.

Of all groups of animals, the insects — sometimes called hexapods, which means 'six legs' — contain the largest number of species; over a million.   Enormously diverse in structure and ways of life, insects are divided into many orders.   Generalisation is therefore dangerous.   Basically insects pass through a number of stages in the course of their life.   Some, like the familiar butterflies, hatch from an egg as a larva, change to a pupa, and are finally transformed into the adult.   These are said to have a complete metamorphosis.   'Metamorphosis' merely means 'change in form'.   Other, less advanced, insects develop without such abrupt changes and have no pupal stage.   They are said to have an incomplete metamorphosis.   Not all insects have wings.   Some primitive forms never acquired them: some specialised insects have lost them.   The body is divided into three parts — head, thorax (which bears the legs) and abdomen, each part being made up of segments.   Each segment has a protective cuticle of chitin — a tough, resilient material that makes up the exoskeleton.   Joints between segments of the body or legs are covered by thin, flexible cuticle — the arthrodial membrane.

Many insects are aquatic for part or the whole of their life.   They include both representatives of groups with an incomplete metamorphosis and of groups that undergo a complete metamorphosis during the course of development.

Aquatic insects are well represented in the Lake District.   Most are winged as adults.   The only primitively wingless insects associated with water in the area are certain spring-tails of the order Collembola.   These are minute animals, generally less than 5mm in length, (the common local species Hydropodura aquatica is not much more than 1mm long), most of which can propel themselves in prodigous leaps by means of a spring-like device located beneath the rear end of the body.   Hydropodura aquatica lives on the surface film of water — whose properties are best described with reference to pond skaters — and has an unwettable coat (cuticle). Black in colour, it occurs sometimes in large numbers, in a variety of sheltered situations.   This is the most primitive aquatic insect to be found in the Lake District.   Nevertheless, its primitive nature has not prevented it from acquiring a remarkable specialisation — its 'spring' or furcula.

The rest of the aquatic insects of the Lake District belong to winged groups though some of them have secondarily reduced, or even lost, their wings.   This is a very different state of affairs from that prevailing among the springtails which, as a group, never developed wings.

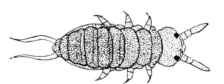

The Water Springtail, Hydropodura aquatica (L.c. 1mm) from above with its 'spring' (furcula) extended and from below with it tucked under its ventral side ready for action

247

Stoneflies — Plecoptera — are primitive insects with an incomplete metamorphosis, that is they develop gradually through a series of larval stages often called nymphs.   There is no pupal stage .   The nymphs are aquatic. Stoneflies are well represented in the Lake District where more than two thirds of the 34 British species have been found.   Most of these frequent rivers and streams, but a convenient species with which to introduce the group is <u>Diura bicaudata</u> whose conspicuous brown nymphs can be found by turning over stones on rocky shores of lakes such as Wastwater, Ennerdale and Buttermere.   Up to about 20mm (about ³/4 in.) in length without 'tails' and somewhat flattened, these nymphs scuttle quickly for cover, being able to grip stones by means of claws at the tip of each leg.   The two anal cerci ('tails') are distinctive of stonefly nymphs.   <u>Diura</u> , which frequents well-oxygenated situations, has no evident gills and presumably employs

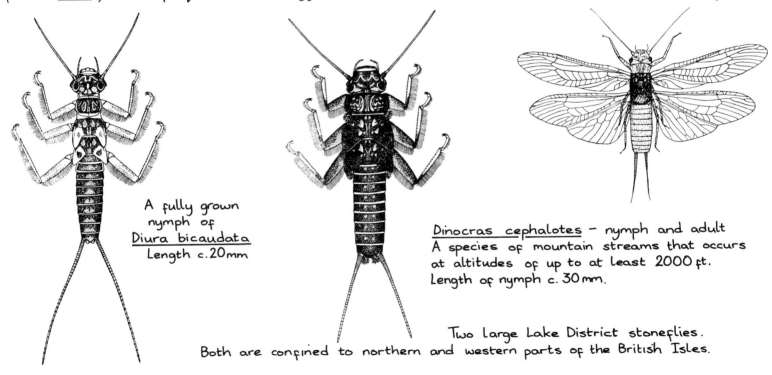

A fully grown
nymph of
<u>Diura bicaudata</u>
Length c. 20mm

<u>Dinocras cephalotes</u> - nymph and adult
A species of mountain streams that occurs
at altitudes of up to at least 2000 ft.
Length of nymph c. 30 mm.

Two large Lake District stoneflies.
Both are confined to northern and western parts of the British Isles.

248

cutaneous respiration — though most parts of the body are protected by thick cuticle.   Some other species have simple gills at the base of the legs which they ventilate by doing press-ups.

Diura is predominantly a carnivore.   It has robust mandibles and feeds largely on midge larvae and other small insects.   Smaller species are herbivores that browse on algae or detritus or, in many cases, ingest bits of mosses and higher plants.

As they grow, nymphs cast their skin many times.   Those of Diura frequent the shore region until about October, migrate to deeper water for winter, return in spring, and emerge as adults mostly over a period of two or three weeks in April and more sporadically until about July.   Nymphal life lasts for one year. A full-grown nymph crawls from the water, its skin (cuticle) splits along the back of the thorax, and the adult escapes.   This looks rather like the nymph but has two pairs of wings.   Nevertheless adults of Diura do not fly but merely scuttle over the stones near the lake margin.   Several other large species show similar behaviour but many smaller species fly weakly.

The courtship of many, perhaps most, stoneflies involves communication by 'drumming'.   Both males and females 'drum' by vibrating the abdomen and striking its tip on such a surface as a tree trunk or twig.   This presumably helps the sexes to locate each other.   Different species 'drum' at different frequencies, which doubtless obviates confusion.   In general 'drumming' is inaudible to the human ear.

After mating the female of Diura swims on the water surface, carrying an extruded mass of eggs on the under side of the tip of the abdomen where they are held together by a sticky substance.   The water dissolves the 'glue' and the eggs fall away and sink.   Other large species behave similarly.   Smaller species fly to the water, dip the tip of the abdomen in it, and release the eggs.

Capnia bifrons is ovoviviparous.   That is, the eggs hatch almost as soon as they touch the water.

Adult life is brief; often a few days only.   Nymphal habits and habitat preferences are therefore more important than those of adults in determining where stoneflies live.   Adults of some species take no food, though they may drink water.   Others scrape algae and lichens from trees and appear to require this sustenance before they can produce eggs.

The life cycle of Diura is typical of stoneflies, but the timing of emergence and the duration of nymphal life differs from species to species.   Some large stream-dwelling species of Perla and Dinocras spend 3 years in the nymphal stage.   Adults of most species emerge in spring and summer, but some do so very early in the year and others are about in late autumn.   Several species, including Capnia bifrons, Leuctra hippopus and Protonemura meyeri begin to emerge as early as February and continue to do so over a 4 or 5 months period.   Leuctra geniculata emerges predominantly at the other end of the year and adults are to be found even in November.

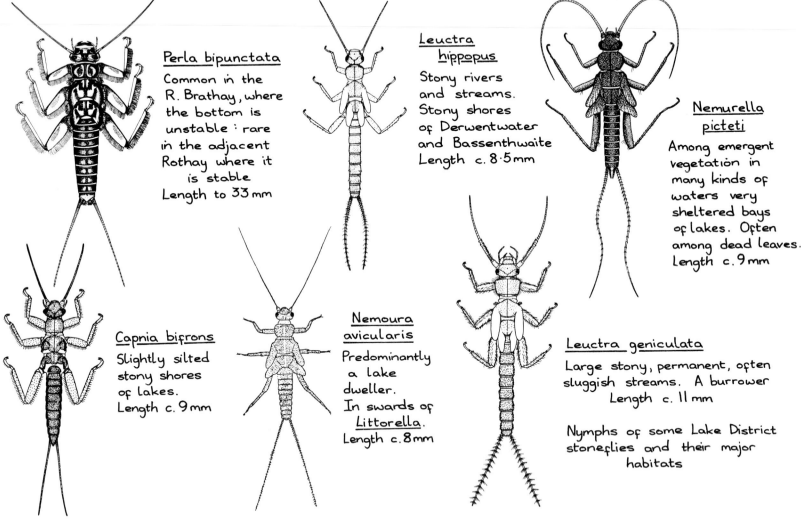

Perla bipunctata

Common in the R. Brathay, where the bottom is unstable: rare in the adjacent Rothay where it is stable
Length to 33 mm

Leuctra hippopus

Stony rivers and streams. Stony shores of Derwentwater and Bassenthwaite
Length c. 8·5 mm

Nemurella picteti

Among emergent vegetation in many kinds of waters very sheltered bays of lakes. Often among dead leaves.
Length c. 9 mm

Capnia bifrons

Slightly silted stony shores of lakes.
Length c. 9 mm

Nemoura avicularis

Predominantly a lake dweller. In swards of Littorella.
Length c. 8 mm

Leuctra geniculata

Large stony, permanent, often sluggish streams. A burrower
Length c. 11 mm

Nymphs of some Lake District stoneflies and their major habitats

250

An interesting phenomenon displayed by the adults of certain small species, notably <u>Leuctra hippopus</u> and <u>Leuctra inermis</u> which can fly, is that the higher they occur in the Lake District hills the shorter are their wings. This brachypterous condition at high altitudes is probably advantageous. It curtails their ability to fly and reduces the chances of being blown away from the stream in which eggs have to be laid. A Lake District species that is confined to mountainous regions is <u>Protonemura montana</u>.

As the nymphs of stoneflies, mayflies and dragonflies may seem confusingly similar to the uninitiated, it is helpful to have illustrations of these side by side. In spite of much diversity of form, representatives of these orders found in the Lake District can be recognised by the following characters.

Stoneflies — 2 filamentous 'tails' (anal cerci). No conspicuous lateral gills.

Mayflies — 3 filamentous 'tails'. Often with a row of lateral gills on each side.

Zygopteran dragonflies (Damsel flies) — 3 leaf-like posterior gills. No lateral gills.

Anisopteran dragonflies — No 'tails'. No lateral gills. Generally robust.

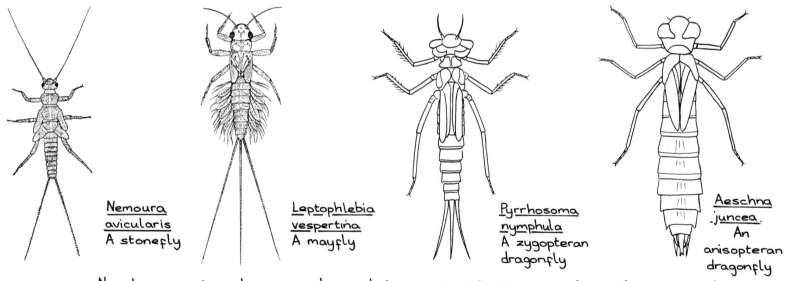

<u>Nemoura avicularis</u>
A stonefly

<u>Leptophlebia vespertina</u>
A mayfly

<u>Pyrrhosoma nymphula</u>
A zygopteran dragonfly

<u>Aeschna juncea.</u>
An anisopteran dragonfly

Nymphs of a stonefly, a mayfly, and two contrasting types of dragonfly compared

251

Mayflies — Ephemeroptera — like Stoneflies, are primitive insects with an incomplete metamorphosis.   Both their technical name, which means 'on the wing for one day', and the old vernacular name 'Day fly' testify to the brief duration of the adult stage, and emphasise the importance of the larvae (again nymphs) in the life history.

Mayflies are well represented in the Lake District in both lakes and streams.   More than two thirds of the 47 British species occur in the region.   Nymphs, recognisable by their three, usually long, anal cerci ('tails'), are diverse in structure, which often shows a beautiful correlation with habits and ways of life.   The species of Cloeon have relatively unspecialised nymphs that generally live in still or slow-flowing water where they often hide among vegetation.   An example is Cloeon dipterum, common in ponds and tarns and sometimes found in lakes.   More streamlined, but not vastly different in form, are the species of Baetis, which are mostly stream dwellers.   Both these genera have a series of leaf-like gills along each side of the elongate abdomen.   In Cloeon these beat in a rhythmic manner, drawing in a stream of fresh water to provide the necessary oxygen, but in Baetis they are stationary.   In this respect Cloeon is the more advanced.

Ephemera danica has very different habits, to which it is beautifully adapted.   Its nymphs, which are common in suitable places in Windermere, Esthwaite Water and other less-rocky lakes, and in rivers and slow streams, are burrowers.   Suitable places therefore have sandy or silty bottoms in which nymphs can excavate their burrows. These are circular in section, open at both ends, and curved with the concave surface uppermost.   They are dug by use of the head, the mouthparts and the first pair of legs. Into them the cylindrical body of the nymph fits neatly. For an animal so ensconced, replenishment of the water around it is vital, but a row of laterally-projecting gills such as those of Cloeon or Baetis would be utterly unsuit-

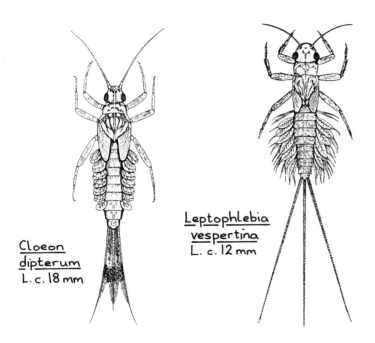

Cloeon
dipterum
L. c. 18 mm

Leptophlebia
vespertina
L. c. 12 mm

Nymphs of two mayflies, common in standing waters, that have rhythmically beating gills.

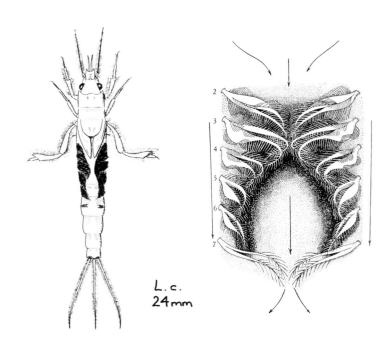

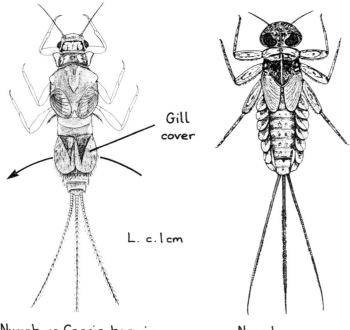

Nymph of <u>Ephemera danica</u> and the feathery gills that drive water backwards through the burrow in which it lives.

L.c. 24mm

Nymph of <u>Caenis horaria</u> and the transverse res--piratory current set up by the protected gills

Gill cover

L. c. 1 cm

Nymph of <u>Rhithrogena semicolorata</u>

—able.   Instead <u>Ephemera</u> has a set of long filamentous, feathery gills arched over the dorsal part of the abdomen which can beat within the confines of the burrow.   (There is a small additional pair — the first — of immobile gills.)   Each gill beats in phase with its partner on the opposite side of the body, but each pair of gills is slightly out of phase with adjacent pairs, that is each begins its cycle of movement just after the pair behind.   Such a rhythm is said to be metachronal and is put to various uses by diverse animals.   Here it draws a current of water over the back of the nymph from front to back, which brings fresh water in at the front of the burrow and drives out 'used' water at the back.

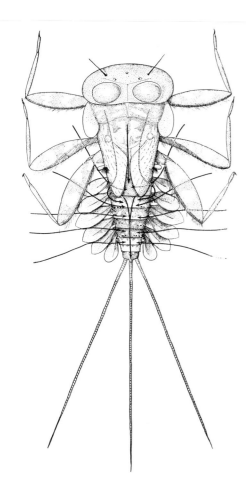

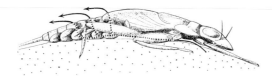

Nymph of <u>Ecdyonurus venosus</u> seen from above and from the side, showing how, in structure and habits, it is adapted to life in fast-flowing water. Arrows show the currents drawn in from each side and from beneath the body.
Length to c. 11mm

Quite different are the way of life and tactics adopted by <u>Caenis</u> of which three species occur in the Lake District. Of these <u>C. horaria</u> frequents soft mud in lakes, tarns, and slow-flowing water, where it lives partly buried —a useful form of camouflage. Here lateral gills such as those of <u>Cloeon</u> would tend to become clogged. The device adopted by <u>Cloeon</u> is to collect its gills into a pile of 4 sets of overlapping plates protected by a lid —

itself actually a pair of gills strengthened and modified for this purpose. Again the gills beat in metachronal rhythm down each side of the body, but the two sides are out of phase. The result is a current that flows not from back to front but <u>across</u> the body. This is gentle, scarcely disturbing the mud, and is reversible.

Nymphs of <u>Rhithrogena semicolorata</u> and of <u>Ecdyonurus</u>, of which there are three species in the Lake District, show progressive stages of adaptation to life in fast-flowing stony streams where they cling, usually to the underside of stones, by use of the claws of the widely spread legs. The body is flattened from top to bottom (dorso-ventrally) and the wide flattened head is held close to the stone facing upstream. In all these respects <u>Ecdyonurus</u> is more special-ised than <u>Rhithrogena</u> which shows as it were a stage intermediate between <u>Cloeon</u> and <u>Ecdyonurus</u>. Just behind the head the thorax of <u>Ecdyonurus</u> is extended as a flange on each side of the body. Note how wide and flat is one segment (the femur) of each leg and how

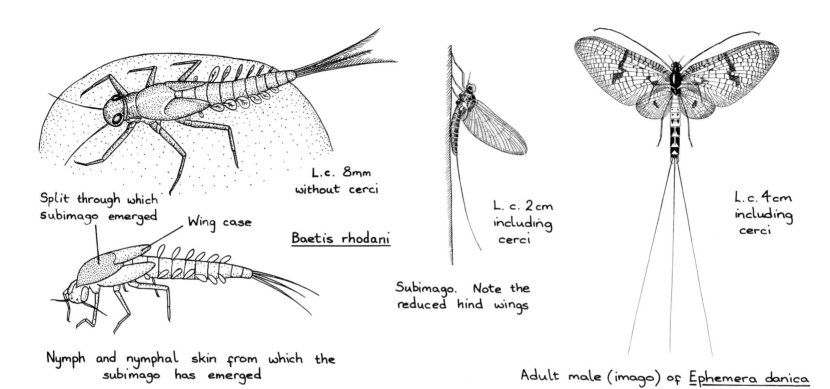

L.c. 8mm
without cerci

Baetis rhodani

Split through which
subimago emerged

Wing case

L.c. 2cm
including
cerci

Subimago. Note the
reduced hind wings

L.c. 4cm
including
cerci

Nymph and nymphal skin from which the
subimago has emerged

Adult male (imago) of Ephemera danica

short are the antennae compared with those of still-water species, and how Rhithrogena displays intermediate conditions in these respects. A conspicuous row of gill plates lines each side of the body. These in fact are paddles which, by beating, lift water from a quiet region beneath the body and draw it from the sides over delicate filamentous gills, which they also protect.

Mayfly nymphs are mostly herbivores, often scraping algae and detritus from surfaces. They undergo numerous moults as they grow. As many as 21 have been recorded in Cloeon in which genus the skin does not split down the thorax as is generally the case, but only on the upper part of the head, the next stage (instar) emerging through the hole so formed. Some species, such as Baetis rhodani, have two generations per year, most have a nymphal life lasting one year or rather less and some, such as Ephemera danica , may spend almost two years as nymphs though the cycle can sometimes be completed in one year.

Many mayfly nymphs are sensitive to acidic (low pH) conditions. This is reflected by their distribution in Lake District streams, such as the R.Duddon (page 105). Several species cannot tolerate a pH below about 6·0. Ephemera danica cannot survive at acidities in excess of pH 5·5 and is seldom found below pH 6·0. Leptophlebia vespertina, however, is remarkably tolerant and can live at pH 4·0, at least for a time.

The transformation from nymph to adult is peculiar in that, interposed between them is a winged stage, the subimago (the dun of fishermen) that looks very much like the adult (the fisherman's spinner). This stage is unique to Mayflies.

In most species, nymphs about to metamorphose rise to the surface of the water where emergence usually occurs, though some species climb out of the water first, and not all individuals of a species necessarily behave alike. The cuticle splits and the subimago emerges and usually flies to nearby vegetation. Emergence is rapid. It needs to be because at this stage the animal is very vulnerable to fishes which feed avidly on these succulent morsels. Splitting of the skin and emergence generally takes only a few seconds. The subimago sometimes moults to give the adult (imago) within a few minutes, as in Caenis horaria. In other cases there may be a delay of up to three or four days. The subimago of some species, such as Ephemera danica, sometimes flies a little, especially on warm sunny days.

Adults, which do not feed, live for only a short time, seldom as long as 2 weeks. Adults of most species emerge only in the summer months, in some cases over short periods, in others over 4 or 5 months. Baetis rhodani ,however, can be found in the adult state from March to November and occasionally even in winter. Although there are primitively two pairs of wings, the rear pair is often reduced, and sometimes even lost, as in Chloeon dipterum.

Swarming of adults is a spectacular feature of Mayflies. In most species, swarms, which can consist of thousands of individuals, consist only of males. These are visited by females which therefore experience no difficulty in finding a mate. In Caenis mixed swarms occur. Most species swarm in daylight but one has to be astir early in the morning to see the large swarms of Leptophlebia vespertina near Windermere, or on the look-out at dusk to see those of Caenis horaria.

Mating takes place in the swarms and is of brief duration. Females then hasten to lay their eggs of which most species generally lay upwards of 500, but seldom as many as 5000. Ephemera danica, however, is particularly fecund and may lay more than 8000 eggs. Egg laying habits are diverse. Most species dip the tip of the abdomen into the water as they fly over it and release the eggs in batches or, in a few cases release them all at once. In a few cases eggs are released as the female sits on a stone and dips its abdomen into the water, while in <u>Baetis rhodani</u> and a few others, the female walks into the water with folded wings and deliberately attaches the eggs to a stone while completely submerged.

<u>Cloeon dipterum</u> is unique, not only among British species, in that the female, which lives for about 2 weeks as an adult before laying, deposits on the surface of the water eggs that hatch as soon as they are wetted. This is an example of <u>ovovivipary</u>, (literally eggs which bring forth young alive).

Eggs of several species can also develop without being fertilised: that is parthenogenetically. Lake District examples include <u>Leptophlebia vespertina</u> and <u>Baetis muticus</u>.

The Lake District boasts one montane (mountain loving) mayfly — <u>Ameletus inopinatus</u> — which is Britain's only Arctic-Alpine species. It is common in streams at altitudes of over 1000 ft and ascends to at least 2200 ft on Helvellyn. <u>Siphlonurus lacustris</u> also favours high altitudes and is found, among other places, in high altitude tarns.

A mass emergence of mayflies: as shown in a 19th century engraving

257

Dragonflies — Odonata — are primitive insects with an incomplete metamorphosis.   The stage of the life cycle with the longest duration is that of the aquatic larva (again a nymph), but adults are longer lived than those of stoneflies or mayflies.   Furthermore they are active, often strongly flying, insects which feed regularly. Adult ecology is therefore of great importance.

While the Lake District is a good place for stoneflies and mayflies this is not so for dragonflies.   Of the 44 British species only 18 can be regarded as local, and then only by including several that are either very rare or occur on, or even outside, the fringes of the district.   Nevertheless representatives of both of the two suborders into which the   British members of the group are divided are represented, some commonly.

Small, slender-bodied adults, whose often brilliantly coloured abdomen is about the size of, and sometimes more slender than, a matchstick, are often called damsel-flies.   These represent the Zygoptera — a not very informative name meaning simply 'paired wings' or 'fused wings', which is not the case.   The larger, robust, types, often several inches long, and with an even greater wing span, represent the Anisoptera — which means unequal wings, though in fact the difference between the two pairs is not particularly great.

Nymphs of the two groups differ in various ways. Zygopterans have slender bodies that terminate in three somewhat leaf-like gills, generally referred to as caudal lamellae : anisopterans are more robust, indeed sometimes bulky, insects without external gills. However, they do not lack an equivalent respiratory organ.   They breathe through their anus.   Water is sucked through it into the capacious rectum — the last chamber of the gut — whose walls are distensible and thrown into complex folds so as greatly to increase its surface area.   Minute branches of the tracheal tubes (air tubes) through which insects transport gases within the body, pass into the folds.   When oxygen has been extracted from it and carbon di-

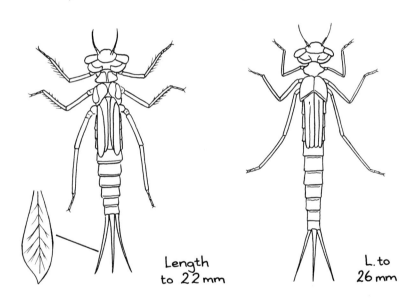

Length
to 22mm

L. to
26 mm

Pyrrhosoma nymphula   Enallagma cyathigerum

Zygopteran (Damselfly) nymphs

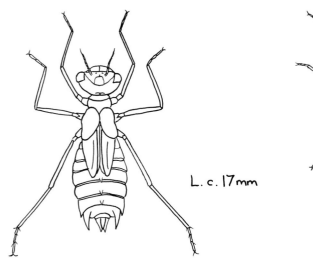

L. c. 17mm

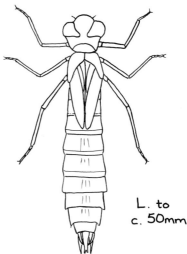

L. to c. 50mm

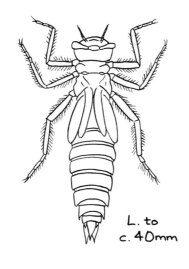

L. to c. 40mm

Sympetrum striolatum

Aeschna juncea

Cordulegaster boltoni

Anisopteran dragonfly nymphs

-oxide dumped into it, the water is expelled by contracting the rectum. For respiratory purposes this takes place gently as required. When necessary a nymph can also eject water from the rectum with considerable force. This propels the creature forward by jet propulsion.

Although zygopterans can swim briskly when necessary using the caudal lamellae as an oar, in general nymphs are sluggish creatures which make themselves inconspicuous in various ways. Zygopterans often align themselves on stalks of vegetation where their colour, green as in Enallagma cyathigerum, or brown as in Pyrrhosoma nymphula — both common in parts of the Lake District — helps to conceal them. Anisopterans are generally dull coloured, often covered with detritus, and therefore well camouflaged. Cordulegaster boltoni which frequents streams, lives partly buried in mud with only the top of its head and the tip of its abdomen protruding. The shape of its small eyes may be related to its habit.

Aeschna juncea has the largest nymph of all Lake District species. It frequents weedy situations and peaty

259

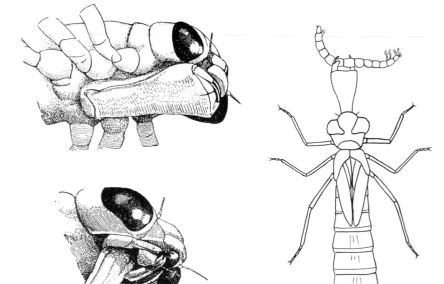

A nymph of <u>Aeschna</u> with its
mask in the closed position
and partly extended

Nymph of <u>Aeschna</u>
seizing prey with
its mask

pools, sometimes high in the fells.   <u>Sympetrum striolatum</u> , which is not rare in at least the southern part of the area, lives in boggy pools.

Dragonfly nymphs are carnivorous and feed on a wide range of prey.   In general they are what are sometimes called ambush predators.   They await the arrival of prey.   Once prey is detected, by the antennae, or the eyes which, as in <u>Aeschna</u>, are sometimes very large, the nymph moves slowly towards it like a cat stalking a mouse.   While still some distance away it shoots out a complex piece of apparatus like a flexed human arm. This is made from the lower lip (labium) of the mouthparts and is often called the mask — an appropriate name as it covers the under part of the head like a mask.   Such a mask is unique to Dragonflies.   It is shot out by blood pressure, aided in the Anisoptera by a diaphragm as far away as the abdomen.   Its terminal spines, open en route, seize the prey and hold it while the apparatus folds and passes the victim to the mouthparts much as the human hand holds an apple as the arm directs it to the mouth.

The nymphal stage is prolonged, even in Damsel flies.   Two or three years is usual.   In one Lake District tarn some individuals of <u>Enallagma cyathigerum</u> and <u>Pyrrhosoma nymphula</u> were found to take three years to complete their development; others only two.   Variation in the food supply in different parts of the tarn may be involved.

When development is complete the nymph leaves the water, usually climbs a suitable support such as a plant stem or tree trunk, its dorsal cuticle splits , and the adult emerges.   Explorers of the Lake District are unlikely to witness the spectacular mass emergences that can sometimes be seen in southern England where certain large species not found here are the performers, but a careful look-out at the appropriate season enables the process to be watched in single individuals. The extraction of the abdomen from the nymphal skin (the exuvia), its extension, and the expansion of the wings, are features of a transformation that is rewarding to watch.

The season of emergence differs from species to species. Pyrrhosoma nymphula is one of the earliest to emerge and can be seen from early May to mid August, while the large Aeschna juncea is on the wing from mid July to the end of September. Adult life spans are often of the order of 40 to 50 days and have been known to exceed two months in some cases.

Unlike mayflies and most stoneflies, adults feed. Like the nymphs they are carnivores. They feed in flight. Well-controlled, often swift and powerful flight, good vision and legs suited to seizing and holding prey are important adaptations for this, as are mouthparts appropriate for its mastication. Dragonflies are opportunistic feeders and capture a wide range of prey in flight and occasionally lift victims from surfaces.

In some species males establish territories — like many birds — from which other males of the same species are chased away if possible. Recognition of the identity and sex of a prospective partner is probably aided by coloration — it certainly is in some cases. Several dragonflies exhibit well marked sexual dimorphism in coloration, males being more brightly coloured than females.

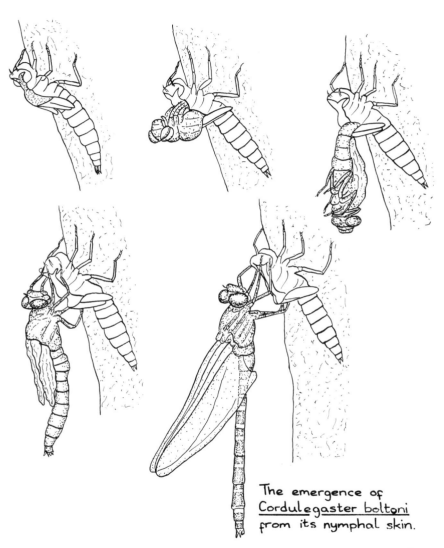

The emergence of Cordulegaster boltoni from its nymphal skin.

261

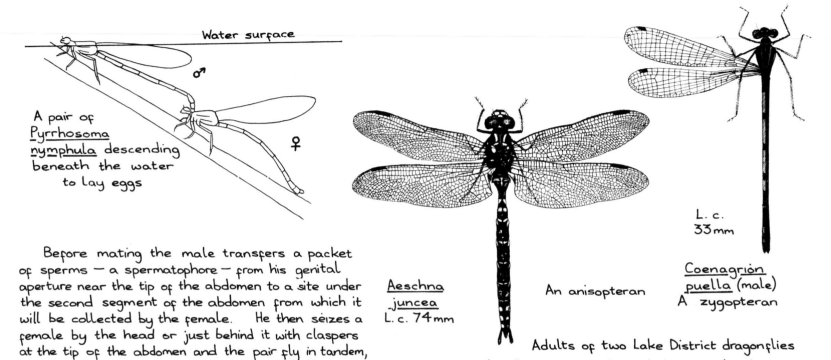

Water surface

A pair of
<u>Pyrrhosoma</u>
<u>nymphula</u> descending
beneath the water
to lay eggs

♂

♀

<u>Aeschna</u>
<u>juncea</u>
L. c. 74 mm

An anisopteran

L. c.
33 mm

<u>Coenagrion</u>
<u>puella</u> (male)
A zygopteran

Adults of two Lake District dragonflies

Before mating the male transfers a packet of sperms — a spermatophore — from his genital aperture near the tip of the abdomen to a site under the second segment of the abdomen from which it will be collected by the female.   He then seizes a female by the head or just behind it with claspers at the tip of the abdomen and the pair fly in tandem, often for some time.   Eventually the female swings her abdomen under that of the male and the genital orifice, towards its tip, collects the spermatophore from the site where the male had previously put it.   Thus is mating accomplished.   This process is unique to dragonflies, though other animals transfer spermatophores in various ways and even rely on the female collecting it.

Egg-laying is performed in various ways.   In some species the male leaves the female who oviposits alone. Any large <u>Aeschna</u> seen alighting at the margin of an upland pool or tarn in the Lake District and dipping most of its abdomen into the water is almost certain to be a female <u>A. juncea</u> laying its eggs.   Its ovipositor (egg-laying tool) makes an incision in a plant and inserts an egg.   Males of damselflies frequently remain in tandem while the female lays her eggs.   In some species only the abdomen of the female is dipped into the water.   In both <u>Pyrrhosoma nymphula</u> and <u>Enallagma cyathigerum</u> both partners descend beneath the water, sometimes to a

262

depth of more than a foot (c. 30cm) and may remain there for up to an hour as the female lays her eggs on suitable objects.

Apart from A. juncea, the other large dragonfly likely to be seen in the Lake District is Corduelgaster boltoni — which has a black body with golden rings and breeds mostly in streams.

Of the other anisopterans recorded in the area, those most likely to be encountered are Libellula quadrimaculata and Sympetrum striolatum. Both are considerably smaller than Aeschna and Corduelgaster. The former has a broad brown and yellow abdomen and dark blotches at the base of the hind wings. The latter has a more slender abdomen, orange in the male, more yellowish in the female, and no blotches at the base of the wings.

Several damselflies are common in the area. The abdomen of Pyrrhosoma nymphula is red with black marks; that of Ischnura elegans black with a broad blue band near its tip. Males of Enallagma cyathigerum have a beautiful electric blue abdomen with black markings; in the female it is mostly black, picked out with green. The abdomen of the male of Coenagrion puella is similar to that of E. cyathigerum; that of the female is black with a thin yellow ring on each segment and blue rings near the tip. In the south of the district Calopteryx virgo is sometimes to be seen. It is easily recognised by its dark body, dusky wings and slow fluttering flight.

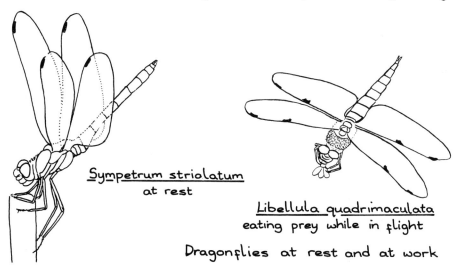

Sympetrum striolatum
at rest

Libellula quadrimaculata
eating prey while in flight

Dragonflies at rest and at work

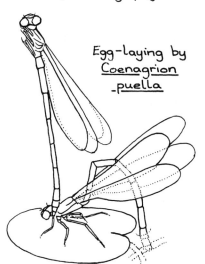

Egg-laying by
Coenagrion
-puella

Although often used in a facetious or pejorative manner, or as a slang term for a bacterium, 'bug' has a perfectly respectable pedigree as a name for a well-defined order of insects — the Hemiptera.   Hemiptera means 'half wing' and is derived from the fact that, when present, the fore wings of many bugs — including all the aquatic ones — have horny bases and membranous tips.   Such bugs belong to the Heteroptera, one of the two sub-orders into which the group is divided.

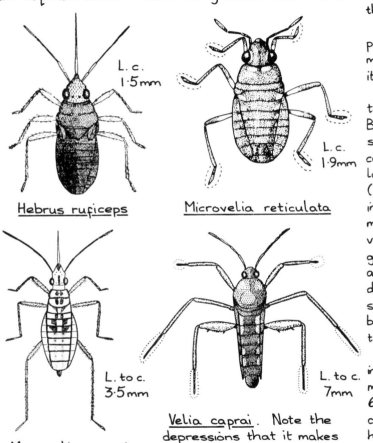

L. c.
1·5mm

Hebrus ruficeps

L. c.
1·9mm

Microvelia reticulata

L. to c.
3·5mm

Mesovelia furcata

L. to c.
7mm

Velia caprai. Note the depressions that it makes in the surface film

Most bugs are terrestrial, but some have exploited the properties of the surface film of water and are among the most skilful exponents of the art of walking or skating on it.   Others are completely aquatic.

Bugs have piercing and sucking mouthparts.   Most terrestrial species suck plant juices: some, such as the Bed Bug, suck blood.   Most aquatic species are carnivores but some are successful detritus feeders.   They have an incomplete metamorphosis, so have no pupal stage and the larvae are sometimes called nymphs.   The number of larval (nymphal) instars is usually five — far fewer than, for example, in Mayflies.   Many adult bugs, including species that spend most of their life under water, can fly, but often there is variation in the degree of development of the wings in a given species, even within a single population.   An apparently fearsome, but quite simple, terminology is used to describe these conditions.   'Pteron' means 'wing' in Greek, so an apterous bug has no wings, while micropterous, brachypterous, and macropterous individuals have wings that are tiny, short or big respectively.

Although the Lake District lacks several water bugs found in southern England, its fauna provides examples of all the major types of freshwater species found in Britain.   Of the 63 British species 44 are recorded in the area.   It is convenient to consider the different types under separate headings according to their ways of life.

To the surface-frequenting bugs — Water Striders and

Pond Skaters — the minute <u>Hebrus ruficeps</u> (length c. 1·5mm) provides a very suitable introduction as its habits are intermediate between those of true surface-dwellers and the terrestrial ancestors from which they came.   It lives among emergent <u>Sphagnum</u> (page 147) growing at the margin of acid pools and streams, where it is very common.   Somewhat more adapted to surface-frequenting habits is the slightly larger (c. 1·9mm) <u>Microvelia reticulata</u> which requires sheltered situations. These are provided by reed beds on lakes, among which it is very common, or stands of sedges at the margin of tarns. A southern species, and a Lake District rarity that has been found only in Moss Eccles Tarn (Claife Heights : near Winder-mere), is <u>Mesovelia furcata</u> (c. 3 to 3·5mm). It is usually associated with floating-leaved plants.

   Much larger (up to 7mm), and better adapted to life on the surface film is <u>Velia</u>

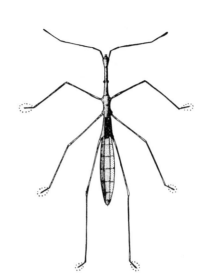

<u>Hydrometra stagnorum</u>
Length c. 1·1 cm
Note the small depressions made in the surface film.

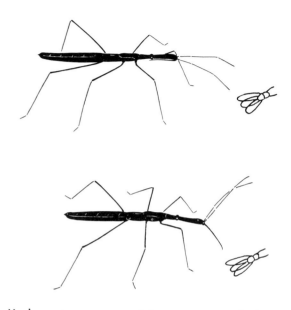

<u>Hydrometra</u> approaching its prey, which is examined by the antennae before the rostrum is lowered. The prey is then speared and its contents sucked out.

<u>caprai</u>, the so-called Water Cricket though, unlike some water bugs, it doesn't chirp.   This is the common bug, of which wingless (apterous) individuals have two longitudinal orange stripes along their upper surface, that is to be seen, often in groups, on the quiet pools and backwaters of almost any Lake District stream, and also on upland pools.   When, as occasionally happens, <u>Velia</u> ventures ashore, it walks.   On the surface it rows.   When it, and other surface-living bugs, stand on the surface film, their legs produce depressions in it but do not break it. The legs are hydrofuge (literally 'flee from water') or water repellant, and virtually unwettable because of a clothing of very fine bristles.   The body surface is also unwettable if its bristles are kept in good order — as they are by frequent grooming by the legs.   The hydrofuge properties of the legs help the surface film to support the weight of the bug, but at the same time allow only very small frictional forces to be transmitted

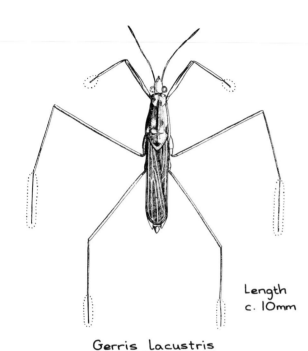

Length
c. 10mm

<u>Gerris lacustris</u>

between the legs and the water.   This has the advantage of allowing the legs to slide easily; the disadvantage that it is difficult for them to push — there is so little resistance.   <u>Velia</u> overcomes the difficulty by rowing with all three pairs of legs, of which, however, the middle pair is much the most important.   A relatively large area of this leg is in contact with the water during the working stroke.   The leg is swung through a wide arc between 10 and 20 times per second.   Brisk skating is thereby achieved.

Much rarer is <u>V. saulii</u>, which has a largely northern distribution in Britain.   It has been found both at lake margins, e.g. Ullswater, and on streams.

<u>Hydrometra stagnorum</u>, the so-called Water Measurer, which is what its **generic name means**, is an exceedingly slender bug, that frequents the sheltered reedy margins of lakes and slow flowing waters, on the surface film of which it walks as it would on land, but, in an emergency, it can move faster by rapid alternate action of the middle pair of legs.   As a walker it makes only small depressions in the surface film.   These stand in contrast to the larger elongate depressions made by skating forms such as <u>Velia</u> and <u>Gerris</u>. <u>H. stagnorum</u> is common in favoured sites.

The other surface-frequenting bugs belong to the **genus** <u>Gerris</u>, the Pond Skaters.   These are larger, sometimes more adventurous bugs, some of which range further from the shore than those previously mentioned.   At least 8 species occur in the Lake District though some are rare.   Each has its own preferences.   The largest, <u>G. najas</u> (17mm) is common on Windermere, but only in extremely sheltered places.   It has a predeliction for boathouses, but only those with dry-stone walls.   Smooth-walled boat-houses provide shelter but not another requirement — crevices in which to hibernate.   It also occurs on some of the larger sluggish streams flowing into the lake.   It seems not to occur on other lakes.   Reed beds provide a home for <u>G. argentatus</u> (8mm) and <u>G. lacustris</u> (10mm), the latter being the more venturesome.   Both are common and both occur also on certain tarns.   <u>G. odontogaster</u> occurs on tarns and pools, while <u>G. gibbifer</u>   frequents peaty pools and <u>G. costai</u>, a northern species in Britain, is a rare inhabitant of similar pools high up on the fells.

All these surface-frequenting bugs feed on other animals.   Food differs according to the size of the insect

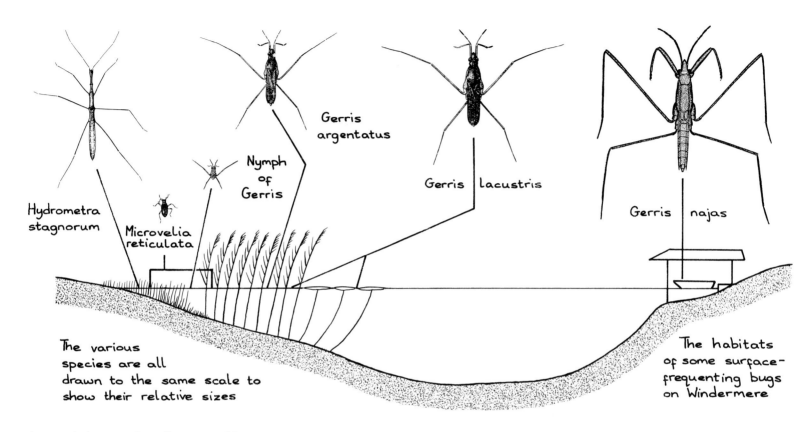

Hydrometra
stagnorum

Microvelia
reticulata

Nymph
of
Gerris

Gerris
argentatus

Gerris | lacustris

Gerris | najas

The various
species are all
drawn to the same scale to
show their relative sizes

The habitats
of some surface-
frequenting bugs
on Windermere

and its ability to handle it.   Most are opportunistic feeders; they get what they can.   Microvelia feeds on small crustaceans trapped in the surface film and on dead or drowning insects.   The feeble Hydrometra scavenges on drowned insects but can also spear tiny organisms through the surface film with its rostrum.   Being sensitive to vibrations it can detect such prey as water fleas (cladocerans — page 236) beneath the surface. Gerrids feed largely on terrestrial insects that fall onto the water and become trapped in the surface film.   Their struggles set up easily detected vibrations.

Life cycles are simple.   Adults hibernate over winter, emerge, mate and lay eggs in spring.   Eggs are laid in various places ; on moss (<u>Velia</u> and some species of <u>Gerris</u>), at or above the water level (<u>Hydrometra</u>), or below it (other species of <u>Gerris</u>).   In <u>Gerris najas</u> the female descends beneath the water, carrying the male with her, as in the dragonfly <u>Pyrrhosoma nymphula</u> (page 262).   Larvae of <u>Gerris</u> (nymphs) look rather different from adults, and are easily recognised as juveniles.   They cannot fly.   Some species have only one gener-ation a year, e.g. the high altitude <u>G. costai</u> ; others, such as <u>G. argentatus</u> and <u>G. lacustris</u> two.

Adults of some species show a great diversity of wing develop-ment, an example of polymorphism ('many forms').   Because it concerns the wings this is sometimes called alary polymorphism. In <u>G. lacustris</u> there are wingless (apterous), fully winged (macro-pterous) and various intermediate forms.   Winged adults can fly and ensure dispersal to new habitats.

Surface-dwelling bugs breathe atmospheric air like a terrestrial insect.   Although fully aquatic, not all <u>bugs that live beneath the surface</u> have emancipated themselves from the need to visit it for air.   One way of getting air is to have a breathing tube — like a submarine's snorkel — and this is the strategy adopted by <u>Nepa cinerea</u> (the so-called Water Scorpion though it is no relation of scorpions).   Its long breathing tube is at the rear and has to be poked through the surface film from time to time.   This would be inconvenient to an active creature, but <u>Nepa</u> has sluggish habits. The tip of the tube is surrounded by hydrofuge bristles to prevent

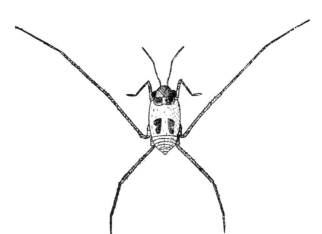

Nymph of <u>Gerris najas</u>

the entry of water.   Very flattened in form, <u>Nepa</u> frequents shallow water in sheltered situations, such as reed beds, at the margin of lakes, where it hunts by stealth.   It is common in the Lake District.   Many small animals, including very young fishes, are seized and held by the powerful front pair of legs — which serve the same function as the mask of dragonflies (page 260).   Indeed, although unrelated, and using very different apparatus, <u>Nepa</u> and dragonfly nymphs have very similar habits.   The former, however, sucks juices from its prey : the latter chew it.

Beneath the protective front wings of <u>Nepa</u> lie membranous rear wings.   Often the flight muscles are poorly developed, but some individuals can fly.   When the wings are spread, the upper surface of the abdomen is seen to be brick red in colour — a surprising feature of an otherwise dull-coloured, well camouflaged animal. This is probably a 'flash colour' which serves to distract enemies.   Although such flash colours are widespread in the animal kingdom, especially among insects, their precise biological meaning is not always clear.   <u>Nepa</u> lays its

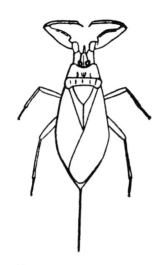

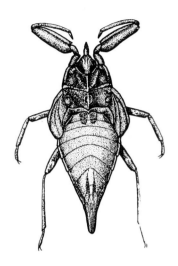

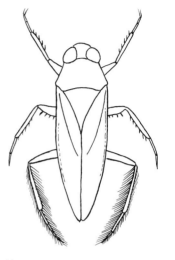

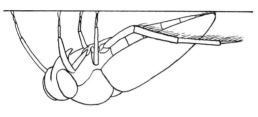

Notonecta hanging from the surface film and replenishing its supply of oxygen.

Nepa cinerea
Length c.3cm

Nymph of N. cinerea

Notonecta glauca
Length c.14mm

eggs, usually on plants, just below the water surface.   Its larvae (nymphs) have a shorter breathing tube than adults and are confined to very shallow water.

Whereas Nepa is a sluggish animal whose activities are constrained by its respiratory mechanism, species of Notonecta are active, robust hunters that are to a greater extent, though by no means completely, emancipated from the surface.   Two species, very similar in form and habits, but with distinctly different ecological preferences, occur in the Lake District.

Notonecta means 'back swimmer' and graphically describes a striking feature of these bugs which swim inverted by powerful thrusts of their stout rear legs.   Atmospheric air is breathed.   A supply is collected as the animal hangs beneath the surface film — a characteristic resting posture — and is carried as a film close to the abdomen as the bug descends.   This reservoir of air is in contact with the spiracles (air holes or breathing pores) of the tracheal system.   Like the air bubble of several water beetles (page 290) it acts as a physical gill.   It sustains the animal for longer than its original oxygen content could.   This is because, as oxygen is used up, slightly reducing the volume of the reservoir, more comes out of solution in the water and replaces it.   This is made possible

269

by nitrogen passing slowly out of the reservoir, and the incoming oxygen restores the equilibrium.   When all the nitrogen has gone or has been reduced to such a level that the surface area of the reservoir is too small to be effective, replenishment at the surface becomes necessary.   The air reservoir renders the animal buoyant and it can dive only by use of its powerful legs.   When it stops paddling it rises to the surface.

Notonecta can detect disturbances in the water.   This ability, plus good vision provided by large eyes, lead it to its prey.   Victims of many kinds are pierced by a stout rostrum and subdued by toxic saliva.   The same combination can cause considerable pain to a man's finger.   The victim's body fluids are then sucked.

There is one generation a year.   Eggs are embedded in plant stems.   When necessary adults can fly well.

In the Lake District _Notonecta glauca_ (length c.15mm) is common in small water bodies and in the reed beds of lakes but is seldom seen in peaty pools.   _N. obliqua_ reverses these preferences, being common in peaty pools at higher altitudes than _N.glauca_ but seldom occurring in lakes.

Corixids are smaller than _Notonecta_ and swim the 'right way up'.   They also fly well.   They are more flattened dorsally than _Notonecta_ and much more associated with the bottom.   Several genera occur in the Lake District, most of which look like _Corixa_, in which genus some of them, such as _Sigara_, were formerly included.   Most bugs, including such corixids as _Cymatia_, _Glaenocorisa_ and _Arctocorisa_, are predators but _Corixa_, _Sigara_ and their close relatives are essentially detritus feeders.   They have the basic sucking mouth-parts of bugs, but the rostrum is short and serves often as a tube up which detritus is sucked like dust up a vacuum cleaner.   The first pair of legs have terminal segments (tarsi) that are modified to allow them to whisk up detritus or scrape it from surfaces in readiness for this, and can also hold particles to facilitate the process.   The rostrum is sometimes used in a more typical bug-like manner and penetrates filamentous algae or small animals, such as midge larvae, whose contents are sucked.   Detritus is 'chewed' or abraded by chitinous 'teeth' (the bucco-pharyngeal 'teeth') at the front end of the gut — an unusual feature in bugs, most of which, being fluid feeders, have no need of such apparatus.   Adults obtain their oxygen by use of a bubble gill, as in _Notonecta_, but the first two larval instars manage on dissolved oxygen.

Most male corixids (species of _Hesperocorixa_ are an exception) 'sing' or stridulate by rubbing patches of bristles on the inner surface of one of the segments of the first legs (the femora) against the margin of the head.   This is used as a courtship 'song'.   In _Arctocorisa germari_, a rare species in the Lake District, females also stridulate, the only known case in corixids.

Typically adults overwinter, but in _Micronecta_ it is the larvae that do so.   Some species have one generation, others two, during the warmer months.   Eggs are generally stuck on water plants, in some cases singly, in others in masses.

270

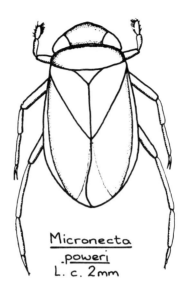

Micronecta
poweri
L. c. 2mm

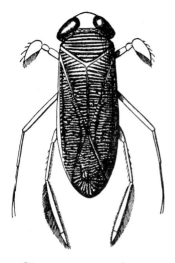

Sigara falleni
L. c. 8mm

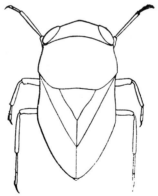

Plea leachi
L. c. 2·5mm

Although many of them are very similar in general appearance, and often in feeding habits, each corixid has its own favourite kind of place — its own ecological preferences. Micronecta poweri the smallest species (length no more than 2mm) is very common on exposed lake shores where the bottom is sandy, or sometimes stony, and occurs over banks of sand in slow stretches of rivers. It is the only species to prefer such places. It shuns organic (peaty) bottoms. Being gregarious — it occurs in shoals — it is sometimes conspicuous even to the naked eye in spite of its small size. It is also so noisy as sometimes to be called the Water Singer. In more sheltered conditions at lake margins it is sometimes accompanied by the very common Sigara dorsalis but the amount of organic matter on the bottom has to increase only slightly to ensure that Micronecta is excluded. A further increase in organic matter sees S. dorsalis joined by S. fossarum and S. distincta which prefer silted places in reed beds (Phragmites). S. scotti prefers even more organic bottoms and occurs in reed beds growing in such places in some of the richer lakes. It also occurs in peaty pools and tarns. Hesperocorixa castanea prefers acidic organic-bottomed places among sedges (Carex) and Sphagnum moss in tarns and pools, but not in lakes, while H. sahlbergi is found in fen areas at the heads of the richer lakes and in lowland fens where the water is not acidic.

Four Lake District corixids, none of them common, are predators. Cymatia bonsdorffii, Arctocorisa carinata and A. germari seize a variety of small organisms, while Glaenocorisa propinqua swims in open water straining out planktonic crust-aceans (page 231) and rotifers (page 179) with long bristles on its first pair of legs as it does so. Five upland corixids occur in the area — Sigara nigrolineata, S. lateralis, S. concinna (one record only), Callocorixa wollastoni and Arctocorisa carinata. At the other end of the scale S. semistriata and S. falleni are confined to the richest lakes.   <u>S. semistriata</u> is known only from Esthwaite Water and a tarn fouled by Black-Headed Gulls.   <u>S. falleni</u>, which is common in southern and eastern England occurs only in the richest lakes — Esthwaite (abundant), Blelham Tarn (plentiful) and Derwentwater (very rare).   It is also recorded from Knipe Tarn.

The minute <u>Plea leachi</u> (length c. 2·5mm) belongs to a family (the Pleidae) related to the corixids.   It favours dense vegetation.   While common in southern England it is very rare in the Lake District.

<u>Aphelocheirus montandoni</u>, perhaps the most remarkable freshwater bug in the Lake District, is generally found on stony bottoms of briskly flowing, but not torrential, streams, but is tolerant of a variety of habitats and occurs on stony shores of Bassenthwaite Lake — its only known Lake District locality.   This completely aquatic bug is a flattened creature about 1cm long and completely different in appearance from any other aquatic insect found in Britain.   Mottled dark brownish grey above, pale grey beneath, it looks like an enormous aquatic Bed-bug.   It is a capable swimmer and also crawls over stones among which it probes with its proboscis in search of such prey as chironomid (midge) larvae, caddis larvae and small molluscs.   Like <u>Notonecta</u> it can inflict a painful 'bite' on man.   Until recently only flightless individuals had been found in Britain.

<u>Aphelocheirus</u> represents an end point in the evolution of aquatic habits.   It never needs to visit the surface.   This independence from atmospheric air it owes to the employment of <u>plastron respiration</u>.   Much of its body is covered by a pile of exceedingly fine bristles.   There are some 2 <u>million</u> on each square millimetre of surface.   This pile is filled with air — only a thin film and far too small in volume to be an air store — is non-wettable at low pressures, and provides an enormous surface area where air and water are in contact.   Via elaborate devices at the spiracles (breathing pores) this film is in contact with the tracheal tubes that carry oxygen into the body.   The volume of gas contained in this plastron remains constant — and very small.   The plastron acts as a gill, transporting oxygen from the water.   Larvae employ cutaneous respiration.

Adults of <u>Aphelocheirus</u> overwinter and lay their eggs in spring.   There is one generation a year.

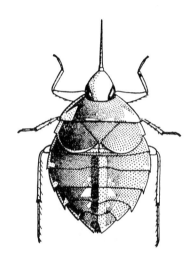

<u>Aphelocheirus montandoni</u>
Length c. 1cm

Adult Caddis flies are dull-coloured, or sometimes black, insects that much resemble moths in general appearance. They are in fact related to butterflies and moths (Lepidoptera) from which they differ in having wings beset with hair-like bristles (Trichoptera means 'hairy wings') instead of scales as in the Lepidoptera. They also lack the coiled sucking proboscis so characteristic of many moths. When at rest the wings cover the body in a roof-like manner. The antennae are long. Many, but not all, are weak fliers and some are nocturnal. Like moths they have a complete metamorphosis with well defined larval and pupal stages. In this they differ from such insects as mayflies and stoneflies whose development is gradual and does not include a pupal stage. These have an 'incomplete metamorphosis.'

The larvae are almost invariably entirely aquatic and much the longest phase of the life cycle is spent as a larva. The best known larvae are case-makers, but by no means all species have this habit. About a quarter of the British species are non-case-makers. Of the 200 or so British species, slightly more than half are known from the Lake District whose fauna reveals a good deal of the diversity shown by the group. Both lakes and streams are frequented, each species having its preferred habitat.

Case-making larvae are rather caterpillar-like in appearance, but much of the body is generally hidden by the case. The head capsule is hard and the first one or two segments behind it (part of the thorax) are protected by tough cuticle, but the rest of the body — mostly abdomen of which there are 9 segments — is soft. The abdomen often bears gills and, at its tip a pair of hooks that are the hallmark of a

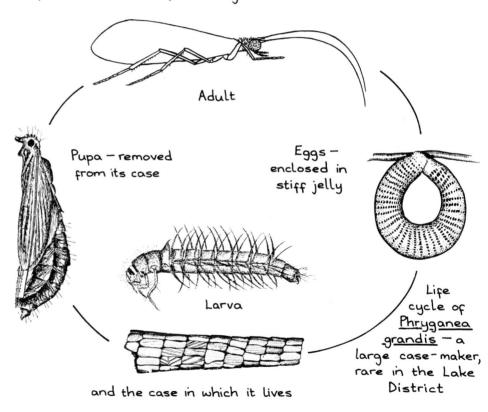

Adult

Pupa — removed from its case

Eggs — enclosed in stiff jelly

Larva

and the case in which it lives

Life cycle of Phryganea grandis — a large case-maker, rare in the Lake District

273

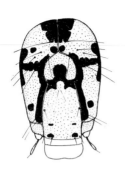

Mystacides nigra and its head seen from in front. Common in both still and running water.

L. c. 12 mm

Agrypnia (= Phryganea) varia
A still-water species of lakes and tarns. Common in Windermere and adjacent tarns

L. to c. 22 mm

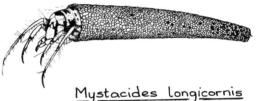

Mystacides longicornis

L. c. 12 mm   Mainly in standing waters - lakes and tarns
Note the subtle differences between its case and that of its relative M. nigra

Some case-making caddis larvae of the Lake District and their habitats.

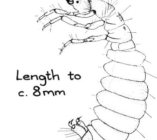

Length to c. 8 mm

Agapetus fuscipes — case seen from the side and below and the larva removed from it. Very common in fast-flowing stony rivers and streams

caddis larva.   In case makers these anchor the larva to its case.   Three fleshy processes are often present on the first segment of the abdomen.   These are retractable and serve to lock the body within the case, allowing plenty of space behind them so that undulation of the abdomen can draw in oxygen-containing water.

   The front end of the body can be extended outside the case to allow the legs to be used for crawling or, some-times, swimming.   Cases take many forms and are constructed from a wide range of materials.   Each species makes a characteristic case, but there is some variation as similar materials are not always to hand.   The case generally has a silken tubular lining.   The silk is produced by salivary glands of enormous size.   A few

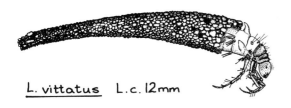

L. vittatus   L.c. 12mm

A still water species but occasionally in the slower parts of rivers such as the Leven.

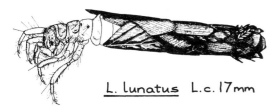

L. lunatus   L.c. 17mm

In most kinds of waters — lakes, tarns, rivers and streams. Often abundant.

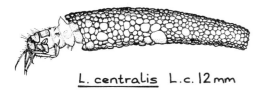

L. centralis   L.c. 12mm

Often in marshy places but also in running water.
Widespread but not particularly common.

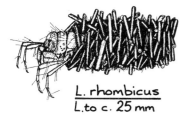

L. rhombicus
L.to c. 25 mm

In still water, associated with submerged and marginal vegetation. Occasionally in slower parts of rivers. Abundant in some localities.

Lake District species of Limnephilus to illustrate the kind of cases made and the habitats preferred

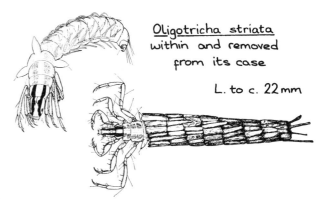

Triaenodes bicolor

L. c. 12 mm

Swims by rapid rowing with the middle pair of legs. Note their great length and fringe of bristles. The lightweight case is made from bits of leaf. Common in lakes and ponds.

Oligotricha striata
within and removed from its case

L. to c. 22mm

Note the protuberances of the abdomen and how the legs of this crawling species differ from those of the swimmer Triaenodes
Widespread but not common:
usually in still water.

A comparison of structure and habits

Molanna angustata removed from and seen within its case, whose shape in section is also shown. Common in lakes and tarns. Length to 17 mm

Length 11 mm

Lepidostoma hirtum — maker of a case of vegetable debris with a square cross section. Common in rivers and on stony shores of lakes.

Glyphotaelius pellucidus seen from beneath. The case is made from pieces cut from leaves and sometimes incorp--orates complete small leaves.
Very common and wide--spread, in lakes, tarns, pools and some streams. L. to 23 mm

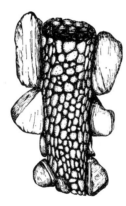

Goera pilosa
Heavy lateral weights are incorporated in the case. Widespread in streams. L. of larva 13 mm.

Anabolia nervosa
Long sticks are added to the case of sand grains. Very abundant in both standing and flowing water. L. 26 mm

Examples of Lake District caddis larvae with particularly characteristic cases.

species make the case entirely of silk, but most bind materials of various kinds — sand grains, pieces of leaf, twigs, or even tiny snails and mussels — to the outside of the silken tube. Some materials such as sand grains, lie to hand because the adult female has laid her eggs in the right kind of place, but have to be sought and sorted; others, like pieces of leaf, have to be cut to size by the mandibles. Similar materials are used in different species to produce cases of different kinds.

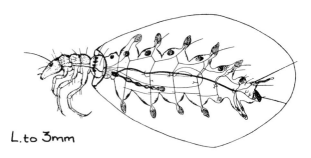

L. to 3mm

Ithytrichia lamellaris, a hydroptilid that makes its case entirely of silk. Widespread and often common in England but rather rare in the Lake District.

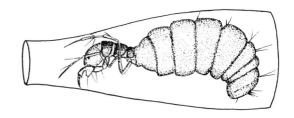

Oxyethira flavicornis in its silk case. Common and widespread in certain lakes, including Windermere and Esthwaite Water, and in tarns.   Length to 3·4 mm.

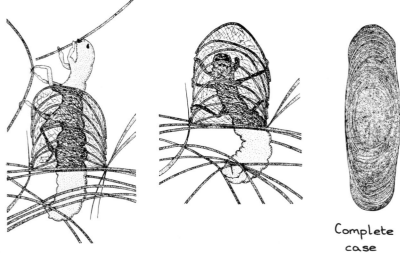

Complete case

Larva of Agraylea making its case.
A. multipunctata is common, and sometimes abundant in Windermere, Esthwaite Water and other lakes. L. to c. 5mm

The case is protective and the larva can withdraw into it should danger threaten.   Some cases probably serve as camouflage against predators such as fishes.   Most case-makers crawl over the bottom with a rather lumbering gait.   A few, such as Triaenodes are swimmers.   These make cases of lightweight materials.   Some crawling stream dwellers adopt exactly the opposite tactic and make heavy cases, sometimes as in Goera and Silo, adding extra weight in the form of a few larger stones at each side.
    Some, but not all, members of the family Hydroptilidae make a case entirely of silk.   These tiny caddises — full-grown larvae are sometimes only 2 or 3 mm in length — do not make a case until they reach the last (5th) instar.   The earlier instars often look quite different from the last.   Agraylea multipunctata uses algal

277

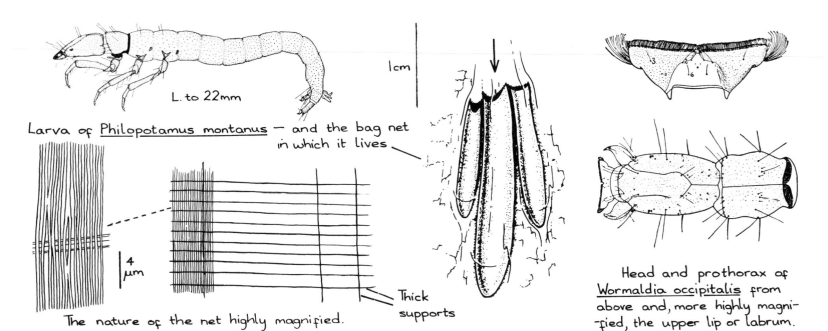

L. to 22mm

Larva of <u>Philopotamus montanus</u> — and the bag net in which it lives

1cm

4 μm

The nature of the net highly magnified.

Thick supports

Head and prothorax of <u>Wormaldia occipitalis</u> from above and, more highly magni- -fied, the upper lip or labrum.

filaments as a framework for its case.   These are cut to length and bent into shape by the larva and bound together by silk.   The whole is then lined by silk.   The algal filaments gradually wear away leaving only a silken case.

Case-making larvae, which generally have robust mandibles, are predominantly herbivores, some exclusively so, but some are opportunists and include a variety of small animals in the diet, and the large <u>Phryganea grandis</u> is markedly carnivorous.   Leaves are often eaten — not entirely surprising when the relationship to caterpillars is remembered.   Thus <u>Limnephilus rhombicus</u> feeds mainly on leaves.   Algae are often important. <u>Agapetus fuscipes</u>, which grazes on algae attached to stones, was found to exert considerable control on the crop of attached diatoms (<u>Achnanthes</u>) in a stream flowing into Windermere.   The stream-frequenting <u>Silo</u> is also a grazer of diatoms.   <u>Ithytrichia</u> also feeds on diatoms but other tiny hydroptilids suck the contents from cells of filamentous green algae, for which purpose they have specialised mouthparts.

<u>Net-spinning larvae</u> have adopted a way of life analagous to that of web-making spiders.   They spin

nets or snares, usually in flowing or trickling water, and catch what the current, or happenstance, bring them. Nets are diverse in form and in details of their construction.

Larvae of <u>Philopotamus montanus</u> and its relatives make sausage-shaped nets of exceedingly fine mesh. These are attached to stones, with the entrance facing the current, usually in small upland streams. Those of <u>P. montanus</u> have a rectangular framework crossed by fine transverse strands less than 1 μm apart (1 μm or micron = 0·001 mm). They collect very fine particles that find their way into them. These serve

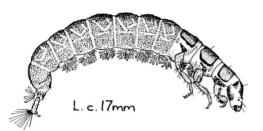

L. c. 17mm

Larva of <u>Hydropsyche instabilis</u>

Net of <u>Hydropsyche angustipennis</u> supported by stones

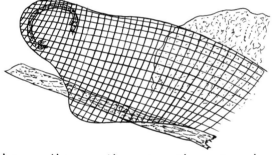

Net of <u>H. angustipennis</u> with captured prey

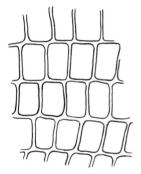

Portion of net of <u>H. angustipennis</u>

Mesh size up to 205 x 112 μm.

as food for the larvae which live in these bag nets and sweep particles from their walls with a plate, the upper lip or labrum, that is fringed with bristles and serves as a besom. The related <u>Wormaldia occipitalis</u> makes similar, but longer, nets. <u>P. montanus</u> is abundant in the Lake District and <u>W. occipitalis</u> is also common. Both species occur at altitudes up to at least 2000 ft.

<u>Hydropsyche</u> and its relatives make a less fine, but beautifully-meshed net which they set in fast-flowing water. Its shape and arrangement vary somewhat according to circumstances but in essence consists of a billowing bag supported by stones or leaves. It is spun from double fibres of silk, cemented at the joints. Its mesh size increases as the larva grows and varies from species to species. In a 5th (last) instar larva of <u>H. angustipennis</u> it is about 205 x 112 μm. The net catches both plant and animal material for

279

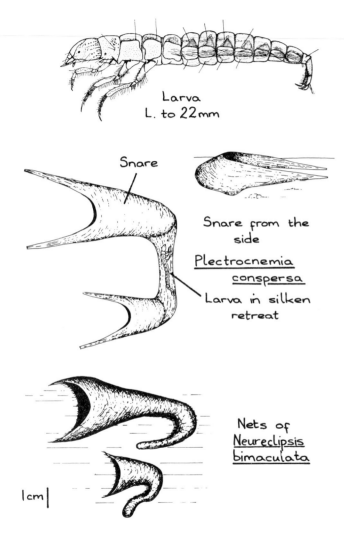

Larva
L. to 22mm

Snare

Snare from the
side
Plectrocnemia
conspersa

Larva in silken
retreat

Nets of
Neureclipsis
bimaculata

1cm|

the larva, which resides in a silken retreat in communication with it.

Nets are often numerous and close together. Spacing may be regulated by communication between larvae using sound. Larvae can certainly stridulate by rubbing a scraper on the fore leg across ridges on the head, but it is not known how they detect these sounds.

Several species of Hydropsyche occur in the Lake District and some are common.

Some larvae of the family Polycentropidae live in silken tubes at each end of which they spin wide-mouthed, slipper-shaped nets, of coarse and rather irregular mesh. Such nets cannot withstand high velocities and are built in slow-flowing or still water. Their shape varies somewhat according to the speed of the current and depth of the water. They act as snares and capture live prey that either drifts or crawls into them. Victims are seized by the larvae, that are exclusively carnivorous and eat whatever small prey presents itself. Plectrocnemia conspersa is a species with such habits. It is widespread in the Lake District where it occurs at altitudes up to at least 1800 ft. Somewhat similar snares are made by another common Lake District species Polycentropus flavomaculatus, but in these, which are built singly, the larva seems to lurk at the bottom of the snare.

Very distinctive nets are made by Neureclipsis bimaculata which is often abundant near lake outflows where it traps planktonic animals that are washed out. Each larva inhabits a long trumpet-like funnel that may be as much as 20cm (8 in) long and whose narrow end, where the larva lives, is turned back upstream. Similar, but shorter, trumpet-like nets, in this case straight, are made by Cyrnus trimaculatus that is very common in lakes and tarns. The rarer Holocentropus dubius makes a tubular net with a funnel-like mouth among vegetation.

Gallery-making larvae belong to the family Psychomyiidae. These construct silken tunnels or galleries in whose walls sand grains or detritus are incorporated. Several species of Tinodes make galleries that snake their way over stones in both lakes and streams. Larvae, which can turn around in the gallery, partly emerge from the front end, anchoring themselves by means of their posterior (anal) hooks, and scrape material from the surface of the stone with their mandibles. When the food supply is exhausted, they demolish the rear portion of the gallery and extend the front. Galleries are therefore not permanently fixed. Tinodes waeneri is abundant in Lake District lakes, tarns, rivers and streams, and ascends to at least 1800ft. Other species of Tinodes are of more local occurrence.

Lype phaeopa, which is recorded from Windermere, Coniston Water and Blelham Tarn, but is probably more widespread, makes its galleries on sticks and branches. These are up to 7cm (almost 3 in) long. The wood is bitten to form a groove, then covered with a skin-like silken tunnel to which sand grains adhere.

Free-ranging larvae are represented by Rhyacophila dorsalis and other species of the genus. These are active carnivores that make no case, net, snare or gallery but roam over stones in fast-flowing streams in search of such prey as chironomid (page 305) and Simulium (page 312) larvae. Their anal hooks serve as grappling irons preventing them from being washed away. R. dorsalis is very common in Lake District streams. Two scarcer species are R. munda, which has a western distribution in Britain, and R. obliterata, which is associated with hilly regions in the northern and western parts of the country.

Most caddis flies have a one year life cycle, most of which is spent in the larval stage. Sometimes a second year is necessary,

L. 10mm

Larva of Tinodes waeneri and the pattern of its galleries on a stone surface

5 cm

Larval galleries of Lype phaeopa on a piece of old wood.

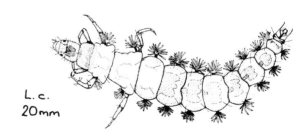

L.c. 20mm

Larva of Rhyacophila dorsalis

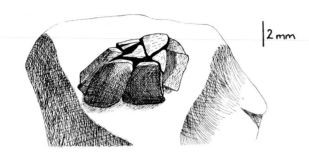

2 mm

Pupal case of <u>Glossosoma intermedium</u> affixed to a stone. That of <u>Goera</u> is similar. The larval case is used : a parchment-like cocoon is produced within it.

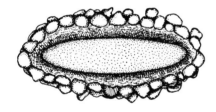

Cocoon of <u>Rhyacophila dorsalis</u> seen within its case after removal from a stone.

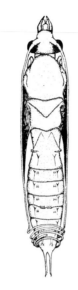

<u>Mystacides azurea</u>
Note how the long antennae are accomm-odated by being wrapped around the abdomen.

Caddis fly pupae

<u>Goera pilosa</u>
side view
Gills omitted.

and under favourable conditions two generations are sometimes produced in one year. Generally at the end of its fifth instar—though 7 or 8 have been reported in <u>Phryganea grandis</u> — the larva moults and becomes a <u>pupa</u>. This is always protected by a <u>cocoon</u> made by the larva before pupation. Case-makers make their cocoon economically by simply blocking both ends of the case and cementing it to a stone, plant or other object. Blocking may be by a stone, bits of cut leaf, algae or detritus, or by a grid of silk spun across the aperture. Hydroptilids block their larval case with a plug of silk. The net-spinning <u>Hydropsyche</u> makes its case by incorporating small stones into the silken larval retreat. Free-living larvae have to make a pupal case rather like the larval case of <u>Rhyacophila</u> secretes a tough, species that use small stones. This they cement to a suitable object. membranous, capsule-like cocoon inside this case.

   In the pupa, an inactive, non-feeding stage, adult features such as wings, large eyes and long antennae are recognisable. This stage often lasts about 3 weeks. The pupa has robust, often sickle-shaped, mandibles, very different from those of the larva. With these it eventually cuts through the cocoon and escapes. They serve this purpose only.   The adult has vestigial mandibles.   The pupa then swims to the surface of the water, to a stone or emergent plant, and splits its skin.   An adult caddis fly emerges.

Adult caddis flies are mostly on the wing from about April to October.   Rhyacophila dorsalis can be found throughout this period but most species are about for only a few weeks or months of the year.   They seldom attract much attention and many of them have to be sought on tree trunks or stones where they shelter.   A few fly in swarms.   Mystacides azurea follows boats, and swarms often accompany the ferry across Windermere in late summer.   These obviously orientate themselves to the ferry as, when the latter accelerates , so do the insects, their long antennae being bent back as a result.   At full speed the ferry leaves its escorts behind.

Adult
Caddis
Flies

Phryganea striata   Length c. 2·5 cm

Tinodes waeneri   L. c. 6mm.

Some adult caddis flies emit an unpleasant odour.   Lake District examples include Phryganea varia and Anabolia nervosa.   Halesus radiatus is aromatic; Limnephilus binotatus smells of Juniper — and often sits on Juniper bushes.

Egg laying habits are various.   Females of the genus Phryganea crawl down plant stems into the water and lay eggs encased in jelly that, like that of frog spawn, swells greatly.   It is not difficult to watch them doing this at the right time of year.   In Phryganea egg masses form characteristic rings (page 273). Other species enter water to lay eggs in strings or clumps.   Sometimes they remain under water for 10 minutes or so while doing so.   Hydropsyche angustipennis has been seen to dive vertically into a stream and swim to a stone, under which it layed.   Eggs in a jelly mass would be unsuited to fast-flowing situations and those of species laying there lack jelly and are stuck to stones.   Limnephilus and its relatives lay eggs on plants above water from which the larvae fall or are washed by rain.

Of the 194 species of caddis flies recorded in Britain, rather more than half have been found in the Lake District.   Here some species ascend to considerable altitudes, several having been found at 2000 ft. Halesus guttatipennis* has been recorded at over 2500 ft, Apatania muliebris even higher.

*Now called Melampophylax mucoreus

283

A. muliebris is not only parthogenetic, reproducing without males, which are unknown, but is an Arctic relict. Outside the Arctic it occurs only in a few isolated areas of northern Europe, its larvae generally living in cold springs. It is presumed that during, or towards the end of, the Ice Ages, it was more widespread, that it retreated north as the ice retreated, but found refuges in certain cold springs in Britain. It has been found plentifully in spring-fed streams at about 2600 ft on Coniston Old Man, less commonly lower down that mountain, in a stream issuing from below ground near the south end of Windermere, and in a locality in the north of the district. It is significant that it could not be found in streams adjacent to that in which it occurs near Windermere that are very similar but warmer.

The Lake District has the distinction of providing the only site, Blelham Tarn, at which one caddis fly, Cyrnus insolutus, has been found in Britain. In the British Isles it is also known from one site in Ireland.

Likewise Glossosoma intermedium was found in Britain for the first time near Coniston in 1925. Since then it has been refound in that locality and discovered in two other Lake District sites.

Limnephilus centralis L.c. 1 cm.

A few moths of the family Pyralidae have aquatic larvae.   As these belong to the so-called 'Microlepidoptera' they tend to escape mention in popular books on butterflies and moths.   Because the wings of adults bear marks thought to resemble those used by potters to mark china, they are called China-mark moths. Nymphula nympheata, the Brown China-mark moth, is very common in the Lake District wherever water-lilies grow in lakes and tarns, and also frequents species of Potamogeton with floating leaves.   On the under surface of a leaf the young larva lives under a patch cut from that or an adjacent leaf — that looks like a puncture patch stuck to the inner tube of a bicycle tyre, — or between two patches fastened together by silken

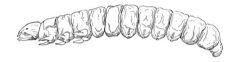

Larva

The Brown China-mark moth
Nymphula nympheata

Case opened to reveal
larva

Film of
air

Larva feeding

Adult

threads to make a case.   In these young larvae the case is full of water, and dissolved oxygen is used for respiration.   These small larvae overwinter on the bottom.   In spring they grow and moult and develop a pelt of fine bristles.   Now they live in an air-filled case and remain dry.   To feed, a larva pushes its head from its case through a small hole and nibbles the adjacent leaf with its mandibles like a typical terrestrial caterpillar.   The pelt of fine bristles prevents the entry of water.   Pupation takes place above the water surface.   A silken cocoon containing the pupa (chrysalis) covered with pieces of leaf is attached, usually to a plant stem.

Mated females deposit eggs by sitting on a floating leaf and dipping the flexed abdomen into the water to reach under it.   There is no entering of the water as occurs in some caddis flies.

The Neuroptera, literally 'nerve-winged flies' — a reference to the network of veins in the wings — include the Alder flies, the Lacewing flies and some related insects.   Of Alder flies — sometimes recognised as an independent order, the Megaloptera—three species occur in Britain, one being rare and little known.   Two species occur in the Lake District, Sialis lutaria whose larvae are very common on muddy and silty bottoms in lakes and tarns, ('lutaria' is derived from the Latin word for mud — lutum), and S. fuliginosa, a stream dweller.   Both are very similar at all stages of the life history.

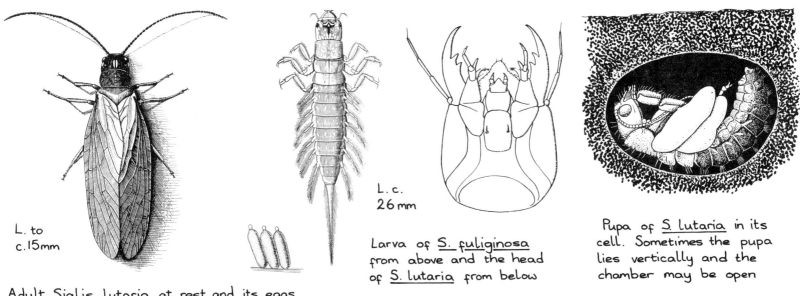

L. to
c.15mm

L.c.
26mm

Larva of S. fuliginosa
from above and the head
of S. lutaria from below

Pupa of S. lutaria in its
cell. Sometimes the pupa
lies vertically and the
chamber may be open

Adult Sialis lutaria at rest and its eggs

Adult Alder flies are easily recognised, soft-bodied, darkly-coloured, weakly-flying insects with long antennae whose wings cover the trunk like a house roof when, as is often the case, they sit on vegetation not far from water.   Both pairs of wings are similar in shape.   Both Lake District species are about in May and June, the commonest, S. lutaria, often in abundance.   Both are variable in size but often about 15mm (c. 5/8 in.) long.

   Although the larvae are aquatic, the eggs of S. lutaria are laid on vegetation overhanging the water; less commonly on stones, bridges or tree trunks : those of <u>S. fuliginosa</u> usually on the leaves of trees overhanging the water.   The tiny larvae that emerge after one to three weeks depending on temperature, either fall into the water or crawl to it.   Larval development, which takes about 2 years, involves passing through 10 stages (instars).   Superficially, larvae appear to have many legs, but only 3 pairs are present, the tubular structures on the abdomen being gills.   The abdomen of <u>S. lutaria</u> is purplish-pink in colour : that of <u>S. fuliginosa</u> orange-yellow.   Provided with formidable mandibles, larvae are voracious carnivores, eating chironomid larvae, worms and small crustaceans.   They are sometimes cannibals.   As they grow, lake-frequenting larvae of <u>S. lutaria</u> venture further and further from the shore and have been found at a depth of 12 m (c. 40 ft) in Windermere.   Towards the end of larval life they return to shallow water prior to crawling ashore and pupating just below the surface in damp soil, sometimes several metres from the water.   No cocoon is made to protect the pupa.   After about a month the adult emerges.

Larvae of <u>S. lutaria</u> are sufficiently common in lakes and tarns in the Lake District to be an important item in the diet of fishes.   Trout in Windermere sometimes gorge on them.   Tough animals, they are swallowed whole by trout and can be found alive in the stomach.
<u>S. fuliginosa</u> is common in Lake District streams.

Only one species of <u>Osmylus</u>, <u>O. fulvicephalus</u> occurs in Britain.   It is rare in the Lake District where it frequents small woodland streams with mossy margins.   Its large size (about 25mm, 1 in.), orange-brown head, blackish body and brown spotted iridescent wings make it readily recognised.   It should be sought in May, June and July.   Eggs are laid on leaves, especially those of mosses, at the edge of streams to which larvae make their way. Wet moss is their habitat.   Larvae are predaceous and pass through only 3 instars.   They overwinter in the moss in a state of torpor, often being sub-merged during this period.   They pupate in spring in a silken cocoon and adults emerge after about a fortnight spent in the pupal stage.

There are 3 British species of <u>Sisyra</u> of which two occur in the Lake District.   These are called

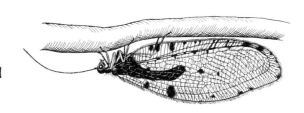

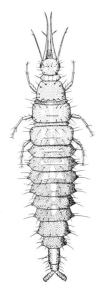

Adult of <u>Osmylus fulvicephalus</u>
(length about 25mm) at rest,
and larva (length about 15 mm)
seen from above

287

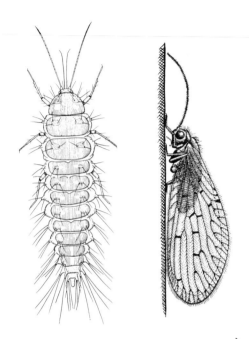

Larva of <u>Sisyra</u> (length c.5mm) and adult of <u>S. dalii</u> (length c. 5mm without antennae) at rest.

<u>Sponge Flies</u> because their larvae live inside, and feed on, sponges. Adults of both Lake District species are about 5 or 6 mm (c. ¼ in) long. <u>Sisyra fuscata</u> has blackish brown wings : <u>S. dalii</u> reddish brown wings with dark brown markings on the cross veins.   Eggs of <u>S. fuscata</u> are laid in early summer and usually give rise to larvae that will become adults a year later, but under some conditions they develop more quickly and produce a second quickly-developing generation, so two generations can be squeezed into one year.   Eggs are laid in batches, each enclosed in a silken web, and are attached to leaves and other objects in the vicinity of water. Larvae hatch within about one to two weeks, find their way into the water and begin to search for a sponge, either <u>Euspongilla lacustris</u> or <u>Ephydatia fluviatilis</u> (page 168).   If successful they attach themselves and begin to feed on the juices of the sponge.   A larva has sucking mouthparts. Sometimes it penetrates inside its host.   There are 3 larval instars, the last being about 5 or 6 mm (c. ¼ in) long.   Being the same colour as the sponge — dirty white or greenish — the larva is inconspicuous.   When fully fed it leaves the sponge and crawls out of the water, there eventually to pupate.   The larva spins a protective silken cocoon that is hidden in crevices among tree bark or stones.   During winter the cocoons actually contain a resting larva : true pupation occurs in spring.   The pupal stage last only about two weeks.

   <u>Sisyra fuscata</u> is common in the Lake District where its distribution is obviously determined by that of its host sponges.   <u>S. dalii</u> is more local but has been found several times in the Windermere – Ambleside area and doubtless occurs elsewhere.

Beetles are among the most numerous and successful of all groups of animals. One facet of this success is their mastery of both terrestrial and freshwater environments. While many insects have aquatic immature stages but terrestrial adults, beetles often live in water at all stages of the life cycle — egg, larva, pupa and adult — but the adult can also often fly if necessary. The basic design of adult beetles has been very adaptable. Many look superficially similar but there is much diversity in structure and habits. The inadequately studied beetle fauna of the Lake District reveals some of the diversity of the aquatic forms. About half of the 220 or so completely aquatic beetles reported in Britain are known to occur in the area, as are several others with aquatic larvae.

Adult beetles are generally well protected by a tough cuticle. Although there are modifications of this plan, they typically have two pairs of wings of which the first is transformed into horny cases (<u>elytra</u>) that protect the second, which alone is used for flying. They have biting mouthparts. Water beetles are often black or dark brown in colour.

<u>Dytiscus marginalis</u> (length almost 1·5 in. (35mm)), the largest water beetle in the Lake District and one of the largest in Britain, exemplifies the family Dytiscidae. Black in colour it has a conspicuous yellow margin — hence its name. Heavier than water, and a powerful swimmer, it propels itself by powerful strokes of the middle and, especially, the hind legs. The legs of a pair operate simultaneously like the oars of a boat. Hydrodynamic efficiency is assisted by air-filled sacs beneath the elytra that grant buoyancy and also

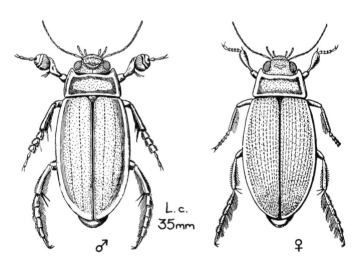

L.c. 35mm

<u>Dytiscus marginalis</u>, male (♂) and female (♀). Note the suckers on the fore-legs of the male.

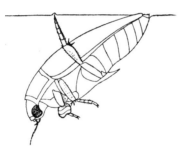

<u>D. marginalis</u> suspended from the surface film ready to ventilate its air sacs.

289

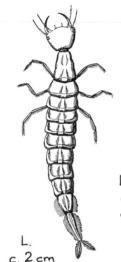

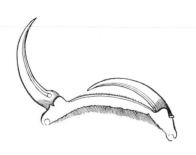

Larva of <u>Dytiscus marginalis</u>
and details of the jaws (mandibles)
one closed, the other extended.

L.
c. 2 cm

Pupa of
<u>D. marginalis</u>

serve for respiration, for <u>Dytiscus</u> breathes atmospheric air.   Fine tubes, the tracheal tubes, carry air from the air sacs deep into the tissues of the body.   Periodic visits to the surface are necessary.   The hind end protrudes and the air chambers are recharged.   Beneath the surface these act as a physical gill: the animal holds a suitable object and from time to time squeezes the air into a bubble at the rear end to facilitate gaseous exchange. <u>Dytiscus</u> flies well when this is necessary. Males have smooth elytra, females either ridged or smooth.   Males also have elaborate suckers on the fore legs to facilitate grasping of the female during mating.   It is commonly thought that the ridged elytra of many females also make grasping easier,
but this is not so.   The suckers grip the under (ventral) surface of the female.

   <u>D. marginalis</u> is a rapacious carnivore.   Almost any animal that it can seize, including small fishes and other creatures larger than itself, serve as prey.   The human finger can be painfully nipped.   A forked spike (the metasternum) on the ventral surface can also inflict a wound.

   Females lay eggs early in the year, inserting them singly into the stems or leaves of submerged plants.   The larva that emerges is also a rapacious predator.   It attains a length of about 2 in. (5cm) after a few weeks or several months of growth, depending on the availability of food.   Like the adult the larva takes in atmospheric air — via two spiracles at the rear end.   Stout sickle-shaped jaws, (mandibles) seize and pierce the prey.   Each mandible is pierced by a duct, actually a not quite completely closed groove — like a hypodermic needle — down which digestive juices are pumped into the victim whose partly digested fluid contents are then sucked in by the same route.   Small amounts of solid food are also swallowed.   A full grown larva burrows into moist earth at the water's edge and is transformed into a pupa.   In summer the duration of the pupal stage is only about 3 weeks.   Should pupation occur late in the year the pupa over-winters.   Adults emerge from pupae. They are long-lived, often surviving for more than a year.

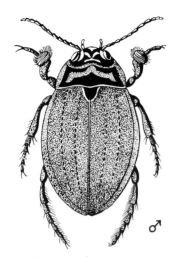
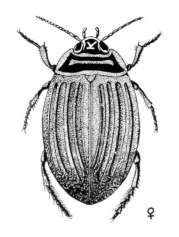

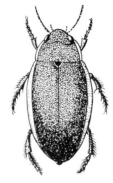

♂ ♀

Ilybius fuliginosus and the head of its larva. Adult bronze with yellow margins. Common in sheltered regions of lakes and tarns. Also pools. L. c. 10mm.

Acilius sulcatus. One of the larger species. Adult somewhat flattened. In various, usually small, water bodies. L. 16-18 mm.

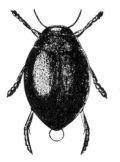
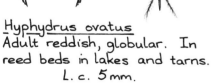
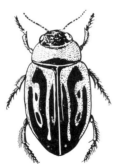

Reddish yellow with black markings. Generally in running water or on exposed lake shores. Also in high tarns. L. c. 8mm

Common and widespread in lakes and tarns, often in exposed places. Also in running water. L. c. 5mm.

Yellowish with fine black marks. Probably commonest in ponds at the fringe of the district. L. c. 16mm.

Hyphydrus ovatus Adult reddish, globular. In reed beds in lakes and tarns. L. c. 5mm.

Platambus maculatus

Deronectes depressus

Colymbetes fuscus

Some Lake District dytiscid beetles.

291

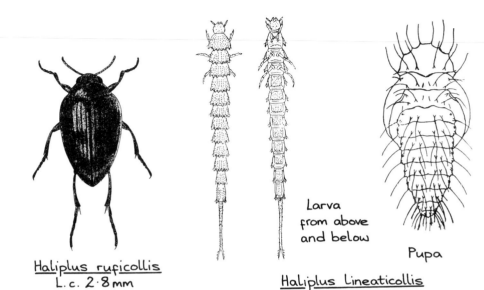

There are many smaller dytiscid beetles. More than 50 species occur in the Lake District and reveal some of the diversity of the family. Often a respiratory bubble is carried posteriorly. Of the species not illustrated Hydroporus palustris and H. pubescens are common and widespread and the latter ascends to at least 2000ft. Other species, such as Agabus congener and A. arcticus also favour high altitudes, the latter being perhaps confined to such, where it is common in pools and tarns. A. congener has been found high up on Scafell, Skiddaw and Blencathra.

At least 11 species of haliplid beetles occur in the Lake District. Yellowish or reddish in colour, they do not exceed about 4mm in length and many are smaller than

Haliplus ruficollis
L. c. 2·8 mm

Larva
from above
and below

Pupa

Haliplus Lineaticollis

this. Unlike dytiscids, which are fine swimmers, haliplids mostly crawl or scramble. When they swim the hind legs move alternately. Air is collected at the surface. There has been disagreement about its use. Broad plates extend from each rear leg under the body and air is trapped between them and the belly. This apparently serves a hydrostatic function as well as for respiration, and air is stored under the elytra for the latter purpose as in dytiscids. No air bubble is carried at the rear end. Because they are slow-moving, visits to the surface are usually infrequent and a resting individual, using little oxygen, can remain submerged for long periods, especially in cold water.

Haliplids live where filamentous algae are abundant and on these they feed. The elongate larvae also feed on such algae. With mandibles like those of Dytiscus, but much smaller, they pierce a filament and suck out its contents — a highly specialised way of feeding. Pupation is in a hole excavated at the water's edge.

Most Lake District species live in reed beds in lakes and tarns or in areas of dense vegetation, but Haliplus fulvus, the commonest species, occurs also in exposed places, as does H. flavicollis, and in running water. H. ruficollis, a typical reed-bed species, has also been found in ponds and streams and on peat mosses.

Whirligig beetles (Gyrinidae) have a very specialised life-style to which they are beautifully adapted.

292

Most belong to the genus <u>Gyrinus</u>. These blue-black beetles live gregariously in sheltered ponds and slow-flowing parts of streams over whose surface they swim at high speed. For this they are streamlined and their propulsive rear legs are broad and paddle-like, the last segment (the tarsus) being divided into segments that can be expanded like a fan as the leg thrusts, and contracted during the return stroke. The eyes are completely divided into an upper portion that is above, and a lower portion, well separated from it, that lies beneath the water surface. These two portions, one for aerial the other for aquatic, vision, differ in their microscopic make-up.

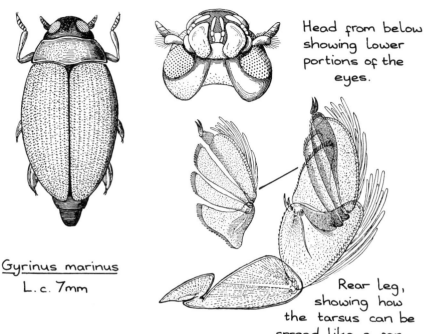

Gyrinus marinus
L.c. 7mm

Head from below showing lower portions of the eyes.

Rear leg, showing how the tarsus can be spread like a fan.

Larva of Gyrinus
L.c. 14mm

Food, often animals stranded in the surface film, is found as the beetles gyrate. If disturbed <u>Gyrinus</u> dives taking with it a bubble of air at its rear end. It can fly well if required.

Eggs are laid on water plants. The carnivorous larva looks superficially many-legged—though it has only the usual three pairs — the rest of the lateral filaments being gills that enable it to use dissolved oxygen. When full-grown it climbs from the water, spins a dull-coloured elliptical cocoon, incorporating bits of detritus, and pupates within it. Adults emerge in late summer and overwinter in a torpid state.

<u>Gyrinus natator</u> is widespread in the Lake District and common in favoured sites, <u>G. minutus</u> local but not scarce, and ascends to Sty Head, <u>G. marinus</u> and <u>G. caspius</u> local. Another gyrinid, <u>Orectochilus villosus</u> tends to live under stones near the edges of streams and is not uncommon. It has also been found in Ullswater.

Hydrophilid beetles are sometimes aquatic, sometimes terrestrial. Some two dozen aquatic species occur in

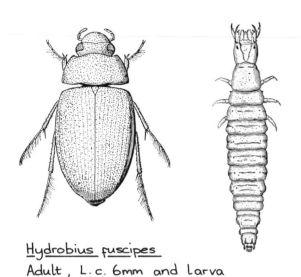

the Lake District. These are mostly feebly swimming vegetarians that crawl among plants. <u>Hydrobius fuscipes</u> (length c. 0·25 in, c. 6 mm) occurs in ponds high and low, ditches, and elsewhere. It particularly favours ponds covered with duckweed. Blackish in colour its ventral surface is covered by a silvery layer of entrapped air. To renew its supply it breaks the surface, not with its rear end as does a dytiscid, but with the front end. It tilts to one side and its reservoir of air is put in contact with the atmosphere via a funnel-like duct between its head and thorax. In making the funnel the antenna which is provided with un-wettable bristles, plays a vital part and is responsible for bursting the film between the reservoir and the atmosphere.

Eggs are laid in small clusters enclosed in a white cocoon spun to protect them. This floats or becomes lightly attached to a plant. Unlike the adult, the larva is carnivorous. It breathes atmospheric air, taken in via a cup-like hollow at its rear end. Pupation takes place at the water's edge in July or thereabouts. From these pupae a new generation of adults emerges in August. These overwinter in a

<u>Hydrobius fuscipes</u>
Adult, L.c. 6mm and larva

<u>Chaetarthria seminulum</u>
L.c. 1·5 mm

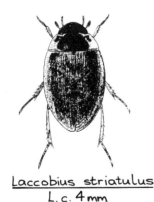

<u>Laccobius striatulus</u>
L.c. 4 mm

L.c. 3·5 mm

Larva and pupa
<u>Laccobius minutus</u>

<u>Coelostoma orbiculare</u>

L.c. 4mm

<u>Helophorus aquaticus</u>
L.c. 4mm

Some hydrophilid beetles of the Lake District

torpid state to breed in the following spring.

Other Lake District hydrophilids include the locally common Chaetarthria seminulum, a species of the muddy margins of ponds, and an inhabitant of wet moss : Laccobius minutus which frequents running water, ponds and ditches and is perhaps commonest on the fringes of the area : the common Coelostoma orbiculare that lives in ponds and among wet Sphagnum moss, and the very common Helophorus aquaticus that is found in both ponds and streams.

Related to the hydrophilids are some minute beetles, the hydraenids. Hydraena gracilis (length c. 2 mm), with its long antennae, looks like a terrestrial beetle. It crawls extremely slowly over stones in streams. Local, but not scarce, in the Lake District, its habits and life history are virtually unknown. The same is true of other species of the genus that occur in the area and of the two species of Octhebius that have been recorded. These are no more than 2 mm long, rather like Hydraena but less slender than H. gracilis, and have shorter antennae. With Hydraena they share

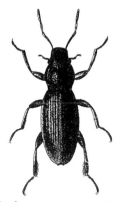
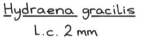

Hydraena gracilis
L.c. 2 mm

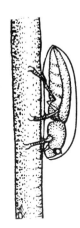

Dryops luridus
crawling down a plant stem enclosed in a bubble of air

the ability to walk upside down suspended from the surface film of water. One of them, O. bicolon is not uncommon at the edges of streams and in wet moss, the other, O. minimus is less frequently encountered.

Dryops belongs to a related family, the Dryopidae. These tiny beetles can crawl about on aquatic plants enveloped in a bubble of air from which only the tips of the legs protrude. D. luridus is common at the marshy edges of ponds in parts of the district and D. ernesti is also common.

The need to visit the surface for air imposes limits on what most water beetles can achieve. For example it makes it difficult to colonise streams, especially fast-flowing streams such as are typical of the Lake District. A plastron, such as that described for the bug Aphelocheirus (page 272) enables oxygen dissolved in the water to be utilised and eliminates the need for regular refills of atmospheric air. Members of the family Elminthidae sometimes called riffle beetles, have acquired a plastron which runs essentially in two broad bands along the sides and undersurface of the body. These are tiny beetles, from about 1.5 to almost 5mm in length, that inhabit swift-flowing water, but sometimes also mossy seepages and occasionally lakes, where they crawl slowly over stones or moss and browse on algae. They cannot swim and most cannot fly. At least 8 of the 11 British species occur in, or at the fringe of, the Lake District.

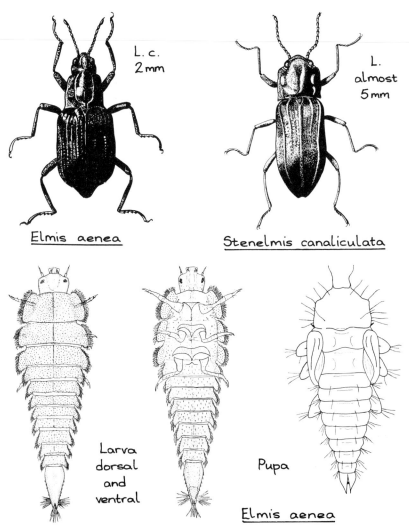

L.c.
2mm

Elmis aenea

L.
almost
5mm

Stenelmis canaliculata

Larva
dorsal
and
ventral

Pupa

Elmis aenea

<u>Elmis aenea</u> , length about 2mm or a little more, and black in colour, is common, as is <u>Limnius volckmari</u>. The brown <u>Stenelmis canaliculata</u>, which at almost 5mm in length is the largest British elminthid, frequents exposed stony shores in Windermere.   When it was first found there in 1960 this was the first time it had been seen in the British Isles.   It has since been found in rivers in Cambridgeshire, Lincolnshire and Wales.

Elminthids lay their eggs on stones or attach them to moss or other plants.   The herbivorous, slow-moving larvae of <u>Elmis</u> are of distinctive flattened form.   In life the gills are regularly expanded like fans from the rear end and then withdrawn.   Larvae of other genera are more tubular in shape.   Pup-ation takes place in soil or among stones at the water's edge.   <u>E. aenea</u> lays its eggs from April to July and these hatch 4 weeks later, or more if the water is cold, live throughout the following winter and pupate about July.   The pupal stage lasts only a couple of weeks.   Adults then overwinter to lay eggs in spring and often survive a second winter to breed again in the following spring.   For their size these are long-lived insects.   This may be related to the exceedingly slow tempo of their lives at all stages.   In the physiological sense their philosophy of life is the exact opposite of 'a short life and a merry one'.

Chrysomelid or leaf beetles are mostly brightly coloured, shiny terrestrial insects that feed on leaves and include important pests such as flea beetles and the Colorado Beetle.   One genus, however, <u>Macroplea</u> (once called <u>Haemonia</u>) spends its time clinging to or walking slowly over submerged vegetation.   It too is a plastron user.   Its plastron covers the entire under surface of the thorax and the abdomen, most of the lower part of the head, and the antennae.   There are at least two records of Macroplea from the Lake District, one referring to M. appendiculata.

Related to Macroplea is the genus Donacia of which adults of several species are terrestrial insects that frequent reeds and other waterside plants.   In the Lake District D. simplex is common on the Yellow Iris.   Larvae of Macroplea and Donacia are white, inactive, maggot-like creatures that live submerged and attached to the roots and stems of water plants whose intercellular gas-filled spaces they tap by means of hollow spines protruding from the rear end of the body.   These spines link the air spaces of the plant to the tracheal system of the larva   which can thus breathe atmospheric air — a remarkable adaptation.   The larvae pupate in ovoid, almost transparent, silken cocoons attached to the 'host' plant with whose air spaces they are in communication via a number of small holes.

Several other beetles have aquatic larvae but terrestrial adults.   One such is Helodes minuta whose flattened larvae, like those of other members of the genus, live under stones in streams.   A number of other beetles are associated with wet places and some of these, such as certain weevils, occasionally enter water.

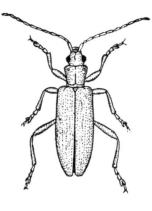

Donacia simplex
L.c. 12mm

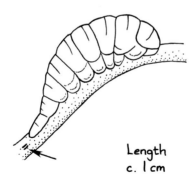

Length
c. 1 cm

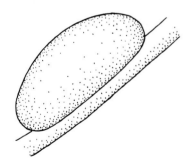

Larva and pupal cocoon of Donacia attached to the root of an aquatic plant.   Arrow indicates holes bored by larva to gain access to the air spaces of the plant.

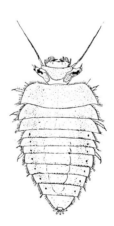

Larva of Helodes minuta
L. 6mm

297

The Diptera, or two winged flies — which is what the Greek-derived scientific name means — are sometimes also called the True flies.   They have only one pair of wings, the hind pair being modified into small club-like balancing organs called <u>halteres</u>.   They have sucking, sometimes piercing, mouthparts.

This is another enormously successful group of insects.   Well over 5000 species are found in Britain and these have colonised a wide range of habitats.   Many have aquatic immature stages — eggs, larvae and pupae — but adults are never aquatic.   In this they contrast strikingly with the beetles.   More than 1100 aquatic or semi-aquatic species have been recorded in Britain.   Just how many occur in the Lake District is uncertain.   Not only are the flies species rich but in terms of the bulk of living matter (bio-mass) larvae of some of the midges are sometimes the most important insects in lakes.

Adults of species with aquatic larvae are extremely diverse but all aquatic larvae share one attribute — they never have jointed legs on the thorax, (nor on the abdomen).

The larvae of many of the almost 300 British <u>Crane Flies</u>, or 'Daddy Long Legs', are 'leather-jackets' that live in soil or other terrestrial situations, but some are aquatic.   Our largest Crane Fly, <u>Tipula maxima</u>, with a wing span of about 65 mm (2.5 in.), which is not uncommon in the Lake District has semi-aquatic larvae.   These live, sometimes submerged, sometimes in very wet soil, at the margins of ponds and streams.   They are maggot-like creatures with a tiny retractable head and three pairs of tubular gill-like structures at the rear end.   While these appear to assist respiration by absorbing dissolved oxygen, the use of atmospheric air is more important.   Two holes at the rear end are brought to the water surface from time to time and air is taken in.   The holes are sealed off when the larva is submerged.

<u>Dicranota bimaculata</u> is another Crane Fly whose larvae are aquatic.   These frequent the mud and gravel of pools and streams.   About 20 mm (3/4 in.) long, and dirty white in colour, they crawl readily through the mud by use of 5 pairs of false legs. (True jointed legs, 3 in number, are always de-

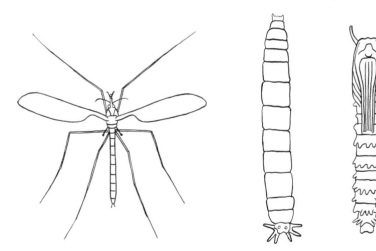

<u>Tipula maxima</u>
Wing span about 65mm (2.5 in.)

A typical aquatic larva
and pupa of <u>Tipula</u>

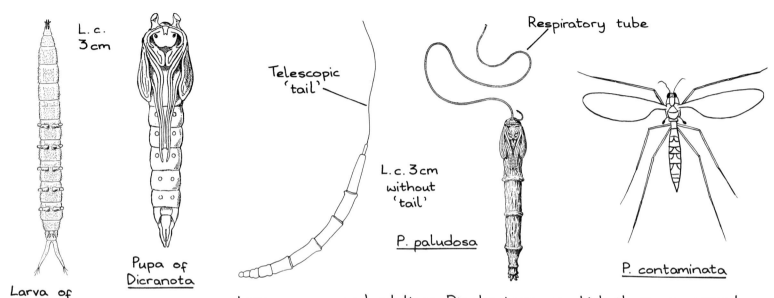

L. c. 3 cm

Larva of
Dicranota bimaculata

Pupa of
Dicranota

Telescopic
'tail'

L.c. 3cm
without
'tail'

Respiratory tube

P. paludosa

P. contaminata

Larva, pupa, and adult of Ptychoptera, of which there are several
Lake District species.

-veloped on the thorax of insects).   The small head can be retracted.   It is provided with powerful jaws with which the larva can seize and masticate such prey as soft-bodied worms larger than itself.   Air breathing is practised.   Two lobes at the rear end each terminate in a spiracle or hole that admits air to the tracheal tubes when the tips of the lobes are protruded above the water surface.   The pupa is also aquatic.   It has a pair of ear-like lobes at the back of its head.   These are respiratory 'trumpets' and are characteristic of many dipterous pupae.

To have to put its rear end to the surface film limits the depth to which a larva can go — or necessitates difficult and dangerous journeys to the surface, which maggot-like larvae are ill-equipped to perform.   A solution which facilitates somewhat deeper penetration is a long telescopic 'tail'.   Such is possessed by species of Ptychoptera, near relatives of the Crane flies.   Their larvae live, usually buried in mud, in shallow water with the long 'tail', through which run two tracheal tubes, extending to the surface.   The pupa also has a long respiratory tube in which are several thin-walled bladders.   These cause the filament to float

299

to the water surface where gases readily diffuse through the walls of the bladders.

As transmitters of malaria, yellow and other fevers, <u>mosquitoes</u> are among the best studied insects. Their larvae live in pools, ditches and other small water bodies so, despite its lakes, the Lake District is not especially favoured by these flies. Female mosquitoes have piercing mouthparts and some suck the blood of vertebrates, including man. Males imbibe juices from flowers and fruits, as also do females. There are two sub-groups of mosquitoes — culicines and anophelines. To man an important difference be-

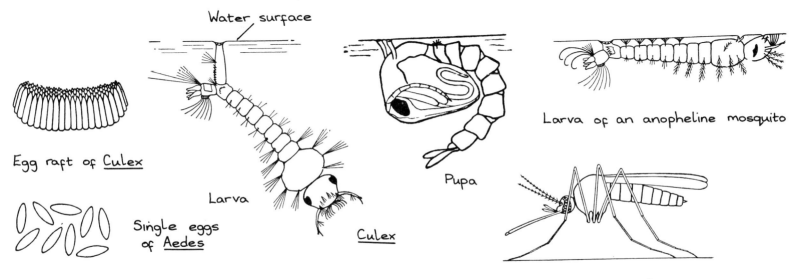

Water surface

Egg raft of <u>Culex</u>

Single eggs of <u>Aedes</u>

Larva

<u>Culex</u>

Pupa

Larva of an anopheline mosquito

Adult female

Stages in the life cycle of culicine mosquitoes

-tween them is that anophelines transmit malaria, culicines do not. Of about 32 British species it is uncertain how many occur in the Lake District.

Eggs of some species, such as <u>Culex pipiens</u> and <u>Theobaldia</u>*<u>annulata</u> are laid in clusters, often of 200 or more, that float on the water surface. In others (e.g. <u>Aedes</u> and the anophelines) they are laid singly. The larvae that emerge display complex adaptations for feeding and respiration.

Larvae breathe atmospheric air. Those of culicines have a respiratory siphon that projects obliquely

*Currently known as <u>Culiseta</u>

from the rear end.   By utilising surface tension a larva hangs from the surface film by this siphon and can take in air via two terminal apertures.   When it dives and swims, which it does by jerkily folding and straightening its body, the apertures are closed by valves.   Water is also prevented from entering by the exudation of an oily secretion.   Anopheline larvae also take in air at the surface and utilise surface tension but stretch themselves horizontally beneath the surface film, using special bristles (float bristles) to enhance attachment.

Some larvae sift exceedingly fine particles from the water as a source of food; some scrape surfaces; a few are carnivores.   Species feeding on fine suspended particles have a complex array of fine bristles on the upper lip at the front of the head.   These make up what is often called the mouth brush.   More graphic is the German term 'Strudelorgane'—whirlpool organ.   The mandibles also have fine brushes and stout bristles.   All these can be folded and protected beneath the plate-like maxillae that lie just behind them.   To feed, the maxillae are lifted, the mouth brush beats rapidly and sets up currents that flow towards the head.   From these the bristles filter particles.   These are combed off by the bristles and spines of the mandibles and passed to the mouth.   Before they are taken in, however, a remarkable process of selection takes place.   Tiny algae and other desirable particles are retained but bits of detritus are rejected, bundled together, and dropped from between the mouthparts as an unbroken stream of tiny spherical pellets.   So, the larva collects <u>all</u> tiny particles but can select from them those it needs, discarding the rest.   <u>Theobaldia</u>*<u>annulata</u>, which scrapes particles from leaves or from the bottom, has stouter bristles on its mouth fan, some beautifully modified as scrapers.   Its mandibles also bear more robust spines than do those of filter-feeders.

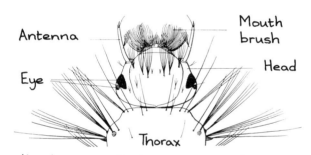

Head of a culicine mosquito larva showing the mouth brush.

The pupa also hangs from the surface film and takes in air via open trumpets whose lining of fine bristles prevents the entry of water during periods of submergence.   The pupa is <u>active</u> and can swim by beating its rear end which is provided with two broad, flap-like paddles.   The adult emerges via a slit along the dorsal surface of the thorax.

The distribution of mosquitoes in the Lake District is poorly known.   Some, such as Culex <u>pipiens</u> and <u>Theobaldia</u>*annulata are widespread, others less common and more localised.   <u>Aedes punctor</u>, a vigorous and persistent biter of man, breeds in acidic pools, often those containing <u>Sphagnum</u> moss or dead leaves of Birch trees with which it is often associated.   Not strictly a Lake District species, though as females

*Now called <u>Culiseta</u>

301

have a flight range of at least four miles perhaps sometimes qualifying, and worth noting for its habits of breeding in saline pools, is <u>Aedes detritus</u>, another vicious and persistent biter, which occurs commonly in nearby estuarine regions.   Of the two commonest species, <u>C. pipiens</u>, which frequently enters houses where it often hibernates, does not bite man (it feeds mostly on birds) but the bites of <u>T. annulata</u>*, which also hibernates in houses, are exceptionally severe.   As the latter sometimes 'awakes' during mild spells in winter one is liable to be bitten at any time of the year.   <u>T. alaskaensis</u>*is a northern species, rare in Britain and at the southern limits of its range in the Lake District and Yorkshire for which there are only a very few records.

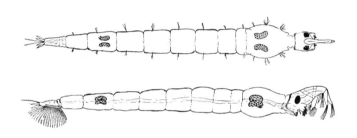

Larva from above and from the side

Stages in the life cycle of <u>Chaoborus</u>

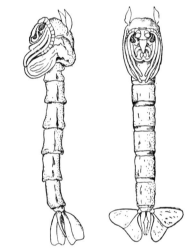

Pupa from the side and below

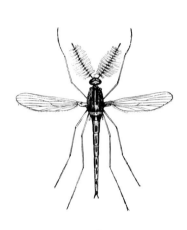

Adult

Related to mosquitoes are certain non-biting flies conveniently called gnats.   <u>Chaoborus</u>, with four British species, and <u>Mochlonyx</u> with two, represent one of these groups.   Adults are mosquito-like but have short non-piercing mouthparts.   The larva of <u>Chaoborus</u> — the appropriately named Phantom larva — is one of the most transparent organisms found in freshwater.   It usually lies horizontally like a submarine, buoyed up by a pair of air sacs forrad and another pair aft.   These are developed from the tracheal system.   Like the swim bladder of a fish they render the larva weightless and allow effortless

*Now <u>Culiseta annulata</u> and <u>C. alaskaensis</u>

302

maintenance of station.   When the larva rises they distend: when it sinks they contract.   Often motionless, the larva moves rapidly when necessary by a sideways flick of the body, thrust being transmitted by a fan of bristles at the rear, analogous to the fin of a fish, which also grants stability.   Its transparency—often the eyes and air-sacs alone betray its presence — is associated with very thin cuticle which readily allows the diffusion of gases.   Dissolved oxygen is used, which renders it independent of visits to the surface. Transparency affords protection against enemies such as fishes.   It also facilitates the capture of prey, for Chaoborus is a predator that seizes small crustaceans and other prey, including mosquito larvae, with apparatus derived from the antennae (usually sensory) as well as mouthparts.   The antennae grasp the prey which is masticated by the mouthparts.

In the Lake District C. crystallinus occurs in a variety of small water bodies.   C. flavicans does likewise but also frequents larger expanses of water, e.g. it is common in Esthwaite Water.   While the larvae of C. cry--stallinus do not appear to do this, those of C. flavicans sometimes burrow in the mud by day and emerge at

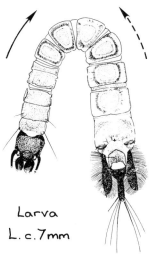

Larva
L. c. 7mm

Solid arrow indicates how, by pushing one limb of the U in that direction, the larva ad--vances over a surface.   The other arm is extended next (dashed arrow).

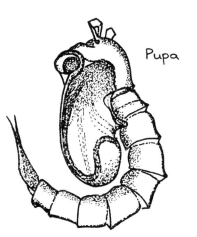

Pupa

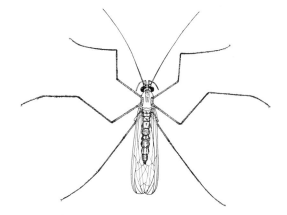

Adult.   Length. c. 5mm.

Stages in the life cycle of Dixa (Page 304)

night.   This may be why they are found by bottom-grubbing fishes in whose diet they appear.   Swarming of adults, such as is described for chironomids, (page 305) sometimes takes place.

Related to the chaoborids are the <u>meniscus midges</u> (Dixidae), so called because their larvae are often associated with the meniscus formed where the water surface meets a stone or plant stem.   The body of the larva is generally bent double on itself, from side to side.   By a characteristic motion, pushing first one arm of the U then the other forward in turn so that the middle part of the body advances first, the larva often crawls above the water surface, dragging a film of water with it.   Larvae also hang suspended from the surface of still water — which includes sheltered places at the sides of fast-flowing streams. Minute particles are collected for food by brush-like organs reminiscent of those of mosquito larvae.

Of the 14 British species at least 8 occur in, or at the fringes of, the Lake District.   Species of <u>Dixa</u> tend to be associated with streams, of <u>Dixella</u> with standing water.   Most Lake District species belong to the former genus.   <u>Dixa puberula</u> is the most characteristic species of rapid stony streams, where it occurs on emergent stones, among accumulations of dead leaves and on emergent grasses and other plants.   By contrast <u>Dixella aestivalis</u> frequents emergent vegetation in pools, swamps, and river backwaters, and at lake margins.

During any evening from early May to the end of August, especially if there be little or no wind, the visitor to the Lake District is likely to be made painfully aware of the presence of tiny <u>biting midges</u>.   These belong to the genus <u>Culicoides</u>, a member of the family Ceratopogonidae.   While less prevalent than in Scotland, one species in particular <u>C. impunctata</u> is sometimes abundant, and females are per--sistent biters of man as they seek a blood meal prior to laying their eggs.   Of these tiny midges, often not much more than a millimetre long, there are several local species.   They have aquatic larvae.   Curiously, although they occur in millions, their eggs have not been found in nature, but have been deposited in captivity. From them slender larvae emerge.   These usually frequent small water bodies — in the case of <u>C. impunctata</u> often pools in boggy places where <u>Sphagnum</u> moss is present.   Other species live in what is little more than a film of water on the sur-face of a dead leaf.   Larvae, which feed on detritus, move by undulatory wriggling.   Most species overwinter as larvae.   After four moults each larva becomes a pupa which is capable of some movement.   The pupal stage lasts only a few days.

Related midges belong to the genus <u>Ceratopogon</u>.   Their larvae, which are very

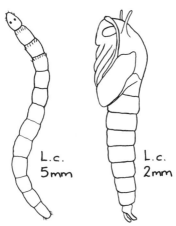

L.c.
5mm

L.c.
2mm

Larva and pupa of
<u>Culicoides impunctata</u>

Larva (above) and pupa (right) of <u>Chironomus</u> <u>tentans</u>. Related species have very similar larvae and pupae.

Stages in the life cycle of <u>Chironomus</u>

Male (left) and female <u>Chironomus</u> <u>dorsalis</u>, a common Lake District species.

common, are similar to those of <u>Culicoides</u> but more slender.

Of all aquatic insects the non-biting midges of the family Chironomidae — <u>chironomid midges</u> — have perhaps the strongest claims to be regarded as the most important. Inconspicuous as individuals, these midges and their larvae often occur in vast numbers. Adults frequently bring themselves to notice when they swarm. Swarms consist of males which are sometimes present in their thousands, sometimes even in millions. Individual females enter the swarm and are quickly seized by a male, and often both fall to the ground. This is conveniently seen when, as sometimes happens, a swarm aligns itself over a light-coloured stationary motor car, onto whose roof and bonnet pairs fall in a steady downpour. These mating pairs permit close inspection of the adults. It is the male that has plumose antennae. Neither sex bites. Mandibles are in fact lacking. To recognise these midges as chironomids is relatively easy. To identify individual species is less so. Some 470 species have so far been recorded in Britain, a large proportion of which occurs in the Lake District.

Eggs, encased in jelly that swells like that of frog spawn, are laid in various places according to species.

Sometimes the egg mass, often of several hundred, sometimes of over 2000 eggs, is a spherical blob, sometimes a long rope : in some cases it is anchored, in others free. The jelly protects the eggs from small predators and sometimes serves as a flotation device. Egg masses of lake-frequenting species are sometimes dispersed widely by water currents.

In appearance chironomid larvae tend to look similar to each other. This similarity belies their diversity in habits, habitat preferences and ways of life. The bottom deposits of lakes are frequented from the shallow margins to great depths, reedy, sandy and muddy bottoms having their devotees ; other assemblages of species occur in upland tarns, streams, boggy situations and even in such places as water-filled tree holes. Chironomid larvae in fact live in practically all habitable situations in freshwater. Different situations call for different life styles. Many larvae feed on algae or detritus, others are carnivores, and within these broad groupings individual species earn their livings in a variety of ways.

Chironomus anthracinus serves to introduce these larvae but those of related species such as C. dorsalis are very similar. The body is 'worm-like' and flexible, the head small, protected by tough cuticle and provided with stout mandibles. The first segment behind the head has short prolegs provided with numerous hooks, and similar appendages are present on the last segment. Tubular gills are borne just in front of them. A striking feature of the larva is its bright red colour. Its blood is red because, like ours, it contains the respiratory pigment haemoglobin. This helps it to snatch oxygen dissolved in the water when it is in short supply. The red colour of several, but by no means all, chironomid larvae gives them the common name 'blood worm' — though they are not worms.

C. anthracinus is common in the bottom muds of several English lakes including Windermere and Esthwaite Water, and is one of the dominant animals in deep water in the soft muds of Esthwaite. It is probably dispersed there in the egg stage or by movements of the first instar larvae that are only about 2mm in length. There are four larval instars, the last being about 16 mm (c. 5/8 in.) long. These make blind burrows in the mud, several times their own length. The burrows are lined with a salivary secretion. This gives stability to a construction made in watery mud — not the easiest medium in which to build. Sometimes a short chimney is built at the entrance to the burrow. The larva reaches out and collects organic matter — mostly dead algal cells falling from the

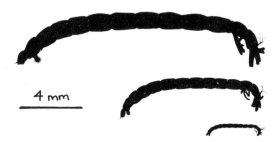

4 mm

The four larval stages (instars) of Chironomus anthracinus to show their relative sizes.

plankton — as food.

Haemoglobin helps the larva to obtain oxygen when it is scarce, but is no help when there is no oxygen at all — as is the case each summer in deep water in Esthwaite. At this time larvae appear to go into a state of suspended animation. In this condition, in which they neither feed nor grow, they can survive for several months without oxygen.

Pupation takes place in the burrow. When ready to escape, the pupa leaves the burrow and rises to the water surface; its cuticle splits, and the adult emerges. Rising pupae are vulnerable to predators, such as fishes; nor does the pupa linger at the surface where 30—40 seconds suffice for the adult to emerge. Emergence is synchronised. In the Lake District it is concentrated into a few days in April. It is at this time that swarms are encountered around Windermere and Esthwaite. The adults are among the largest of the local chironomid midges and are black in colour.

Larvae of <u>Chironomus anthracinus</u> appear to collect their food in a simple manner. Related tunnel-frequenting species have adopted more elegant methods. <u>C. plumosus</u>, another Lake District species, makes a U-shaped tunnel in mud, open at each end, within which it anchors itself with its posterior prolegs. Its head circles round and round within the tunnel and the anterior prolegs help to draw out strands of salivary secretion that are attached to the walls of the tunnel and stretched to form a loose saucer-

Larva of <u>Chironomus plumosus</u> with its net inside its tunnel. The arrow shows the direction of the food-bearing current.

shaped sheet. The larva now retreats from the sheet dragging a salivary thread from its centre. This pulls the sheet into the shape of a cone — like a minature child's fishing net, which indeed it is. By undulating its body about twice a second the larva draws a current of water through the tube, and therefore through the net which retains tiny particles. The larva then eats both the net and its contents. A new net is then made. The entire cycle is enacted in only about 1½ to 2 minutes, half of which time is devoted to eating and making the net, half to undulating. This process is often continued without respite for an hour or more. In nature one could not observe such details but <u>C. plumosus</u> helpfully performs in a glass tube, thus revealing all!

Particularly interesting is the fact that while the larvae of <u>C. dorsalis</u> and <u>C. riparius</u> are so similar to that of <u>C. plumosus</u> that they cannot with certainty be separated from it — though adult males are re-cognisably distinct — and although they also make U-shaped tubes, they spin no net. This is an ex-cellent example of animals that appear to be the same in structure (or, as the biologist says, appear to

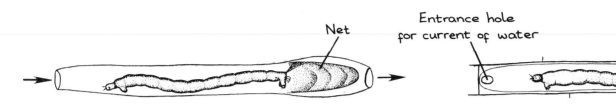

Endochironomus in a tube of its own secretion on the surface of a leaf, and the net it has spun within it. Arrows show the direction of the current set up by the undulating body of the larva

A larva of <u>Glyptotendipes</u> ensconced in a tube that it has excavated inside a leaf and within which it has spun a net.

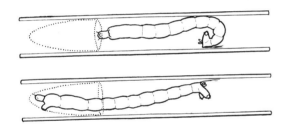

Endochironomus making its net. In this case the larva has been put in a glass tube the better to reveal its activities

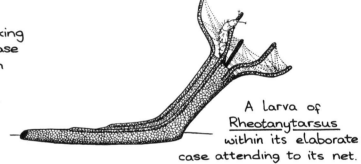

A larva of <u>Rheotanytarsus</u> within its elaborate case attending to its net.

be morphologically identical) but which differ strikingly in behaviour. Such an example emphasises the need to study the living animal before its role can be understood.

Chironomus plumosus is not, however, the only net-spinning chironomid larva. Species of <u>Endochironomus</u> make a straight tube of salivary material on the surface of a leaf, open at each end, and live within it. Near one end they spin a net, more thimble-like in shape than that of C. plumosus. Having made it they turn around before undulating and thus face away from the net. After undulating they turn again and devour both the net and its contents. <u>E. albipennis</u> is a common Lake District member of this genus.

Similar nets to those of <u>Endochironomus</u> are made by leaf-mining larvae of the genera <u>Pentapedilum</u> and <u>Glyptotendipes</u> that burrow into leaves — like leaf-mining terrestrial insects — making a tunnel open at

308

each end.   <u>G. glaucus</u>, a common species in the Lake District where the reed <u>Phragmites</u> occurs, burrows in decaying stems of that plant.   Elaborate nets are spun by stream-dwelling species of <u>Rheotanytarsus</u> that also construct spacious and complex tubes or cases in which they live.   The case, made from particles of sand or silt, is elevated at one end which, in fully-grown larvae, terminates in five spreading arms facing upstream.   Using the arms as supports, the larva spins a network of threads that make a net to catch particles brought in by the stream.   It then retreats for a few minutes into its tube, emerges and examines its net.   Unwanted particles are bitten free and cast aside to be borne away by the current.   The net is then cut free and gathered into a ball by the mouthparts and anterior prolegs, usually only one section being so treated at any one time.   The larva takes its prize within the tube and eats it or part of it.   Any left-overs are stuck at the end of the tube ready for use as wall material when the tube is extended.   A new section of net is then spun.   Larvae pupate within the tube, making a perforated lid across the entrance before doing so.   Larval tubes of <u>Rheotanytarsus</u> are easy to recognise but the exact identity of the larvae is often difficult to ascertain.

Chironomid larvae and certain caddis larvae (page 278) have independently adopted the habit of net-spinning.   This is an example of convergent evolution.   Similar convergent evolution is shown in the habit of case-building.   Some chironomid larvae make portable cases that are very similar to those of caddis larvae.   Those of <u>Stempellina bausei</u>, a species recorded from Windermere, for example are constructed from tiny sand grains and look rather like those of a caddis larva such as <u>Mystacides longicornis</u> or <u>Limnephilus vittatus</u> (pages 274 and 275), but are smaller.

While many chironomid larvae are detritus feeders or eat algae, others are carnivores.   Such are the species of <u>Tanypus</u> and <u>Ablabesmyia</u>. These are slender, long-headed larvae with long prolegs of which the anterior pair are fused together for much of their length.   They move around briskly in a manner that suggested to one observer that they appear to have wooden legs.   They prey on other chironomid larvae and on small crustaceans.   The pupa, which can swim actively, is superficially more similar to that of a

L.c.
7mm

Larva and pupa of <u>Ablabesmyia monilis</u>,
a common Lake District species.

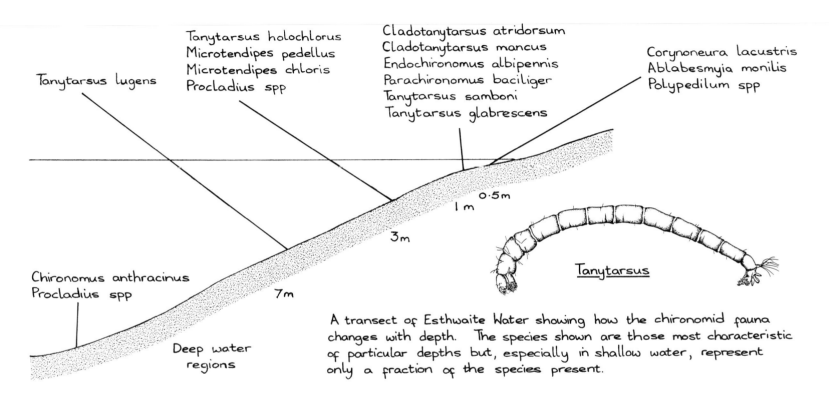

Tanytarsus lugens

Tanytarsus holochlorus
Microtendipes pedellus
Microtendipes chloris
Procladius spp

Cladotanytarsus atridorsum
Cladotanytarsus mancus
Endochironomus albipennis
Parachironomus baciliger
Tanytarsus samboni
Tanytarsus glabrescens

Corynoneura lacustris
Ablabesmyia monilis
Polypedilum spp

0·5m
1 m
3m
7m

Chironomus anthracinus
Procladius spp

Deep water
regions

Tanytarsus

A transect of Esthwaite Water showing how the chironomid fauna changes with depth. The species shown are those most characteristic of particular depths but, especially in shallow water, represent only a fraction of the species present.

culicine mosquito (page 300) than to the pupa of Chironomus.

The diversity of chironomid larvae, of which only a fraction is indicated here, is matched by their abundance. Lakes often harbour many species, sometimes in vast numbers. In the well-studied Esthwaite Water 120 species have been found. In winter at depths down to 6m (20ft) these are present on the bottom at a mean density of about 21,000 per square metre. At a depth of 2m, where 70 species have been found, as many as 76,000 larvae may be present on a square metre of bottom. Numbers are fewer in deeper water but between 8 and 15m about 3,500 larvae per square metre are present in winter.   The fall-off in numbers with increasing depth is paralleled by a reduction in diversity.   This is easy to understand.   Habitat diversity is greater in shallow than in deep water.   In the shallow littoral zone there are various types of bottom and both emergent and submerged vegetation is present.   In deep water there is a monotonous desert of mud and the variety of foods is limited.

Although there are so many species in Esthwaite, many of them are relatively uncommon, and a few species dominate the fauna.   Thus at depths down to 6m about 90% of the fauna consists of species of Tanytarsus and Procladius.   Below 6m, Chironomus anthracinus and species of Procladius account for about 85% of the fauna.   Many species feed on algae so a limit is set to the depth to which such species can occur by that at which algae can get enough light for photosynthesis.   This is at about 8m in Esthwaite.   Detritus feeders or consumers of sedimenting plankton, such as Chironomus anthracinus, or roving predators such as species of Procladius suffer no such restrictions and can penetrate much deeper.

The chironomid faunas of Lake District tarns differ considerably among themselves.   The most acidic tarns have assemblages of characteristic species that include Protanypus morio, Heterotrissocladius grimshawi, Macropelopia goetghebueri and Psectrocladius platypus.   In less acidic tarns these are replaced by such species as Polypedilum pullum and species of Stictochironomus.   Hard water, calcareous, tarns at the fringe of the area have different faunas.   Acid-loving midges are here replaced by such species as Endochironomus impar.   Some species, such as Psectrocladius obvius, are versatile and can tolerate both alkaline and acidic (but not the most acidic) conditions.

Rivers and streams have their own assemblages of chironomids.   In the Lake District high altitude streams have distinctive chironomid faunas.   One such, at about 2160 ft (660m) on Helvellyn, produced 20 species.   The name of one of these, Micropsectra monticola indicates a 'love' of mountainous habitats.

In the Lake District most chironomids either have a lifecycle that lasts for one year (and are said to be univoltine) or produce two generations a year (are bivoltine).   Under certain circumstances some of the large species, such as Chironomus anthracinus require two years to complete their life cycle. (Some tropical species have several generations a year.)   Each species has its own time, or times, of emergence, mostly during the period from late April to the end of October.   Some emerge over a period of several weeks — six in the case of Microtendipes pedellus that emerges in July and August — others concentrate their emergence into a few days.   More than 80% of the Esthwaite population of Microtendipes chloris emerges in four days in late April.   Emergence is sometimes at a particular time of the day or night.   Thus Psilotanypus rufovittatus, one of the commonest midges of Esthwaite, emerges mostly between midnight and 6.00 am B.S.T.

Certain species of <u>Chironomus</u>, <u>Corynoneura</u> and <u>Tanytarsus</u> are capable of reproducing without the intervention of males (that is, by parthenogenesis). Even pupae of some species of <u>Tanytarsus</u> can lay parthenogenetic eggs. Because of their abundance chironomid larvae are an important source of food for many animals. Fishes consume them in vast numbers; others are eaten by many invertebrates, including other chironomid larvae, some of which are themselves eventually eaten by fishes. Adults are eaten by many birds, especially by aerial feeders such as swallows, martins and swifts, but also by wagtails and other insect eaters.

<u>Simulium flies</u>, sometimes called Black flies, are small, (2 to 7mm long), somewhat hump-backed flies with plump bodies, short legs and large broad wings. Females of some species bite and suck the blood of man and domestic (and other) animals. While sometimes a source of intense irritation they are a less serious pest in Britain than in parts of Africa where some species transmit a nematode worm, <u>Onchocera</u>, the cause of onchocerciasis or river blindness, a disease sometimes resulting in blindness. <u>O. guttorosa</u> infects cattle in Britain and is transmitted by <u>Simulium ornatum</u> but seems not greatly to inconvenience its host. At least 16 of the 35 British species occur in the Lake District and others at its fringes. All are associated with flowing, often briskly flowing, water in which the larvae and pupae live.

Egg-laying habits are various. In some species the female enters the water, in others eggs are stuck to objects washed by the stream. Sometimes several females lay communal masses of eggs.

Larvae are superbly adapted to life in flowing water. Up to about 10mm (almost ½ in.) in length, they have a tubular body somewhat swollen posteriorly. The head bears a pair of fan-like mouth brushes that can be extended or closed. These collect the food. Posteriorly the body terminates in a 'sucker'—actually a ring of numerous minute hooks — by means of which the larva attaches itself to a stone or leaf on whose surface it has spun silken threads to give the hooks something to grip. To feed, the larva, which is inevitably aligned head downstream by the current, expands its mouth brushes and uses them to catch drifting particles. Such a mechanism is more efficient in regions of smooth (technically laminar) than turbulent flow as turbulent eddies might remove captured particles, so <u>Simulium</u> larvae tend to congregate in regions where flow is smooth rather than rough. Captured particles are passed to the mouthparts and ingested.

Before it pupates, the larva spins a simple cocoon, usually shoe- or slipper-shaped that lies, toe

<u>Simulium ornatum</u>
Female

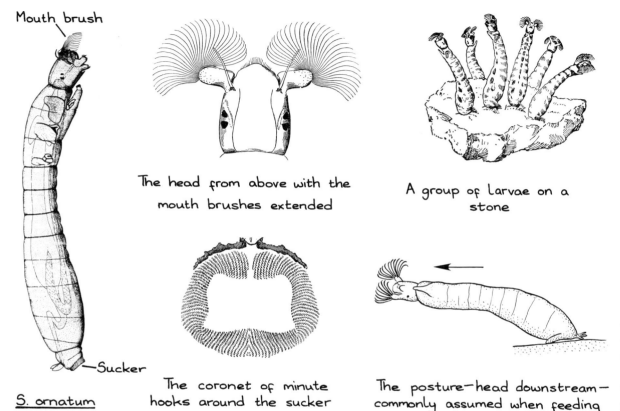

Mouth brush

The head from above with the mouth brushes extended

A group of larvae on a stone

S. ornatum
L.c. 9mm

—Sucker

The coronet of minute hooks around the sucker

The posture—head downstream— commonly assumed when feeding

Simulium larvae

upstream, and covers the pupa within, preventing it from being swept away by the current. The rather ovoid pupa, whose head end protrudes from the wide end of the cocoon, is provided with a pair of conspicuous, branched respiratory organs that are directed downstream. Escape of the adult fly from a pupa anchored in fast-flowing water presents problems, to which an elegant solution has been evolved. The pupal stage lasts about two weeks. Towards the end of this period the pupal skin becomes inflated with air extracted from the water and passed, apparently through the spiracles of the developing fly, into the space around it. Eventually the distended pupal skin splits, and a bubble of air, which surrounds the adult fly, rises to the surface carrying the adult with it.

As simuliids are associated with fast-flowing rivers and streams, physical conditions in the Lake District are suitable for several species. Some of those present, such as <u>Simulium latipes</u> and <u>S. ornatum</u>, are widespread in Britain, but as these favour lowland situations they are less common than several others, such as <u>S. variegatum</u>, <u>S. niti-difrons</u> and <u>S. monticola</u> that have northern and western distributions.   As the name of the last indicates, it favours hilly or mountainous regions where it frequents briskly flowing rocky streams.   The primitive <u>Prosimulium hirtipes</u> is a northern form which is near the south-ern limit of its range in the Lake District. It is a torrential hill stream species.

<u>Moth flies</u> (Psychodidae) are tiny flies, often about 2mm in length, whose bodies, including the wings, are adorned with long bristles.   Of no med-ical importance in Britain their overseas relatives — Sand flies — carry the protozoans that cause leishmaniasis in man, one type of which is Kala-Azar, a sometimes fatal disease. Another is Oriental boil, an unpleasant skin ulcer.

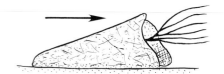

Pupa of <u>Simulium variegatum</u> in its cocoon.   Arrow shows direction of current

S. brevicaule   S. latipes   S. aureum

Cocoons of Lake District species of <u>Simulium</u>.   From above.

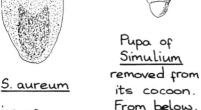

Pupa of <u>Simulium</u> removed from its cocoon. From below.

<u>Pericoma</u>, a Moth fly
L.c. 4mm

The tiny larvae of psychodids are cylindrical and tapered at each end and in most species frequent aquatic habitats, but sometimes only small volumes or films of water. One such site is sewage works filter beds from which adults sometimes emerge in vast numbers and constitute a nuisance.   In the Lake District adult psychodids are more likely to be found on tree trunks or the under-sides of leaves , but are not infrequently seen on window panes.

<u>Hover Flies</u> (Syrphidae), which are sometimes exquisitely coloured, have remark-

-able powers of flight.   They can hover motionless and even fly backwards as well as dash forward with great rapidity.   While the larvae of many of them are terrestrial, several are aquatic.   These include the so-called rat-tailed maggots.   Of several syrphids with such larvae, <u>Eristalis tenax</u> is very common. The adult, sometimes called the Drone Fly because of its superficial resemblance to the male or drone of the Hive Bee, is often seen in Lakeland gardens.   Its larvae, and those of its relatives, frequent small, often stagnant, pools but are not inconvenienced by lack of oxygen as they breathe atmospheric air through a telescopic 'tail' reminiscent of that of <u>Ptychoptera</u> (page 229).   The larva has seven pairs of short false legs, each armed with hooks, but its most remarkable possession is its telescopic 'tail'.   This consists of two tubes, one sliding within the other.   The inner tube can be extended from the outer and in addition the outer behaves rather like a concertina and can be greatly extended, becoming reduced in diameter as it does so.   A larva only about ⅝ in. (c. 16 mm) long can extend its breathing tube to the water surface from a depth of about 5 in. (about 13 cm) Food consists of organic particles.   Pupation takes place out of water in damp soil.

Eristalis tenax, wing span about 2·3cm, and its larva, a rat-tailed maggot

Telescopic breathing tube

A very handsome Lake District syrphid fly with a 'long-tailed' larva is <u>Sericomyia borealis</u> that frequents boggy and peaty pools.   Adults have a wasp-like black and yellow abdomen.

Various other Lake District flies , including tabanids such as some of the species of <u>Tabanus</u> (Horse flies) and <u>Haematopota</u> (Clegs) that bite man and his domestic animals, have larvae that live in wet situations and sometimes in water, and other flies with aquatic larvae that are known elsewhere in Britain have as yet remained unstudied in the area.   Even in relatively well-studied groups , such as the chironomid midges, the relating of larval and pupal to adult stages is sometimes difficult or impossible , and a vast amount remains to be learned about the habits of most species.   Such studies offer abundant scope for the enthusiastic field worker provided with very modest equipment.

A wasp that swims under water using its wings as oars and lays its eggs in the eggs of Dragonflies seems a most improbable insect, yet it exists.   <u>Polynema natans</u> is only about a millimetre in length. While able to fly, it spends much of its time swimming under water, driving itself along with its bristle-fringed wings and often remaining submerged for several days without visiting the surface.   Bouts of wing beating that look like slowed-down flapping for flight are interspersed with periods of rest.   The bristles are not an adaptation to swimming for non-aquatic relatives of <u>P. natans</u> have similar bristle-fringed wings.   Indeed while remark-ably at home under water — it even mates there — <u>P. natans</u> shows few obvious modifications for aquatic life.   It has a tracheal system like aerial insects and does not apparently take in dissolved oxygen through its wings as once thought.

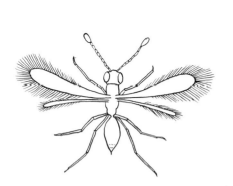

Polynema natans
L.c. 1mm

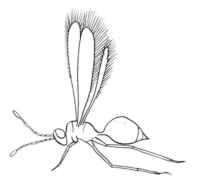

P. natans 'flying'
under water

Eggs are laid in the eggs of dragonflies or the water bug <u>Notonecta</u>, and the larvae develop there.   Only one larva develops in each dragonfly egg; 4 or 5 is more usual in each egg of <u>Notonecta</u>.   When the whole contents of a victimised egg have been con-sumed, which takes only a few days, the larva pupates there.   The pupal stage generally lasts only about 10 or 12 days.

<u>P. natans</u>, which belongs to the family Proctotrupidae, and is sometimes called a Fairy Fly, is just one of a host of tiny relatives of the familiar bees and wasps, that have parasitic habits of various kinds but is perhaps the most truly aquatic of these usually terrestrial insects.   Not specially sought in the Lake District, it has been encountered in collections of tiny aquatic crustaceans and may be commoner than realised.

Another group of insects that, like ants, bees and wasps, belongs to the vast group the Hymenoptera (meaning 'membrane winged') is that which comprises the ichneumon flies.   Of these there are many terrestrial species whose larvae develop on or in the body of other insects whose substance they convert to their own flesh.   Caterpillars are frequent victims.   One aquatic ichneumon, <u>Agriotypus armatus</u>, selects caddis pupae of the genera <u>Silo</u> and <u>Goera</u> as its victims.   About 1 cm long, the almost black

316

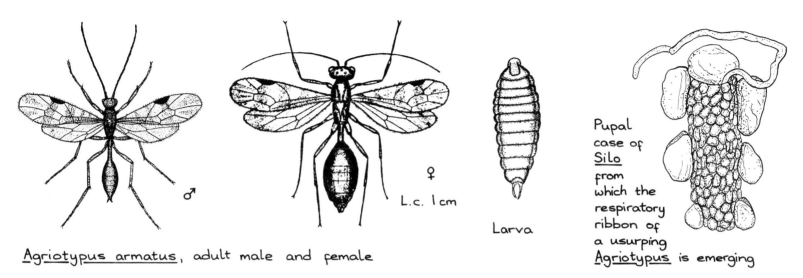

♂

♀

L.c. 1 cm

Larva

Pupal case of Silo from which the respiratory ribbon of a usurping Agriotypus is emerging

Agriotypus armatus, adult male and female

adult female flies over suitable streams in May and June.   From time to time it alights on a stone from which, surrounded by a bubble of air, it creeps under the water in search of a caddis pupa in which to lay an egg.   Its quest is often time-consuming and it may remain continuously submerged for as long as 5 hours.   Several such excursions are necessary.   Eggs are laid inside the pupal case of the host on the surface of the pupa.   More than one egg may be laid on a host but only one larva develops.   The larva that soon emerges is maggot-like in form.   It begins to feed on the caddis pupa and grows rapidly, passing through five instars by August by which time it has completely consumed the caddis pupa and is it-self ready to pupate.   It constructs a cocoon of silk from which extends a long, flat, hollow ribbon up to about 1·5 cm (c. 5/8 in.) long.   This is curled and springy and like the cocoon proper, is full of gas. Its wall is composed of an outer layer of wet, closely woven silk and an inner layer of dry tangled silk. When the larva pupates in the cocoon in August the ribbon acts as a plastron (page 272).   If it is cut off the pupa dies.

Development is complete by October but the adult remains in the pupal case all winter and emerges in the following spring.

A. armatus occurs in Lake District streams.   Although encountered only in small numbers it is probably not particularly rare and is likely to occur wherever its hosts are found.

317

Spiders and mites belong to a large group of jawless arthropods, the Arachnida that also includes harvest-men, ticks and several other groups, some not represented in Britain. These, with the king crabs and some extinct forms including the giant eurypterids, comprise the Chelicerata. Although they lack jaws, spiders (Aranea) are predators. Prey is seized by a pair of chelicerae. Each chelicera is two-segmented, the terminal segment being a fang or poison claw. With these the prey is quickly killed. Salivary glands exude a digestive ferment which digests the prey externally and the resulting fluid is sucked into the stomach. Other characteristic attributes of spiders are four pairs of legs and the ability to spin silken threads from posteriorly located spinnerets.

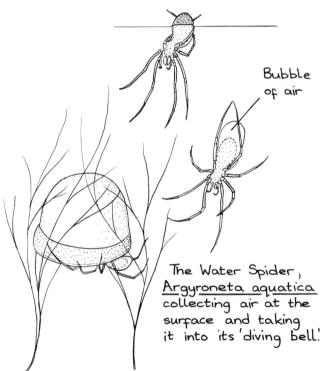

Bubble of air

The Water Spider, Argyroneta aquatica collecting air at the surface and taking it into its 'diving bell.'

Several spiders are associated with wet places and some of these occasionally enter water but only one British species is truly aquatic. This is the aptly named Water Spider Argyroneta aquatica which occurs in certain Lake District tarns. Females usually grow to a length of about 15 mm, exceptionally more: males are a little less. Seen out of water Argyroneta shows few obvious signs of adaptation to an aquatic life, but it swims efficiently and as it dives beneath the surface it carries with it a silvery film of air that covers the rear end of the body (technically the opisthosoma: not quite the equivalent of the abdomen of insects) and the under surface of the more anterior parts. Its silk-producing ability enables it to construct beneath the surface a remarkable air-containing bell that serves as a retreat. A curved platform of silk is spun among vegetation and the spider proceeds to fill it with air.

When exploring under water only a thin film of air is carried: a bubble would render the spider too buoyant. When the bell is being filled, large bubbles are entrapped at the surface by a special movement, and with such a bubble the spider swims or scrambles to the silk platform under which the bubble is released. A series of such trips, interspersed with adjustments to, and extensions of, the bell, gives rise to a usually thimble-shaped, but sometimes irregular, air-filled chamber. As happens in the gas bubbles carried by insects, as the carbon dioxide content of the air in the bell rises as a result of the spider's respiration, it diffuses into the water and oxygen diffuses in. This, plus replenishments by the spider, provides a permanent air-filled underwater dwelling.

The spider sits with its legs protruding from the bell and pounces on passing insects, and also makes excursions, especially at night, in search of food. As digestion is external, prey has to be consumed inside the bell, or occasionally out of water.

As in terrestrial spiders, prior to mating the male charges his palps, that lie immediately behind the chelicerae, with sperm. After courtship he passes the sperm from the palps to the female. Eggs, 50 to 100 in number, are laid in the upper half of the bell from about May to July, two, or sometimes three batches being produced in a season. The young hatch within three to four weeks and generally remain in the bell for two to four weeks before departing to lead an independent existence.

The winter is spent in a state of torpidity in a bell of stouter texture than the summer home that is built in deeper water.

Ticks (that have no aquatic representatives) and mites make up the Acari. Aquatic mites comprise the Hydrachnida (or Hydracarina). Unlike the Water spider adult water mites are independent of atmospheric air. Seen from above they generally have a rounded or oval body with no boundary between the prosoma and opisthosoma. Like spiders they have four pairs of legs. Many are brightly coloured, often red or orange, sometimes bluish or greenish and include some of the most conspicuous invertebrates. This is related to the fact that they are distasteful to fishes and other predators. Their bright colours are warning colours. Others, however, are brown and inconspicuous. Their

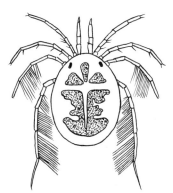

Limnesia
Several species common
in lakes

Hydrodroma despiciens
Females c.2mm. Reddish orange.

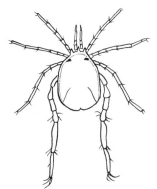

Aturus scaber
L.c. 0.5 mm

Lake District water mites

319

mouthparts are modified for piercing and sucking.   Of the 300 or so British species, about 100 are known in the Lake District.   Females are generally larger than males.   The largest species (up to about 8mm — ⅓ in.) generally frequent shallow, weedy lakes and ponds and are often active swimmers.   Others are slow-moving crawlers.   Mites of running water are generally small, inconspicuous crawlers.   Adult mites are predators.   Prey includes small crustaceans, midge larvae and nymphs of mayflies and stoneflies.

The life cycle is generally complex, and in many species still unknown. The often reddish eggs are usually deposited in rows or clumps on a variety of firm objects, but some species of Hydrachna insert them into plant stems, other species shed them freely, and species of Unionicola lay them inside mussels or sponges. In most species a tiny larva emerges but in some it is passed through in the egg. The larva has three pairs of legs.   Larvae are often active swimmers and generally seek an insect on which to become parasitic.   Adult midges, water beetles and water bugs are frequent hosts.   Many such larvae, often red and conspicuous, may be carried by a single host.   To become attached to such a host as an adult midge, which emerges quickly from its pupal skin, presents problems.   Larvae often sit on the pupal skin and, as it splits, transfer themselves with alacrity to the emerging adult.   Some leave the host after becoming engorged and enter a resting stage prior to emerging as a so-called deuteronymph.   Others change into a deuteronymph before leaving the host.   This larva is an active predator and has 4 pairs of legs.   After feeding it enters another resting stage where it changes into the adult.

Common water mites in the Lake District include Hydrodroma despiciens, a reddish-orange species found in a variety of habitats, mostly tarns and smaller water bodies, where it feeds on chironomid eggs and whose larvae parasitize adult chironomid midges.   Common too is the greenish Limnesia undulata (length c. 2mm)

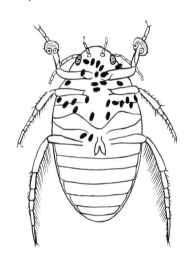

Larvae of Hydrachna attached to the beetle Dytiscus marginalis

that is found in both lakes and tarns.   Unionicola crassipes (females about 1.5mm, males smaller) is a greenish yellow mite found in lakes and large tarns.   Here it lays its eggs in sponges.   Its larvae parasitize adult chironomid midges but all the post-larval resting stages are passed through in sponges.   Among the running water species the tiny Aturus scaber (0.5mm) often occurs in large numbers in moss in fast-flowing streams, and the larger, yellowish, Hygrobates fluviatilis (females c. 2mm) is also common, and sometimes occurs in lakes. The largest species is Hydrachna geographica of which females attain a length of about 8mm, males about 6mm. This is a handsome red mite with more or less cruciform black markings dorsally.   It has been found in certain tarns.

320

Tardigrades are minute arthropods, seldom as much as 1mm long, whose relationship to other animals is obscure. Possessing four pairs of legs, each terminating in 2 or 4 claws, (more in some marine species) they have a slow, ambling gait (the name Tardigrade means 'slow walker') and display a fanciful resemblance to bears — hence their common name. A few species are truly aquatic but many are aquatic only insofar as they live in a thin film of water among mosses and in similar situations. Here they are often abundant.

Of the 70 or so British freshwater species, very few are recorded in the Lake District, but they are certainly plentiful in some places and the abundant mosses of the area are likely to be productive. They also occur at lake margins. As numerous species have been found around Scottish lochs, similar results

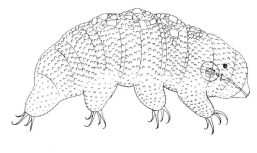

Hypsibius verrucosus

Two species known from Scottish lochs that are likely to be found in the Lake District.

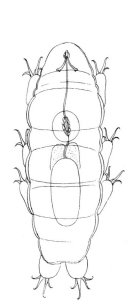

Hypsibius chilensis, one of the few species as yet recorded in the Lake District

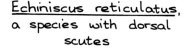

Echiniscus reticulatus, a species with dorsal scutes

Some typical tardigrades

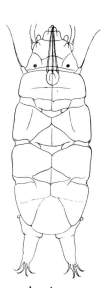

Pseudechiniscus suillus a common species

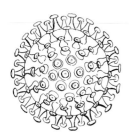

The egg of <u>Macro-biotus hufelandi</u>, probably our most common tardigrade and found in several habitats in the Lake District.

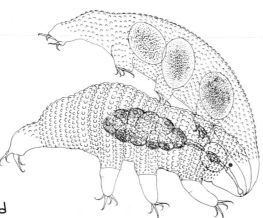

<u>Macrobiotus annulatus</u>, a common species, carrying eggs in a moulted skin

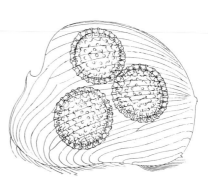

Eggs of <u>Macrobiotus hastatus</u> inside a cast carapace of the 'water flea' <u>Alonella nana</u>

A hatching egg of <u>Macrobiotus</u>

are likely in the Lake District and the group would be a rewarding one for the amateur.

In some species the dorsal cuticle is provided with a series of plates or scutes : in others it is simple. The terminal mouth is provided with a pair of piercing stylets with which plant or animal tissues can be pierced. A sucking pharynx enables material to be drawn in.

The sexes are separate. In some species males are unknown. Eggs are laid, sometimes freely — in which case they are spiny or viscous — or, several together, in the cast skin when the female moults — in which case they are smooth. One species, <u>Macrobiotus annulatus</u>, has the apparently unique habit of moulting its cuticle ('skin'), casting three eggs into it, and carrying the entire ensemble around until the eggs hatch. <u>M. hastatus</u> has repeatedly been found to deposit its eggs, always three in number, in the cast carapace of the 'water flea' (cladoceran) (page 236) <u>Alonella nana</u>. In some species the emerging offspring looks very much like the adult : in others several moults are necessary before the adult form is achieved.

Some tardigrades display a remarkable form of encystment. This is little known and even less understood. One species in which it is known is <u>Macrobiotus dispar</u>, which is common and widespread in ponds, lakes and bogs. Encystment begins by casting the old skin but the newly moulted individual remains within it.

322

An adult
individual

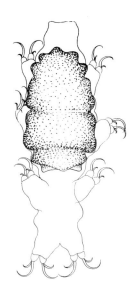

A cyst within the
old skin (from above)

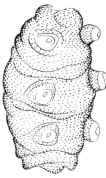

A cyst seen
from below

Elliptical cyst
from within a
mature cyst.

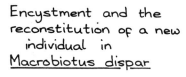

Encystment and the
reconstitution of a new
individual in
Macrobiotus dispar

Contents
squeezed
from an
elliptical cyst.

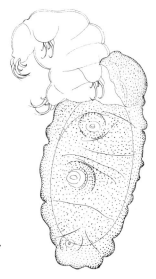

A reconstituted individual
emerging from a cyst.

This individual, which has a dark yellow skin, moves feebly and gradually becomes smaller. As it does so it exudes a viscous secretion to which extraneous material adheres. The legs are gradually withdrawn and eventually the animal becomes a dark cyst, about half its original length, still contained within the old skin. If, after some days, the cyst is ruptured it is found to contain an elliptical cyst with its own skin. If the contents of this cyst are squeezed out they are seen to consist of a largely amorphous mass of cells, though the eye spots are recognisable and some dark central cells probably represent the gut. Eventually an entirely new individual is reconstituted within the cyst, which ruptures near one end to release it. The significance of this remarkable process, which must require the expenditure of a great deal of energy, is not known though in some cases it may help to tide the animal over an adverse period.

Tardigrades do not, however, always have to go through such a performance to survive adverse conditions. Many can simply dry out. In this condition they are almost unbelievably resistant. Not only can they withstand the worst conditions that nature can impose but can tolerate much greater extremes. Some tardigrades have revived after 2 hours at a temperature only a fraction of a degree above absolute zero (-273°c). This means that, during that period, all biochemical and physiological reactions (life processes) were slowed essentially to zero. If reactions are possible at -200°c they would be about 8 million times slower than at 20°c. At these low temperatures the cell constituents are drastically altered and even their molecular states are changed, yet on warming and wetting normal activities are resumed.

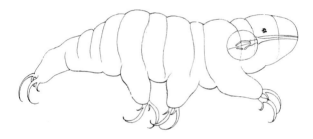

A <u>Macrobiotus</u> at speed!

Compared with the freshwater fish faunas of the tropics, that of Europe is meagre. As the British freshwater fish fauna is a depauperate version of the European fauna, and the fauna of the Lake District an impoverished version of that of more southern parts of the country, it must be admitted that it is somewhat lacking in diversity. Nevertheless the species represented are sufficient to give at least some inkling of the range of structure and habits of this most diverse of all groups of vertebrates (back-boned animals), and the Lake District is the home of certain fishes with rather restricted distributions in Britain, which to some extent compensates for its poverty of species.

Whether lampreys should be referred to as fishes is a moot point. Unlike true fishes they lack jaws. This is recognised by their assignment, along with their nearest relatives, to a superclass, the Agnatha — which means 'without jaws'. Their relatives are not modern fishes but creatures that flourished some 300 million years ago. Lampreys are in fact survivors from the distant past and as such can throw light on the organisation of the earliest vertebrates. Modern lampreys are called cyclostomes — which means 'round mouths' — and are smooth-skinned creatures, eel-like in shape. Their relatives of Silurian and Devonian times were the heavily armoured cephalaspids, pteraspids and others.

Two lampreys occur in the Lake District*. One is the Brook Lamprey, <u>Lampetra planeri</u>. The name <u>Lampetra</u> comes from the Latin 'lambere', to lick and 'petra' a stone and refers to the way in which lamp-
    * See however page 342 for recent information.

The Brook Lamprey.   <u>Lampetra planeri</u>
Length to about 20cm (7 in. or rather more)

Ammocoete larva of the Brook Lamprey

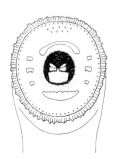

Mouth and sucker
of the
Brook Lamprey

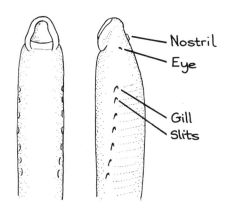

Head of ammocoete from
below and from the side.

325

River Lamprey. <u>Lampetra fluviatilis</u>
Length to c. 40cm (16 in), occasionally
longer.

Mouth and sucker. Note the teeth.
These rasping structures distinguish
it from the Brook Lamprey.

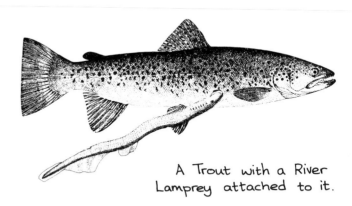

A Trout with a River
Lamprey attached to it.

-reys attach themselves to stones by means of the sucker that surrounds the mouth. The Brook Lamprey, like some insects, spends more of its life as a larva than as an adult. The larva is called an ammocoete. When first discovered this creature was not recognised as the larva of a lamprey and was given a name of its own, <u>Ammocoetes</u> — hence its present name. It is rather worm-like in general appearance, lives buried in the sand and gravel of streams and is seldom seen. It has rudimentary eyes, a toothless mouth surrounded by hood-like lips, and a row of small external gill openings. Water is sucked in through the mouth and pumped out through the gill openings. En route any food particles in it are entangled in a string of sticky mucus produced by an organ called the endostyle. About 3 or 4 years is spent in the larval state. Metamorphosis takes about a month. Among the remarkable changes that occur is a trans-formation of the endostyle to a structure similar to the thyroid gland of more advanced animals. Adults live for only a few months, spawn from about March to May and then die. They never feed.

Spawning is a communal affair. Several members of each sex make a 'nest', clearing small stones from the bottom by holding them with the sucker and dragging them away. In the depression so formed males and females intertwine, mate, and lay eggs.

Brook Lampreys may be commoner in streams and small rivers in the Lake District than is generally supposed. Without specially looking for them I have seen them in considerable numbers in a stream flow-

-ing into Grasmere and have watched them spawning in Borrowdale.

The River Lamprey, <u>Lampetra fluviatilis</u>, is similar in general appearance to the Brook Lamprey but is larger and the sucking disc is armed with stout teeth. By means of the sucker the lamprey attaches itself to a fish, the teeth rasp the victim's flesh, and its blood is sucked. The life history is similar to that of the Brook Lamprey but the adult is longer lived and, while the Brook Lamprey lives permanently in freshwater, some, but not all, River Lampreys migrate to the sea like the Salmon. Not much is known about the River Lamprey in the Lake District but it has been seen in the southern part of the area, and in the Caldew and other tributaries of the Eden. The even larger Sea Lamprey, <u>Petromyzon marinus</u>, which enters freshwater to spawn has been seen in estuaries in the south of the area and may occasionally enter Lake District rivers.

Although salmonid fishes (Salmon, Trout and their relatives) are esteemed as 'game' fishes and in some quarters have a greater snob value than the so-called 'coarse' fishes, they are in fact more primitive than the latter. As a rough analogy a primitive organism can be regarded as a prototype of the more advanced models that are to follow.

The Salmon, <u>Salmo salar</u>, ascends, and spawns in, several Lake District rivers. The celebrated leap of upstream-migrating adults can be watched, for example, at several places on the R. Kent. Salmon move upstream at all times of the year, but often towards its end. Rivers sometimes differ in this respect. In the Cumbrian Derwent the main run is in summer. Although they leap clear of the water at times, Salmon more frequently negotiate obstacles by chosing a place where the flow of water over it is smooth, and swimming

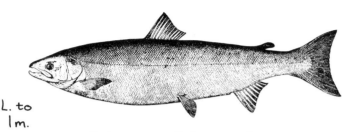

L. to 1m.

Salmon, <u>Salmo salar</u>

A leaping Salmon

327

up it, which is not too demanding of energy.   Leaping is resorted to where the flow gives rise to a standing wave beneath a fall or weir.   The Salmon leaps from the crest of this wave, apparently without taking a run at the outset, which demands an enormous propulsive effort, though of short duration.   These migrating Salmon seldom or never feed.   En route for the spawning grounds some pass through lakes such as Windermere, Bassenthwaite and Derwentwater.   Spawning, usually between October and January, involves the excavation by the female of a shallow trough or 'redd' among suitable gravel, for which purpose the tail is used as a scoop. Here eggs are deposited, fertilized by an attendant male, and covered by further sweeps of the tail.   Spawning is a prolonged process and may continue in bouts for up to about 2 weeks.   During this period several thousand eggs, more than 20,000 in large females, are deposited, and the redd may extend over several feet.   Spent adults return to the sea to feed, but some perish.   Such returning adults are called <u>kelts</u>.

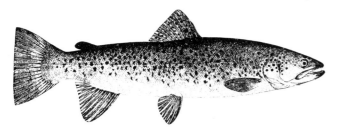

Trout,   <u>Salmo trutta</u>

After passing through the early stages young Salmon are referred to as <u>parr</u>.   When about 2 years old or a little more they become silvery in colour and, as <u>smolts</u> some 13 to 15cm (c. 5 or 6 inches) long, return to the sea where they grow rapidly.   They return to breed as <u>grilse</u> after a little over a year in the sea when they are 3½ to 4 years old.   They then weigh about 6 to 6½ lbs.   Others remain in the sea for another year and weigh about 13 lb on return.   If they remain a further year they weigh up to 20 lb.

The Trout, <u>Salmo trutta</u>, is common and widespread in the Lake District.   Its success reflects its adaptability.   It can live equally well in a small upland beck or a large lake, and is catholic in its diet, eating whatever invertebrates are available.   Notwithstanding its success, its abilities, such as swimming speeds, tend to be overestimated by fishermen or those who see a Trout dash away.

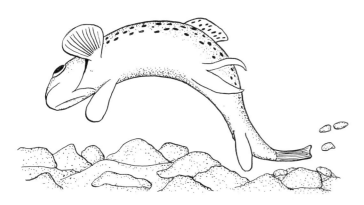

A female Trout, belly towards the observer excavating a redd prior to laying its eggs

5 m.p.h. is about the maximum speed, and this can be sustained for no more than a short burst.

Size and growth rate are enormously variable. Trout of small becks often attain a weight of only 2 or 3 oz. : monsters of up to about 10 lb exist in Windermere and several other lakes. A 14 lb trout has been netted in Crummock Water and fishes reputed to weigh up to 56 lb are said to have been caught in the past. These large individuals are predominantly fish eaters.

Growth rates differ according to the kind of habitat frequented. A 4 year old Trout in a Lakeland beck may be only about 18 cm (c. 7 in.) in length. In lakes a fish of this age is generally larger than this but not the same size in all lakes. Growth is faster in rich lakes than in poor — another illustration of the differences between lakes (page 90). A 4 year old Trout in Wastwater averages about 7·9 inches (c. 20 cm) in length, in Ullswater about 9·3 inches (c. 23·6 cm) and in Windermere about 11·2 inches (c. 28·5 cm)

Several factors influence growth rate. They include the acidity or alkalinity of the water (page 65) — growth is best in alkaline waters — the amount of food available, generally least in acidic waters, and the number of individuals present.

Breeding behaviour resembles that of the Salmon. In November or thereabouts a redd is excavated by the female for the reception of the eggs, usually in a stream, occasionally on a gravelly lake shore. Successful egg laying in a Lakeland stream does not necessarily mean a successful brood. A sudden spate can wash out eggs or newly hatched young fishes and cause great mortality, even to the extent of virtually eliminating a year's recruitment to the population. Exceptionally dry years, such as 1984, can have similar consequences.

Young trout, still hidden in the gravel, begin to swim feebly as soon as they have hatched. At this stage they carry a massive yolk sac that sustains them, and are called <u>alevins</u>. As the yolk is gradually absorbed the alevin grows and begins to feed on tiny invertebrates. By the time they are about 25 mm (1 in.) long all the yolk has been absorbed and the young fishes are referred to as <u>fry</u>. These gradually assume the adult form.

Two forms of the Trout, the Brown Trout and the Sea Trout, occur in the Lake District, but both belong to the same species, <u>Salmo trutta</u>. The basic difference is in the migratory habit well-developed in the Sea Trout which goes to sea like the Salmon,

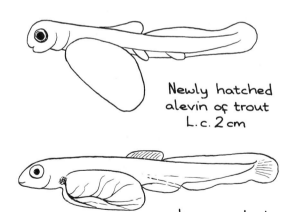

Newly hatched
alevin of trout
L. c. 2 cm

Larger alevin

much less so in the Brown Trout.   It is not known if migratory habits are inherited but the evidence suggests such is not invariably the case.   Brown Trout occur throughout the Hebrides, and in Orkney and Shetland (where there are no true freshwater fishes such as members of the Carp family (cyprinids) e.g. the Roach).   The presence of Trout can only be interpreted as indicating that they arrived by sea since the Ice Ages, that is as Sea Trout.

The Char, <u>Salvelinus alpinus</u>, a relative of Salmon and Trout, represents an Arctic–Alpine element in the fauna of the Lake District, and is one of its most distinctive fishes.   Indeed the Char is some-times called the Arctic Char.   In Britain Char occur mainly in cool, stony, oligotrophic lakes and are con-fined to freshwater.   In Arctic regions — they extend north to at least latitude 82°— although there are permanent freshwater populations, many are migratory like the Salmon, living much in the sea and entering fresh-water to spawn.   This habit they doubtless had in Britain whenever rivers were open during the last Ice Ages, at which time they extended further south than they do today.   When the ice retreated northwards so did the Char.   In the far north migratory habits were often un-interupted.   Further south, deterred by warming seas, some populations became land locked in cool lakes, where they remain to this day.   In continental Europe

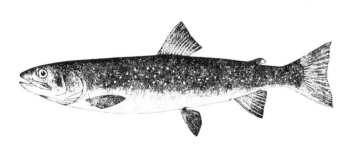

Char, <u>Salvelinus alpinus</u>
Maximum length c. 40 cm

only Alpine lakes were sufficiently cool and the Char died out elsewhere, so today it displays a <u>disjunct</u> <u>distribution</u>, the Arctic and Alpine populations being widely separated from each other.   In the British Isles the Char is found only in the north and west, especially in Scotland and Western Ireland.   The only English populations are those of the Lake District.   Further south in Britain it occurs in only two isolated localities in Wales.

The Char is a handsome fish, especially in the breeding season when the male develops a bright orange belly while the anterior margins of the pectoral, ventral and anal fins are milk white.   Adults are usually from about 25 to 40 cm (10 to 16 inches) in length.   (Some migratory Char achieve a considerably greater size.) In the Lake District the main food is zooplankton, mainly the small crustacean element, which is filtered from the open water by means of sieves (gill rakers) that lie above the rows of gills.   The same flow of water thus serves for respiration, by bathing the gills, and as a food-bearing current.   Larger items are sometimes eaten.   I have seen stomachs of Ennerdale Char packed with Sticklebacks!

The Char populations of lakes in different valleys are isolated. Since becoming land locked, each has undergone small changes in form or coloration and these have not been the same in each lake. Although very small, these changes enable the populations from several lakes to be distinguished from each other. This is evolution in action. Given another 50 thousand, or perhaps 100 thousand years, these populations may become even more distinct and each lake could conceivably come to have its own species.

By comparing measurements and counts of various structures (morphometrics), and by comparisons of proteins by a technique known as electrophoresis, it is possible to see how similar, or different, are the Char populations of the different lakes. The results show that the Ennerdale population is the most distinctive. What is more this is the only Lake District population to harbour the parasitic copepod Salmincola edwardsii (page 235). These facts are in harmony with the belief that the history of the Ennerdale population was different from that of the other lakes (page 26) and that it has probably been isolated for longer than the other populations.

Lake District Char spawn from about November to February. Many run up rivers and spawn in much the same manner as the Salmon and Trout though the process is a more communal affair and takes place mostly at night. In some rivers hundreds of fishes congregate in small areas to spawn. The situation in Windermere is particularly complicated. Some individuals spawn in November in the River Brathay. Others spawn on stony shores in the lake at the same time, yet others in the same places in February. Individuals show fidelity to spawning sites and times in successive years and there may therefore be two or more, more or less segregated populations in the lake. A difficulty here is knowing whether Char have been transferred to Windermere from other lakes. Char spawn has certainly

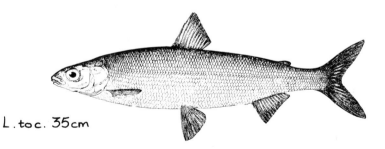

L.to c. 35cm

Schelly, Coregonus lavaretus

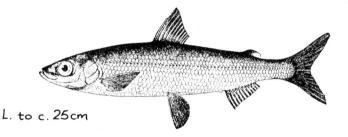

L. to c. 25cm

Vendace, Coregonus albula

331

been collected for stocking purposes, and records of introducing Char into Windermere exist.   Even the monks of Furness Abbey may have indulged in such practices several centuries ago.   (The lakes in which the Char is present are listed on page 93).

As distinctive of the Lake District as the Char, having similar histories, and of even more restricted distribution in Britain, are two fishes of the related family Coregonidae.   These are the Schelly, Coregonus lavaretus, and the Vendace, C. albula.   Both, but especially the Vendace, have a rather Herring-like appearance.   Like the Char both feed on zooplankton, but the Schelly also eats larger bottom animals. The Schelly (length to about 35cm : 14 inches) is confined to Ullswater, Brotherswater, Haweswater and Red Tarn, Helvellyn : the Vendace (length to about 25 cm : about 10 inches) to Derwentwater and Bassenthwaite. Both are shoaling species which though seldom seen are probably common and are sometimes caught in large numbers in nets.   They are seldom caught by anglers, but in 1986 a local enthusiast devised a new technique and landed the largest rod-caught Schelly to date in Haweswater — 2lb. 1½ oz. (c. 950gm). The Schelly spawns mainly from mid January to mid February, congregating in large numbers for this purpose. In Ullswater spawning takes place at a depth of about 8m (25 ft.) The Vendace probably spawns mostly in December but there are old references to it as doing so in spring.   An unusual attribute of the Schelly is that it smells of cucumber!

The Pike, Esox lucius, is one of the most distinctive fishes of the English Lakes, in which it fulfils the role of top predator.   In contrast to the generalised Trout, the Pike is a specialist, beautifully adapted for a particular way of life — fish-eating.   Its form reveals its habits.   The dorsal and anal fins are set well back on the elongate body — like feathers on an arrow and for similar reasons — the eyes are large and in a position to give frontal vision with binocular vision over a field of view of 30°—40°, the snout sharp, the mouth with a wide gape and beset with formidable backwardly-directed teeth.   All these attributes contribute to its efficiency as a hunter of other fishes that have to be swallowed whole.

The Pike is an ambush predator that lies in wait for its prey which, having come within range, is carefully stalked.   It is well-equipped for catching its prey in this way.   A camouflaged, greenish, color-ation is one asset.   A rapid dash culminates in the victim being seized crosswise and then swallowed head first.   Binocular vision is important here.   It gives better distance judgement than does monocular vision — which is all that some fishes have.   Only binocular vision enables a Pike to strike with the accuracy that it does.   Its body — about 60% muscle — is flexible and can bend into a deep curve, which, aided by the rear fins, presents a large surface area to the water and gives a powerful thrust.   This gives good acceleration but can only be repeated a few times in quick succession before the fish tires, and is un-suited to persistent swimming.   Fishes that cruise throw their body into smaller waves and undulate gently.

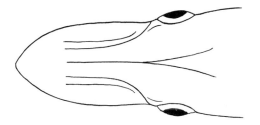

Pike, <u>Esox lucius</u>. Length occasionally more than 1 metre.

The head of a Pike from above

Such fishes are also better at manoeuvring than is the Pike, to which this ability is less important than it is, for example, to the Perch.

The Pike is widely distributed in Lake District lakes and tarns but is not found in the barren Wastwater or Ennerdale Water.   It attains a respectable size.   Several individuals more than 1 metre in length have been caught in Windermere where the largest caught (in a net) weighed 35 lb (c. 15·9 Kg.) and had a length of 110 cm (3 ft 7 in.).   Individuals of almost similar size have been recorded in Derwentwater and Bassenthwaite, though these fall short of the largest sizes recorded in Britain.

Except when very small the Pike feeds almost entirely on fishes.   Which species are consumed depends to a large extent on availability.   In Windermere Perch and Trout are the major prey species, Char are frequently captured, and Sticklebacks and Minnows are also regularly taken.   Cannibalism is sometimes practised.   Very small Pike, up to about 2 cm in length, feed entirely on tiny crustaceans, Cladocera and Copepoda.   By the time they are about 3·5 cm (nearly 1½ in.) in length they have become largely fish-eaters, feeding mostly on Perch fry which are usually abundant at this time, but also take some insects and the large cladoceron <u>Eurycercus</u> (page 241).   From that size upwards fishes dominate the diet.

Individuals of both sexes usually breed for the first time when 2 years old, by which time, in Windermere, a male is about 38 cm (15 in.) in length and a female about 42 cm (16½ in.).   Windermere Pike spawn from mid March to the beginning of May.   As breeding Pike smell more strongly than non-breeding individuals it seems that odour plays some part either in courtship or as an attractant.   The sticky eggs adhere to plants growing on bottoms that are silty with some stones.   The number of eggs is related to the size of the female.   A 2 Kg (4·4 lb) fish produces about 50,000 eggs, one twice that weight about 100,000, and one four times as heavy about 200,000.   The newly hatched young, only 7 or 8mm long, have a yolk sac, which serves as an initial food supply, and a small sucker on the head that produces a sticky substance by means of which they attach themselves to plants, and thus clear of the silty bottom, for the first four days or so of their life.   The oldest Pike recorded in Windermere was 17 years old.

Although fishes of the Carp family (Cyprinidae) dominate the British freshwater fish fauna there is only one member of this group that can be said with certainty to be native to the Lake District.   This is the Minnow, <u>Phoxinus phoxinus</u>.   A frequenter of clear stony lakes, rivers and streams, the Minnow, which as an adult seldom achieves a length of more than 10 cm (4 in.) is a gregarious species that moves around in shoals.   It is widespread in the Lake District and ascends as high as 1960 ft. in Grisedale Tarn.   The Minnow is active from about the beginning of April to the end of October.   In lakes, such as Windermere the warm shallows are frequented during summer.   With the onset of cold weather there is a movement to deeper water (a depth of

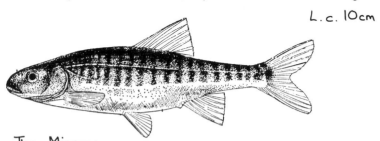

L. c. 10 cm

The Minnow
<u>Phoxinus phoxinus</u> , and head of male in breeding season showing spinous tubercles

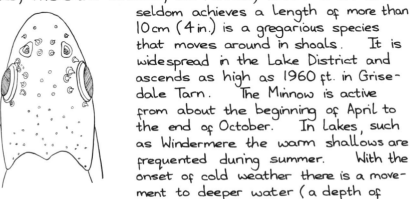

about 2m (6ft.) seems to be preferred) and the winter is spent hiding under stones.   There is, however, some feeding activity during this period though less than in summer.   Both plant and animal matter is eaten.   The composition of the diet depends on availability.   In Windermere Cladocera are the main food but other invertebrates, filamentous algae and diatoms are also important.   In some streams algae play a more important role but a wide range of invertebrates is eaten.

In warm weather shoals of Minnows can often be seen in shallow water.   Shoals, which number hundreds, or even thousands, of individuals, are composed of fishes of the same age/size.   Shoaling, and the coordinated movements that it involves, call for complex interactions.   It offers protection against enemies. Many pairs of eyes are on watch (though this is offset by the conspicuousness of the shoal) and not all members of the shoal need be on the alert all the time.   This gives more time for foraging.   If attacked, an individual in a shoal has a smaller chance of being caught than has a solitary fish.   Predators, such as the Pike, are confused by the movements of the many members of a shoal.

Shoaling and predator evasion are complicated processes.   On the near approach of a predator a shoal may become compact and cease to forage.   Escape from an attack can involve various strategies.   These include skittering, leaping out of the water, or swimming away from the predator then doubling back, some individuals passing to the right, others to the left, of the pursuer — like water from a fountain.   Sometimes a shoal 'explodes', scattering in all directions and confusing the predator.   As a last resort individuals can hide under stones.

Non-hunting predators, such as a Pike, are sometimes 'inspected' by shoaling Minnows.   Two or three Minnows may swim to within a couple of feet or so of a Pike then return to the shoal.   This behaviour seems to be a means of obtaining information on the motivational state of the predator and perhaps enables the Minnows to acquire familiarity with a potential enemy.

Minnows have a chemical means of warning their fellows of danger.   In the skin are certain cells that, if damaged, produce an 'alarm substance'.   This rapidly diffuses, and minute amounts of it can be detected by Minnows in the vicinity.   Related species of fishes also produce alarm substances.   These can be detected by Minnows, but less readily than that of their own species.   The closer the relationship, the more effective and easily detected   is the alarm substance.

A few Minnows breed when they are one year old ; most first do so a year later.   The breeding season extends from May to July when the already attractive coloration, which includes a dark green or brown dorsal region, becomes enhanced.   The male is then dark green dorsally, has metallic emerald green sides, with dark vertical stripes, and develops an intense scarlet ventral region.   The coloration of the female is similar but less intense.   Both sexes also develop white spots at the base of the paired and anal fins and at the edge of the opercula, and spinous milk-white tubercles on the upper surface of the head, though the latter are usually most strongly developed in the male.   Many, but not all, lake-frequenting Minnows enter inflowing streams to spawn.   In Windermere spawning Minnows formerly frequented the ferry landings, finding the gravel on which the ferry beached, and the regular turbulence caused by its arrival and departure, much to their liking.   The modern concrete ramps offer no such attraction and the Minnows no longer entertain ferry passengers.

Spawning is a communal affair.   Males predominate in spawning shoals, remaining at spawning sites longer than females which depart after laying their eggs.   From about 180 to 550 eggs are shed by each female depending on its size, and adhere to the under side of suitable stones.   Some Minnows undergo sex reversal.   Having functioned as females, in old age they are transformed into functional males.   In Windermere relatively few Minnows survive beyond the age of 3 years.

Whether the Roach, _Rutilus rutilus_ is a true native of the Lake District is doubtful.   What appears to be an old established population occurs in Priest Pot — a pool cut off at the head of Esthwaite Water —

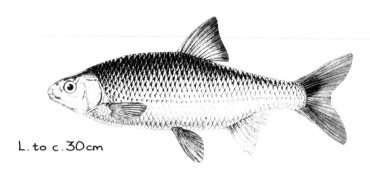

L. to c. 30cm

The Roach, <u>Rutilus rutilus</u>

and it now seems to be established in the latter Lake and in Windermere, but in both cases introduction is suspected. Anglers bring Roach as live bait and some are released. This is a long established practice, for Roach suspected to be of such provenance were found in Windermere long ago, but never apparently established themselves, as they now appear to have done. It occurs in several waters on the southern fringes of the area.

The Stone Loach, <u>Noemacheilus barbatulus</u> is a member of the family Cobitidae. It cannot be confused with any other Lake District fish. With a usual maximum length of about 12 cm (less than 5 in.) it has an elongate, more or less cylindrical body whose scales are so small that it appears to be naked. In contrast to most of our freshwater fishes it relies to only a limited extent on vision. Its eyes are small but it is provided with three conspicuous pairs of tactile (touch sensitive) barbels by means of which it can feel its way around under the stones among which it usually lives. These it also uses to detect its prey. The barbels surround the mouth which is located on the ventral side of the head and therefore in close proximity to the bottom from which the food is taken. Scents are also perceived not, as some have wrongly assumed, by the barbels, but by the same sort of olfactory (smell detecting) organs as those of other fishes. The nostrils admit water to a closed chamber where scents are detected.

The food consists of bottom-living invertebrates of which chironomid (midge) larvae (page 305) are particularly important, though a wide range of other animals, especially insect larvae and crustaceans, is eaten.

In the Lake District proper the Stone Loach appears to be largely, perhaps entirely, confined to the southern part of the area, though its detailed

L. to c. 12 cm

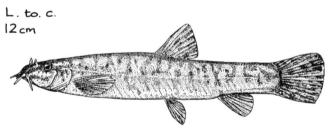

The Stone Loach, <u>Noemacheilus barbatulus</u>, and the mouth with its surrounding barbels as seen from below

distribution remains to be mapped.   Here it is rather rigorously restricted to rivers and streams, and does not usually venture into the lakes into which these flow.   Thus it has not been found in Windermere though it occurs in several inflowing streams.   It has been found plentifully on one short stretch of shore in Esthwaite Water near an incoming stream but nowhere else in the lake.

Of largely nocturnal habits, the Stone Loach usually spends the daylight hours hidden beneath a stone.   Spawning occurs in May.   Some individuals spawn when one year old, others do so for the first time when two years old.   Not much is known of spawning behaviour which appears to take place at night beneath stones.   The ovaries often contain about 5000 or 6000 eggs.   In the Lake District the maximum life span is usually 5 years.

The Eel, Anguilla anguilla (family Anguillidae) is widely distributed in the Lake District, occurring in rivers and lakes, and ascending to some of the mountain tarns.   As is well known all the Eels found in freshwater in Britain are born in the Sargasso Sea on the western side of the Atlantic Ocean. Towards the end of the crossing, which, for English Eels, takes the better part of 3 years, the larvae are transformed into elvers — which look like miniature eels — and it is as elvers that they invade and ascend rivers, often in very large numbers.   Spring is the season at which they enter Lake District rivers.   'Ropes' of elvers are sometimes to be seen as they strive to ascend weirs and other obstacles. Eels remain in freshwater for several years.   In Windermere females remain for between 9 and 19 years, males for 7 to 12 years.   Not surprisingly females grow to a larger size than males.   While few of the Eels caught in Windermere are more than about 60 cm (2 ft) in length, occasional individuals are larger.   A 3 ft (90 cm) Eel weighs about 6 lb (c. 2.7 kg).   There is an old reference to a 9 lb Eel having been taken from Windermere.

Lake District Eels feed largely on invertebrates. Fishes constitute a negligible part of the diet.   In Windermere, molluscs, both snails and small bivalves, are the most frequent components and larval stages of aquatic insects are also important.   The latter are the single most important category in some Lake District rivers and streams.   Various other invertebrates — crustaceans and worms — are eaten.   Very occasionally small fishes are taken, and the Eel is not averse to eating the eggs of Trout and Char during the spawning season of these fishes.

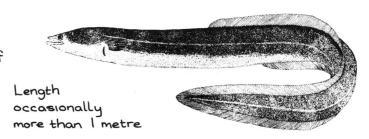

Length
occasionally
more than 1 metre

Eel, Anguilla anguilla

Eventually physiological changes, which include an enlargement of the eyes and the development of a silvery coloration, take place and, as so-called Silver Eels, the adults leave the lakes and rivers and return to the sea, a migration that occurs in autumn. Although it is generally assumed that they return to the area in which they were born, this is not proven. Little is known of the fate of European Eels after their return to sea and it is conceivable that all our Eels are the offspring of parents from American rivers whose progeny supply not only the rivers of that continent but those of Europe as well.

The Perch, Perca fluviatilis, is the only Lake District representative of the family Percidae. It is of distinctive form and coloration. It has two dorsal fins of which the anterior is supported by stiff, sharp-tipped spines and can be erected at will, thereby providing a defensive structure. Its back and the upper part of its flanks are olive green in colour. It is more golden below, and the belly is white. Five or more dark vertical bars run down the flanks and to some extent act as camouflage when the fish ventures among vegetation. Red ventral, anal and caudal fins complete its livery.

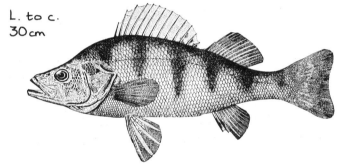

L. to c. 30 cm

The Perch, Perca fluviatilis

The Perch is widely distributed in the lakes and tarns of the Lake District, but is not present in the two least productive, oligotrophic, lakes, Wastwater and Ennerdale Water. It is a gregarious species which lives in shoals. A carnivore, its diet depends to some extent on what is available, and on its size. Initially it feeds on minute crustaceans, changes to larger, bottom living invertebrates, especially insects, as it gets bigger and, when large, also takes such fishes as it can obtain. In Windermere individuals over a wide size range feed on bottom-living invertebrates for much of the year but switch largely to zoo-plankton from July to October, during which months they also consume many young of their own species.

Of all the Perch populations in Britain that of Windermere is the best studied. Here its numbers have been followed for many years. In spring adults move inshore from the deeper water in which they have spent the winter. Here they spawn at depths of from about 1·5 to 6 m (5 to 20 ft) from about the end of April till early June. Eggs are deposited in long strings. Each string is attached to a stone, plant or other object and become entangled in vegetation. The number of eggs laid is large, upwards of 7,000, per female, the number increasing with the size of the fish.

During the 1930s Perch were abundant, and mostly small, in Windermere. Their numbers were reduced by a fishery that began in 1941 as a contribution to wartime food production and continued until 1948 during which time about 90 tons of Perch were caught, canned, and sold as 'Perchines'. The fishery was based on spawning fishes that freely enter unbaited traps, rather like steel-framed lobster pots covered with wire netting, whose design was inspired by traps employed in Africa. Since the end of this venture traps have been set annually at selected sites and samples of Perch collected. From these it is possible to calculate the size of the population and to follow its fortunes from year to year and to relate success, or failure, of the outcome of a year's spawning — a year class — to various factors. The success or otherwise of a year class can be gauged two year later when the fishes concerned are big enough to be trapped. Factors conducive to a good year class include a warm summer, a low density of adult Perch, and few Pike (whose numbers depend in part on the intensity of a netting programme). A cool summer, high Perch population and many Pike tend to give rise to a poor year class. Sometimes one factor exerts an influence in one direction, another in the opposite one.

Before 1941, when the population was large, the Perch in Windermere grew slowly. Reduction of the size of the population meant more, and more easily obtained, food and more living space for the survivors, so growth rate increased. It continued to do so for some time. On average a female hatched in 1955 reached just over 16 cm (about 6 ¼ in.) when 3 years old, at which age spawning usually takes place for the first time, and laid about 7,600 eggs. Females hatched in 1968 averaged just over 20 cm in length when 3 years old and laid almost 20,000 eggs. Growth rate falls off rapidly after about 5 years. Some Windermere Perch are over 20 years old.

In 1976 a still mysterious disease specific to this species killed more than 98% of the Perch in Windermere. More than a million fishes died. Recovery was, however, rapid. Competition between the few survivors must have been virtually nil. By 1982 there were more Perch in Windermere than in the early 1950s.

Among large Lake District Perch an individual of 5lb from Ullswater may be the heaviest. Others not far short of this weight have been recorded in other lakes, including Windermere.

The Bullhead, <u>Cottus gobio</u>, is the only British representative of the family Cottidae. In the Lake District it is near the northern limit of its range. Recent records refer only to the southern part of the area though there are old reports from the Eamont, in which river it probably still occurs. In the Lake District, where it frequents streams whose flow rate is slow to moderate, and also the stony shores of certain lakes, an 8cm Bullhead, which would be 4 years old, is a large specimen. Elsewhere, especially in 'hard' waters on limestone rocks, it attains a considerably larger size. Of distinctive appearance, with its broad head, to which its common names of Bullhead and Miller's thumb refer, it is a scaleless fish with two dorsal fins of which the anterior is spinous. The pelvic fins also have a spine and when these and the dorsal spines are extended they make up a formidable defensive device. The colour is a mottled brown or olive dorsally but can be changed rapidly according to the background against which it rests or according to its emotional state.

Seldom
>8cm in
Lake District
Larger elsewhere

The Bullhead, <u>Cottus gobio</u>

Bullheads live under stones, each individual zealously guarding its retreat and driving away intruders of its own species. Most of the daylight hours are spent in such solitary concealment. Feeding takes place chiefly at night. The food consists mainly of insect larvae — in the Lake District especially those of stoneflies (page 248), mayflies (page 252), and caddisflies (page 273) — but includes other invertebrates such as <u>Gammarus</u> (page 227).

The breeding habits of the Bullhead are among the most interesting of any British freshwater fish. In the Lake District spawning takes place in April. The male enlarges the space beneath a stone by 'digging' and removing small stones. Here he waits until a female passes. He seizes her by the head with his jaws and attempts to pull her into the chamber. Immature females react by wriggling free : ready to spawn females remain quiescent and allow themselves to be pulled into the chamber. Once within, the female usually spends between 20 and 30 hours lying quietly upside down against the stone forming the roof of the chamber, before laying her eggs. By contrast the male displays much excitement. He twists and turns, presses against the female and lashes his tail from side to side. Eventually the female deposits a clump of from about 50 to 250 yellow eggs which are stuck to the roof of the chamber and these are fertilized by the male. The female then leaves the chamber. Occasionally a second female will enter and deposit a clutch in the same 'nest'. The male remains, guarding the eggs and fanning them almost continuously by means of the large pectoral fins. This drives a current of water over them, providing aeration and preventing the settlement of fungal spores. Care continues until the eggs hatch in four to six weeks depending on temperature (about 4 weeks at 10°c) Although it takes about four weeks for the young to absorb their yolk sacs, they appear to disperse soon after hatching so the male's duties terminate shortly after the young emerge.

The Three-spined Stickleback, <u>Gasterosteus aculeatus</u>, is widespread in the Lake District, especially in the south.   Seldom as much as 3 in. (c.7cm) in length its distinguishing features include the three stout dorsal spines and a pelvic spine on each side that can be locked in position.   As experiments have shown, this provides an effective defence mechanism against at least young Pike and Perch.   The Stickleback is itself a predator, feeding on a variety of invertebrates and sometimes on small fishes.

For most of the year it is a shoaling species and is cryptically coloured.   ('cryptos' means 'hidden'). Greenish hues prevail.   Things are very different in the breeding season which is concentrated in May and June.   Like the Bullhead, the Stickleback indulges in complex breeding behaviour and the male exhibits parental care, but unlike the secretive Bullhead the Stickleback conducts its affairs in public.   Males leave the shoals and establish individual territories, like Robins in a garden.   They share with Robins another feature. At this time they develop a brilliant red breast.   This startling colour is accentuated by changes in the upper parts that become a shining bluish white.   The eyes are bright blue.   Territories are vigorously defended against other males.   Besides dashing at intruders, territorial males sometimes adopt a 'threat posture', hovering head down with one or both pelvic spines erected, and moving jerkily.   The importance of the red breast is

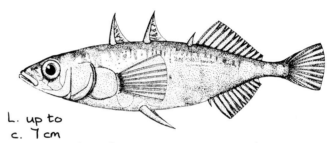

L. up to
c. 7 cm

The Three-spined Stickleback
<u>Gasterosteus aculeatus</u>

dramatically revealed by experiments.   Provided its lower part is red, even a crude model whose shape bears scant resemblance to a Stickleback elicits a vigorous attack if introduced into a territory.   An accurately shaped model, or even a freshly killed Stickleback, is much less effective if it lacks the red breast.   While fights sometimes occur, threat is often sufficient to drive off an intruder.   Regular fights to the death would be detrimental to the species.

Within its territory the male builds a nest.   A pit is dug in the sand or debris, material being re-moved by the mouth.   Bits of vegetation and debris are then piled on it and glued together by a secretion of the kidneys.   The male now assumes an even brighter coloration and attempts to attract a female, now silvery and swollen with eggs.   This is achieved by a zig-zag courtship 'dance'.   A willing female follows the male who pushes his head into the nest and turns on his side.   The female then pushes her way into the nest so that her head protrudes at one side and her tail at the other.   Encouraged by prods from the male, she eventually spawns and leaves the nest.   The male then enters and fertilizes the eggs.   Two, three or sometimes even more, females may be so enticed into the nest.   The behaviour of the male then changes.   He now guards the nest, driving water through it by fanning with the pectoral fins.   Within a week, or a little more, the eggs hatch.   When the young leave the nest the male guards them, keeping them in a group.   If one wanders, it is retrieved by the male who seizes it in his mouth and spits it back among its companions.   Within about two weeks the young swim as a shoal.   The male gradually loses interest in them, loses his bright colour, and the habits of the non-breeding season are resumed.

Whether the Ten-spined Stickleback, <u>Pungitius pungitius</u> occurs in the Lake District is uncertain.   It was reported as occurring in Ullswater and its streams by the Rev. W. Richardson in 1793.   Confirmation of this is much desired.

A postscript on lampreys

No book of this sort can ever be fully up to date at the time of its publication.   New information is always being produced.   An example is provided by recent work on lampreys.   Our two lampreys appear to be very distinct.   The River Lamprey, <u>Lampetra fluviatilis</u> is usually migratory and is parasitic on fishes as an adult, in relation to which habits it has rasping teeth.   The Brook Lamprey, <u>L. planeri</u> is non-migratory, does not feed as an adult, and has no rasping teeth.   Careful comparison restricts the differences to those of ecology and to features concerned with feeding or the lack of it. Otherwise, apart from size, the two are remarkably similar.   They have identical karyotypes (that is, their chromosomes are the same), and the haemoglobin of their blood gives identical electrophoretic patterns. Thus in spite of obvious differences it is possible that both may be merely forms of one species just as the Sea Trout and Brown Trout are forms of <u>Salmo trutta</u>.   If they are forms of one species, that is that the Brook Lamprey is actually a non-migratory form of the River Lamprey, the occurrence of the former in Ireland becomes easier to understand.   The post-glacial history of Ireland was such that it was difficult for any but migratory fishes to get there.   If the Brook Lamprey actually arrived as a River Lamprey (if one can put it this way) the problem is solved.

Like the rest of Britain the Lake District has an impoverished amphibian fauna.   Of the tail-less amphibians (Anura) the Common Frog, <u>Rana temporaria</u>, is widespread and its spawn can be encountered in spring in pools at considerable altitude in the fells, though here it sometimes suffers from what some believe to be frost damage, though this needs further investigation.

The Common Toad, <u>Bufo bufo</u>, is also plentiful in many parts of the area and even lays its long strings of eggs on certain lake shores.   On the Cumbrian coast the Natterjack Toad, <u>B. calamita</u>, frequents sandy places — it needs light, sandy soil in which to burrow — and breeds in pools among the dunes.   Now of restricted distribution in Britain, it is an officially protected species.

Of the newts (Urodela), all three British species occur in the Lake District.   Commonest and smallest is the Palmate Newt, <u>Triturus helveticus</u>, adults and tadpoles of which can be encountered in many tarns and pools at the appropriate times.   In spring adults are often found wandering even on roads as they make for the water in which they are to breed.   This is the most montane of our newts and occurs at considerable altitudes in the Lake District, being known from several tarns above 1500 ft.   On Haystacks it has been seen at about 1700 ft.

The Smooth Newt, <u>T. vulgaris</u> tends to occur at lower altitudes than the Palmate Newt, than which it is less common in the Lake District.

The Great Crested (or Warty) Newt, <u>T. cristatus</u> is rare in the area and is known from a limited number of pools whose whereabouts are best left unspecified.   It too is a protected species.

Palmate Newt, <u>Triturus helveticus</u> under water

Common Frog, <u>Rana temporaria</u>

Natterjack Toad, <u>Bufo calamita</u>

The lakes, tarns and streams of the Lake District provide habitats for a variety of birds of diverse habits, ranging from those whose way of life is completely dependent on these waters to others that merely favour waterside habitats.   Not all are present all the year round and not all breed in the area.

Among the species that can be termed entirely aquatic, though it can still fly, is the Cormorant, <u>Phalacrocorax carbo</u> that breeds in coastal parts of Britain but frequents many of the lakes in winter and is occasionally to be seen in summer.   Breeding has been attempted at Haweswater but was frustrated by anglers.   Cormorants catch fishes by diving from the surface.   In Windermere one met its fate by becoming entangled in a net at a depth of 12–13m (c. 40ft give or take a foot or two), which is a good deal deeper than is acknowledged in textbooks.   Underwater, Cormorants propel themselves with their feet, using their wings and tail for balance.   Captured prey is often brought to the surface before it is swallowed.

Cormorant, <u>Phalacrocorax carbo</u>

The Great Crested Grebe, <u>Podiceps cristatus</u>, another fish-eater, also dives from the surface in pursuit of its prey, for which purpose it is beautifully adapted.   It has an elongate, streamlined body, a long neck, a long, pointed bill, small wings, and feet located well back, by the simultaneous beating of which it propels itself.   In its breeding plumage this is a handsome species.   Its complex courtship behaviour has many components, none more striking than the so-called 'weed-dance' during which each member of the pair, holding pieces of soft weed, tread water and, facing each other, rise in a vertical posture above the surface.   The Great Crested Grebe breeds intermittently on various lakes and low-lying tarns in the Lake District, favouring the most eutrophic situations.   In autumn and winter, when it has lost the distinctive tippets (ruffs) of the head, shows little crest, and is more uniformly coloured, it is more widespread and is to be seen on most of the lakes.

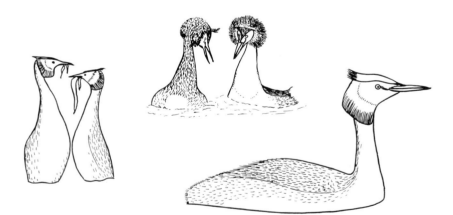

Great Crested Grebe, <u>Podiceps cristatus</u>.   An adult male in breeding plumage and, in the background, aspects of court- -ship, including the weed-dance

344

The smaller Little Grebe, <u>Tachybaptus ruficollis</u>, also eats fish, but feeds largely on invertebrates — insects, crustaceans and molluscs. The fishes it takes are generally smaller than those eaten by its larger relative. This is a more dumpy bird than the Great Crested Grebe, with a shorter neck and bill. It is present all the year round in small numbers and breeds on small, and occasionally large, water bodies. Other grebes — Slavonian, Red-necked, and Black-necked — are generally rare winter visitors though the last has bred in the area.

Some of Lakeland's ducks are also fish-eaters. These are the 'sawbills', the Red-breasted Merganser, <u>Mergus serrator</u> and the Goosander, <u>Mergus merganser</u>, both recent colonists from the north that now breed in the area. The serrated bill is an adaptation that enables them to grasp their slippery prey which is caught by diving. When it swims under water the Red-breasted Merganser propels itself by means of both its wings and its feet, the Goosander by its feet alone. Both species are slender-bodied ducks that show convergent similarity in shape to the Great Crested Grebe and contrast sharply with such dabbling ducks as the Mallard. Broods of young, often 8 or 9 in number, sometimes amalgamate and are cared for by one female. Large flotillas of Merganser ducklings are sometimes to be seen in summer even on the boat-infested Windermere.

Red-breasted Merganser, <u>Mergus serrator</u>
An adult male in breeding plumage and in flight.
Note the long slender body

Related to the sawbills is the Goldeneye, <u>Bucephala clangula</u>, a winter visitor that frequents rivers and estuaries and is regularly present on Windermere where it dives in search of molluscs, crustaceans and insects. Two other diving ducks, the Tufted Duck, <u>Aythya fuligula</u>, and the Pochard, <u>A. ferina</u>, are widely distributed in the area. Both breed, the former sparingly, the latter very rarely, and it is as winter visitors that they are chiefly represented. The Tufted Duck is omnivorous, eating various invertebrates and much plant matter, especially seeds; the Pochard feeds predominantly on plants but takes some invertebrates.

Dabbling ducks, that feed particularly, but not exclusively, by dabbling and upending, are represented by the Mallard, <u>Anas platyrhynchos</u>, an omnivorous and opportunistic species that has learned to benefit

Goldeneye, Bucephala clangula

Tufted Duck, Aythya fuligula.

Pochard, Aythya ferina

Three ducks familiar in winter on large lakes such as Windermere.

346

from the tourist trade and congregates in large numbers at such places as Bowness Bay on Windermere where it is fed by visitors. Such confiding habits contrast strongly with its behaviour in remote situations where it is cautious and difficult to approach. Its smaller relative the Teal, Anas crecca favours rushy up-land tarns and other small water bodies. It too is omnivorous but in winter feeds mainly on seeds. In summer insects feature more prominently in its diet. Both species breed in the Lake District.

   The area is generally unsuitable for the Shoveller, Anas clypeatus which favours shallow, productive waters from which it sieves creatures as small as 'entomostracans' (page 229) with its specialised beak. It is not common on the lakes but breeds on Bassenthwaite and has done so on Haweswater. The Widgeon, Anas penelope, which favours shallow water where it feeds on vegetable matter of all kinds, and grazes on land, occurs on certain tarns in winter but it is rare on the lakes. It occasion-ally breeds, and the Pintail, Anas acuta, has also done so though it is not much associated with lakes and tarns.

   An essentially marine duck, the Shelduck, Tadorna tadorna, has nested intermittently around Windermere and, less commonly, Coniston Water.

   The Lake District ducks display very nicely the sharing of the available resources (fishes, invertebrates and plant matter) which they exploit via different habits and subtle modifications of structures common to them all; such as the beak. They also illustrate sex-ual dimorphism. Males are more brightly coloured than females

A male Mallard, Anas platyrhynchos in flight. Compare its shape with that of the diving, fish-eating Merganser.

whose drab colours often serve as camouflage as they brood their eggs. The bright colours of the males are employed during the sometimes complex courtship behaviour. All lose their colours for some weeks, and are said to go into eclipse, when, each year, they shed all their flight feathers simultaneously and become flightless. Camouflage is then doubtless an asset.

Geese were merely winter visitors until the artificial introduction of the native Grey Lag, _Anser anser_, and the alien Canada Goose, _Branta canadensis_. Although the Grey Lag is not really a lake lover it is now often to be seen in places such as the grassland adjoining Rydal Water. Large flocks of the Canada Goose are often to be seen alongside the shallow southern end of Thirlmere.

The Mute Swan, _Cygnus olor_, breeds on several lakes, including Windermere, and on certain tarns. All those colonising Ullswater appear to die within a few weeks, apparently as a result of lead poisoning. Traces of lead, especially in the past, entered the lake from the adjoining lead mines and were taken up by the vegetation on which the swans feed — an interesting parallel to the fate of swans that in some places die of lead poisoning by picking up the discarded lead weights of anglers, whose use is now banned.

Swans are white and conspicuous. This they can afford to be because, being so large (the Mute Swan is the world's heaviest flying bird) they have few predators. Indeed they have exploited their large size and whiteness and made a virtue of conspicuousness. As swans are territorial, and as each pair requires a considerable area, it is advantageous to be able to see a rival while he is afar off. An approaching rival elicits a spectacular response from a male with an established territory. With the secondary and tertiary feathers of the wings raised to form an arch over its back and the neck held back— a posture that enhances its size — the male sculls majestically towards the intruder. This alone may be sufficient to induce retreat. If not a 'take-off' run towards the interloper, accelerating over the water with beating wings and noisily pattering feet is usually sufficient to accomplish the task. Such dramatic displays can be seen early in the year on Windermere.

The Whooper Swan, _Cygnus cygnus_, is a regular winter visitor to certain favoured tarns and to some of the lakes, especially Derwentwater and Bassenthwaite; Bewick's Swan, _C. columbianus_, less so. Elterwater, which still proves attractive to Whooper Swans, has evidently long done so for its name is derived from the Old Norse 'Elptarvatn' which means 'Lake of the Swans'.

The Coot, _Fulica atra_, and the Moorhen, _Gallinula chloropus_ breed on various lakes and tarns, up to an altitude of about 1000 ft. in the case of the former, to somewhat higher in the case of the latter, which also prefers smaller waterbodies than does the Coot but sometimes nests in bays of large lakes. The number of Coots is greatly enhanced in winter when, for example, the traveller on the Windermere ferry can watch them repeatedly diving for the plants on which they largely feed. Flocks of over 500 sometimes

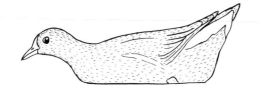

Moorhen, _Gallinula chloropus_

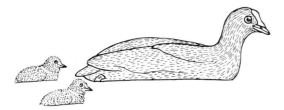

Coot, _Fulica atra_

occur on Windermere during hard weather.   A relative of the Moorhen, the Water Rail, _Rallus aquaticus_ is much less common and, because of its skulking habits, is seldom seen.   It frequents dense aquatic vegetation, such as reeds, sedges and their assoc- iates, that develops on areas of flat, muddy ground adjacent to lakes and tarns, often where small willows are growing.

A truly aquatic bird of a very different kind is the Dipper, _Cinclus cinclus_.   Thrush-like in general form, but representing a distinct family, the Dipper is a bird particularly of upland areas. An habitual frequenter of streams or certain rocky lake shores, it is very characteristic of the clear stony streams of the Lake District where it can be found at altitudes of over 2500 ft and breeds up to about 1500 ft.   Streams are partitioned into elongate territories sometimes more, sometimes less, than a mile in length, presumably depending on food supply.   The Dipper feeds chiefly on invertebrates, but sometimes takes small fishes.   Some prey is caught as it wades in shallow water, but much is obtained as it completely immerses itself and runs over the stream bed or propels itself with its wings. Largely black, with a conspicuous white breast, the Dipper has the habit of bobbing persistently as it stands or walks on the rocks of a stream.   It also has the pleasing attribute of singing even in the depths of winter.

A very different bird, not aquatic but haunting the mar- gins of similar streams to those favoured by the Dipper, is the Grey Wagtail, _Motacilla cinerea_, the most elegant of

Dipper, _Cinclus cinclus_

the wagtails.

The most colourful aquatic bird of the Lake District is the Kingfisher, <u>Alcedo atthis</u>. Near the northern limits of its range, it is scarce in many parts of the area but occurs on certain favoured rivers and streams, including the Kent, and is occasionally seen on some of the lakes. A fish-eater, the Kingfisher catches its prey by plunging into the water but is otherwise aerial in habits.

The Grey Heron, <u>Ardea cinerea</u> is often to be seen in what appears, deceptively, to be slow and measured flight. In fact it generally exceeds 40 km p.h. (25 mph). It is also to be seen standing in the water at the margin of lakes and tarns as it waits for its prey to pass. It feeds extensively on fishes but in such streams as harbour them it also stabs crayfishes. Its food is not, however, obtained exclusively from water; mammals up to the size of moles, but especially voles, are also eaten. There are several small heronries in the Lake District.

Of the waders the most closely associated with water is the Common Sandpiper, <u>Tringa hypoleucos</u> whose bobbing gait, fluttering flight and high-pitched calls make it easy to recognise and whose arrival is one of the signs of spring in the Lake District. It frequents the stony shores of lakes and tarns and stony streams from low-lying lakes such as Windermere to tarns at over 2000 ft, at which altitude it sometimes breeds. It is interesting that it occurs around low-lying lakes, as in Britain it is essentially an upland species.

Grey Heron, <u>Ardea cinerea</u>

Gulls are frequently seen around the lakes. While a few pairs of the Lesser Black-backed Gull, <u>Larus fuscus</u> now breed regularly, and the Great Black-backed Gull, <u>L. marinus</u> and Common Gull, <u>Larus canus</u>, do so occasionally—the latter did so for several consecutive years recently on the solitary rock in the middle of Easdale Tarn — it is the Black-headed Gull, <u>L. ridibundus</u>, that is the commonest breeder. Small colonies are established on several tarns.

In winter a variety of other water birds is to be seen on the larger lakes. These include the three British divers, and storm-driven marine species ranging from ducks to such waifs as the Little Auk.

Unfortunately the days when the White-tailed Eagle, <u>Haliaetus albicilla</u>, and perhaps the Osprey, <u>Pandion haliaetus</u>, not only graced the English lakes but bred in the area, are long gone. Happily the former is now breeding again in Scotland following its re-introduction and the latter, sometimes seen on passage in the Lake District, has re-colonised Scotland and is increasing in number. Given good-will these species, as the Golden Eagle has recently done, may yet again give pleasure to those who appreciate the splendid sight of birds of prey in flight and the even more magnificent spectacle of these fish-eaters swooping to catch their prey.

The Lake District boasts few aquatic mammals.   One insectivore, the Water Shrew, <u>Neomys fodiens</u> is probably widely distributed but seldom seen.   Larger than the familiar Common Shrew, its upper parts are almost black and its belly white.   It frequents streams, probably mostly at low levels.   For example it lives in some of the smaller streams that flow into Windermere, and I have seen it in the Troutbeck Valley, but information on its distribution is scarce.   It hunts its food — a variety of invertebrates and sometimes small fishes -- mostly by swimming to the bottom, but also forages on land.   As it swims it is enveloped in a bubble of air and appears silvery white.   Its sharp teeth are well adapted to seizing, slicing, and dissecting its prey which is carried ashore for consumption.   Like other shrews it has to feed at frequent intervals and is active almost around the clock.   It breeds mostly in spring, but as two, sometimes three, litters (of 3 to 8) are produced each year, breeding continues to September.   Its life span seldom exceeds 18 months.

Water Shrew, <u>Neomys fodiens</u>

Water Vole

<u>Arvicola</u>

<u>terrestris</u>

Bats are often seen near water.   These are usually either the Pipistrelle, <u>Pipistrellus pipistrellus</u>, the commonest Lake District bat, or Daubenton's Bat, <u>Myotis daubentoni</u>, sometimes called the Water Bat for obvious reasons.   Both are small species whose wing spans do not exceed about 27 cm (10½ in.).   The Pipistrelle is by no means restricted to the vicinity of water, and even Daubenton's Bat sometimes strays from the waterside.   The attractions of water include the insects that emerge from it.   Midges and Caddis Flies are important in the diet of the Pipistrelle.   Daubenton's Bat is more restricted in distribution in the area than the widespread Pipistrelle, but more information is required.   In summer it appears to have a particular liking for bridges where nursery colonies are established

A rodent, the Water Vole, <u>Arvicola terrestris</u>, has an apparently inappropriate scientific name.   It was **indeed** formerly called <u>A. amphibius</u> and there has been much discussion as to what constitutes its specific limits.   It is now thought that there is but one species that, in most of Britain, is largely aquatic (or amphibious), but which in some parts of the Continent, and even of Britain, is more terrestrial in habits.

Water Voles like narrow, slow-flowing, deep waterways with firm banks, covered with dense vegetation, that offer facilities for making burrows.   Many Lake District streams do not provide such conditions.

They are briskly-flowing, stony bottomed and often shallow, and their banks are often stony and scantily vegetated. Such streams are shunned.   Water Voles occur, however, beside various lowland streams and on the shores of some of the richer lakes such as Grasmere, Rydal Water and Windermere.

Water Voles are essentially vegetarians and feed largely on grasses and the reed Phragmites, but some animal food is taken.   They are particularly active at dusk but can be watched feeding by day.   Like many rodents they are fecund animals, producing 4 or 5 litters of usually 4 to 6 young in a season, nests being made in burrows or in dense reed beds.   Males, which are slightly larger than females, are about 200 mm (8 in.) in length.

The most impressive aquatic mammal in the Lake District, now unfortunately rare, is the Otter, Lutra lutra, which frequents lakes, rivers and streams.   An adult male is generally about 120 cm (4 ft.) long, including tail, and weighs over 10 kg. (22 lb).   Females are somewhat smaller.   Although capable of brisk movement on land it is superbly adapted for swimming underwater, where it can achieve speeds of up to 10 or 12 km/h. (c. 7.5 m.p.h.) which is sufficient to enable it to catch fishes of almost any species.   These it seizes with its teeth.   Not all the fishes it catches are large.   Species such as Sticklebacks are not despised, and it eats crayfishes and even such small crustaceans as Gammarus, as well as occasionally amphibians, mammals and insects.

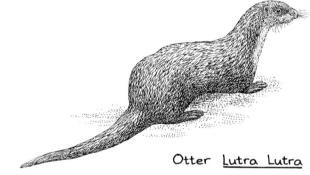

Otter Lutra Lutra

Otters breed at any time of the year, females giving birth usually to 2 or 3 young in a den or 'holt'.   Mostly nocturnal, they are seldom encountered in the Lake District unless specially sought, and their recent decline reduces the chances of seeing them even more.   Their presence is revealed by their droppings ('spraints').

A recent, unwelcome, arrival in the Lake District is the Mink, Mustela vison, a larger relative of the Stoat and Polecat.   Males are up to 43 cm (17 in) in length.   Descendants of escapees from Mink farms are now well established and frequent the vicinity of a variety of waters, from which they are sometimes erroneously reported as Otters. Mink swim well and are also active on land.   They prey on fishes, mammals and birds — Coots and Moorhens being particularly vulnerable.   I have seen the remains of a Wood Pigeon and a Mallard outside a temporary hideout.

Mink   Mustela vison

351

This book has tried to say something about some of the situations in which organisms live in lakes and streams and to show how their lives are affected by such things as the chemistry of the water, the penetration of light, the stratification of lakes and other environmental variables.   Each species has its own particular prefer-ences regarding just where it lives, what — if it is an animal — it eats, whether it is active by day or by night and so on.   Each has its own role in the economy of nature.   That role is called its <u>niche</u>, or <u>ecological niche</u>.

Although each species has its niche, organisms do not live in isolation: they interact in various ways. The destruction of algae by fungal parasites, the eating of algae by snails or small crustaceans, and the eat-ing of these animals in turn by fishes, are obvious examples of direct interactions.   When one organism consumes another the interaction is an element in a <u>food chain</u>, or more usually a <u>food web</u> for there are often cross connections as well as continuous chains.   Interactions between predators and their prey have led to specialisations in predators — as in the Pike (page 332) and dragonfly nymphs (page 260) — and to the development of defensive contrivances by their prey.   The latter include rapid escape movements, camouflage, a protective case or shell, an unpleasant taste and other subterfuges.

Animals and plants also interact in other ways.   They <u>compete</u> for vital necessities when these are in short supply.   Plants of all kinds may compete for nutrients such as nitrates and phosphates : higher plants growing in close proximity to each other may compete for light.   Animals may compete for food, or for places in which to live, or deposit their eggs, or rear their offspring.   Competition may be between different species (interspecific) or between individuals of the same species (intraspecific).   Spaces under stones may be desirable residences for animals of various kinds, but limited in number, so both inter- and intraspecific competition for them may take place.   The number of sites at which a net-spinning caddis larva can spin its net may be limited at any particular place and the same is true for the number of territories available to young Trout in a stream, so in both cases intraspecific competition may occur.   In the case of the Trout, competitors may be literally driven out.   Failure to establish a territory is often a death sentence.   In other cases competition is more subtle.

Interactions between species span the entire spectrum from beneficial to detrimental and may be far from simple.   Even predators may be beneficial to potential prey species by eating some of their competitors. Other organisms live together gaining mutual benefit by so doing, as in the symbiotic association of green algae and <u>Hydra</u> (page 173).   Some animals utilise the partly digested faeces of others, while algae are to a large extent dependent upon materials released as metabolic by-products or 'wastes' by animals and by the dis-integration of organisms after death, in which process bacteria are involved.

These and other interactions link organisms together into <u>communities</u>.   Communities usually involve both plants and animals and differ much among themselves. Those found in the open waters of lakes that make up the plankton are quite different from those of stony shores, or of the muddy bottoms of deep lakes, or of torrential streams. However communities are not always isolated from each other and interact in various ways. Some animals spend time in different communities at different times of their life. Such are some of the complexities of <u>ecology</u> to which this book is no more than a prologue. The subject is indeed too complex fully to understand, but two things are obvious. It is impossible to appreciate many of the subtle interactions between organisms — how communities are structured and how they 'work' — until the habits and ways of life of their constituent species are known. Those who delight in the making of mathematical models and enjoy playing with computers sometimes like to think otherwise. Their contributions and insights can be very valuable, but are sometimes misleading. Until they possess basic information, some of which can be provided by any intelligent observer, they are treading on dangerous ground. The other obvious thing is that man can all too easily upset the balance established by nature. He can interfere in many ways : by drawing down lakes to meet his needs for water, by enriching or polluting lakes and rivers, by introducing alien species, dredging streams, or simply by creating disturbance. Lakes and streams will always be used : they should not be abused.

The Lake District is a wonderful area. Its scenery, which reflects its geological history, is superb, and its waters are full of fascinating, beautiful and useful organisms that deserve our protection. However, the area is small and fragile. If future generations are to continue to enjoy what we are priviledged to enjoy today it should receive sympathetic, careful and intelligent treatment. Such treatment depends largely on common sense and unselfish behaviour but sometimes calls for scientific understanding, to which amateurs as well as professionals can contribute. This is one reason for looking carefully at the world around us. Another, given more than three centuries ago, seems an appropriate note on which to end :—

> The wisedom of God receives small honour from those vulgar heads that
> rudely stare about, and with a grosse rusticity admire His workes ; those
> highly magnify Him, whose judicious enquiry into His acts, and deliberate
> research of His creatures, returne the duty of a devout and learned
> admiration.
> Sir Thomas Browne   <u>Religio Medici</u> 1642

INDEX

Both the common and scientific names of all fishes, amphibians, birds and mammals are listed. Otherwise, except in a few cases where an animal has a familiar common name (e.g. the Crayfish) only scientific names of organisms are given. Pages where the indexed entry is illustrated are indicated by underlining. For convenience, entries relating to major water bodies are gathered together under the water bodies in question as well as, in most cases, being separately indexed.

354

This book has been published by The Freshwater Biological Association, an independent research organisation and registered charity with over 60 years of experience in freshwater scientific research, currently carried out by honorary research fellows and by awarding grants and studentships, usually to young scientists. The Association has an internationally renowned library, and publishes a variety of bibliographies and booklets, manuals on methods, and definitive keys for the identification of the British freshwater fauna and flora. Membership of the Association is open to anyone with an interest in freshwater science and includes the opportunity to purchase at a discount various services offered by the library, and the publications of the Association. Members are kept informed on the activities of their Association by *Freshwater Forum*, published three times each year and sent free to members. It contains short articles, reviews, news and views contributed by the world-wide membership. Further information may be obtained by writing to the Director, The Freshwater Biological Association, The Ferry House, Far Sawrey, Ambleside, Cumbria LA22 0LP, England.